introduction to servomechanism system design

PRENTICE-HALL SERIES IN ELECTRONIC TECHNOLOGY

Irving L. Kosow, editor

Charles M. Thomson, Joseph L. Gersho, and Joseph A. Labok,
consulting editors

introduction to servomechanism system design

WILLIAM M. HUMPHREY

President, Humphrey Instruments, Inc.
Lawrenceville, New Jersey

Prentice-Hall, Inc., Englewood Cliffs, New Jersey

Library of Congress Cataloging in Publication Data

HUMPHREY, WILLIAM M.
　　Introduction to servomechanism system design.

　　1. Servomechanisms. I. Title.
TJ214.H85　　　629.8′32　　　72–8488
ISBN 0–13–495960–4

© 1973 by
Prentice-Hall, Inc.
Englewood Cliffs, N.J.

10 9 8 7 6 5 4 3 2 1

Printed in the United States of America

Prentice-Hall International, Inc., *London*
Prentice-Hall of Australia, Pty. Ltd., *Sydney*
Prentice-Hall of Canada, Ltd., *Toronto*
Prentice-Hall of India Private Limited, *New Delhi*
Prentice-Hall of Japan, Inc., *Tokyo*

Bus & I
R

13.95

contents

preface   **xi**

1   introductory concepts   **1**

1-1. What are Servos? 1
1-2. Basic Servo Characteristics 3
1-3. Drive Motor Selection 3
1-4. Servo Performance 4
1-5. The Standard Diagram 5
1-6. The Frequency-Response Approach 9
1-7. Frequency-Response Testing 10
1-8. The Integrator 11
1-9. Bode Plots 12
1-10. Integration in the Time Domain 13
1-11. Summary 16
      Problems 16

2   servomechanism analysis techniques   **18**

2-1. Frequency-Response Analysis 18
2-2. Transient Analysis 21
2-3. Introduction to Laplace Transforms 23
2-4. Transfer Functions 24
2-5. Block-Diagram Algebra 25

2-6. Gain of an Integrator   28
2-7. Frequency-Response Solution of an Integrator in a Loop   30
2-8. Ideal Motor Servo   32
2-9. Summary   35
      Problems   36

3   Laplace transforms   **39**

3-1. Basic Properties   39
3-2. Transform Examples   40
3-3. The Laplace Transform Table   41
3-4. Stability   45
3-5. The Integrator   46
3-6. A Simple Servomechanism   48
3-7. Summary   50
      Problems   51

4   simple servo performance   **53**

4-1. Velocity Constant   53
4-2. First-Order Approximation of a Servo   55
4-3. Linear Mechanical Elements   57
4-4. Reflected Inertia   62
4-5. Summary   65
      Problems   65

5   servo motors   **68**

5-1. dc Servo Motor Characteristics   68
5-2. Dimensions of ω_m 73
5-3. Effect of Drive Amplifier Impedance on ω_m 76
5-4. Armature Inductance   78
5-5. Servo Constants   81
5-6. Relationship between K_{mTE} and K_{mTI} 82
5-7. The Effect of High-Value Poles   83
5-8. dc Motor Maximum Power Point   84
5-9. Summary   86
      Problems   86

**6   elementary servo design;
      torque stiffness**   **88**

6-1. Electrical Break Frequency   88
6-2. Gear Ratio at Maximum Power Point   89

6-3. Motor Break Frequency, ω_m 89
6-4. Closing the Loop; ω_{cp} 89
6-5. Calculating Amplifier Gain 95
6-6. Velocity Constant 97
6-7. Torque Stiffness 97
6-8. Torque Disturbances 98
6-9. Linearity 104
6-10. Direct Design 104
6-11. Summary 107
      Problems 108

7   tachometer and back emf stabilization   **111**

7-1. Tachometer Stabilization 111
7-2. Position Loop Around Tachometer Loop 121
7-3. Block-Diagram Alternatives 124
7-4. Torque Stiffness 126
7-5. Block-Diagram Algebra of Disturbances 129
7-6. Back EMF Stabilization 130
7-7. Summary 134
      Problems 134

8   stability   **136**

8-1. Poles and Zeros 136
8-2. S-Plane Quadratic Response 139
8-3. A Closed-Loop Example 142
8-4. The Standard Quadratic 145
8-5. Geometric Properties of Standard Quadratic Poles 147
8-6. Transient Response from Pole Location 149
8-7. Phasor Gain 150
8-8. M Circles 153
8-9. Gain and Phase Margin 154
8-10. Nichols Charts 156
8-11. Nichols Chart Example 160
8-12. Summary 165
      Problems 165

9   integral network compensation   **167**

9-1. Integral Networks 169
9-2. Position Loop 171
9-3. Integral Network Servo Performance 172
9-4. K_v Form 176

9-5.   Integral Network Servo Torque Stiffness   177
9-6.   Integral Network Gain Expressions   178
9-7.   Integral Network Servo Design Example   180
9-8.   Specifying Hardware   184
9-9.   Summary   186
        Problems   187

**10   lead network and viscous coupled
        inertial damped servos   188**

10-1.   Lead Network Characteristics   188
10-2.   Lead Network Servo Position Loop   191
10-3.   Lead Network Servo Torque Stiffness   192
10-4.   Lead Network Servo Velocity Constant   193
10-5.   Lead Network Servo Design Example   194
10-6.   Introduction to Viscous Coupled Inertial Damped Servos   197
10-7.   Servomotors and Simple Servos   197
10-8.   Viscous Coupled Inertial Dampers   201
10-9.   The VCID Servo Position Loop   204
10-10. VCID Servo Performance   207
10-11. Summary   210
        Problems   210

**11   resonance, limits on ω_{cp}; scaling,
        saturation, and tracking systems   211**

11-1.   Analysis of Load Resonance   211
11-2.   Bandwidth Limits in General   215
11-3.   Empirical Bandwidth Data   216
11-4.   Scaling   217
11-5.   Saturation   219
11-6.   Introduction to Automatic Tracking Systems   225
11-7.   Secant Correction   225
11-8.   Manual Position Follow-Up Servo   229
11-9.   Rate Memory   230
11-10. Scanners   231
11-11. Summary   231
        Problems   232

12   error budgets   234

12-1.   Disturbance Errors   236
12-2.   Static Friction Error (Static)   239

12-3.   Motor Starting Voltage Error (Static)   240
12-4.   Tachometer Noise Error (Static)   241
12-5.   Component Errors (Static)   241
12-6.   Transducer Errors (Static)   244
12-7.   Gearing Errors (Static)   245
12-8.   Deflection Errors (Static)   247
12-9.   Steady Torque Errors (Static)   247
12-10. Wind Gust Errors (Static)   248
12-11. Tachometer Ripple Error (Dynamic)   250
12-12. Target Motion Error (Dynamic)   250
12-13. Error Constants   252
12-14. Passing Track Method   256
12-15. Tracking Noise (Dynamic)   260
12-16. Summary   265
         Problems   265

13   electrohydraulic servos   267

13-1.   Basic Relations   267
13-2.   Motor-Valve Analysis   272
13-3.   Leakage Flow   275
13-4.   Compressibility Flow: Hydraulic Resonance   275
13-5.   Hydraulic Servo Systems   279
13-6.   Summary   280
         Problems   280

14   design—an approach; system performance comparison   281

14-1.   Drive Power   281
14-2.   System Bandwidths   282
14-3.   Performance Calculation   283
14-4.   Saturation   284
14-5.   System Performance Comparison   284
14-6.   Servo Configuration Performance Comparison Example   288
         Problems   289

appendix A   operational amplifiers   290

appendix B   performance comparison curves   296

appendix C   conversion equivalents   300

appendix D   moment of inertia calculations   *302*

appendix E   answers to selected problems   *304*

appendix F   experiments   *307*

index   *311*

preface

This book is intended to bridge the gap between mathematical servo theory and practical design. It has been prepared for use as a text, for reference by the practicing engineer, and as a medium for individual study.

The material starts with the basic concepts of analysis and design, develops the significant properties of various types of servos, and concludes with a semiquantitative comparison of the performance characteristics of the five basic servo configurations. The emphasis of the book is on the exposition of techniques required for rapid system analysis and design and on the development of valid approximations which are adequately accurate for engineering purposes. Practical examples are given as demonstrations. Problems with selected answers are provided to allow the serious student to evaluate his understanding of the material.

Minimum background for this book should include introductory courses in differential and integral calculus, linear differential equations with constant coefficients, Laplace transforms, and linear circuit theory. Much of this material is lucidly presented in *Network Analysis*, by M.E. Van Valkenburg (Englewood Cliffs, N.J.: Prentice-Hall, Inc., 1955). The physics of linear translational and rotational systems, and operational amplifier theory and practice are also valuable background.

The separate laboratory manual is keyed to this textbook. Experiment procedures, recommended equipment configurations, and summarized theory are presented. The basic theoretical developments that form the background for the various experiments are those presented in this book. The combination of this book and the laboratory manual comprises a complete lecture and laboratory course in elementary servomechanism system design.

I wish to gratefully acknowledge the debt I feel to George A. Biernson who contributed a great deal to my understanding of servos, to Dr. Paul R. Johannessen whose clear understanding of servos and of solid state devices was apparent on so many occasions, and to Dr. Thomas C. Searle who has made many indirect contributions to this book. Special gratitude is due to my wife, Ruth, who has spent so many hours typing drafts and manuscript copy.

WILLIAM M. HUMPHREY

Lawrenceville, New Jersey

introduction to
servomechanism system
design

1

introductory concepts

The purpose of this book is to present material that will allow the reader to obtain a physical visualization of practical closed-loop servomechanism (servo) systems while developing the necessary theoretical base. The approach taken is to develop rapid design techniques that are based on valid approximations and that are adequately accurate for most design situations.

1-1. what are servos?

Let us say initially that servos are closed-loop control systems used to determine the position, velocity, or acceleration of mechanical loads. To elaborate on this initial definition and at the same time to make it more exact, let us investigate the meaning of the phrase "closed-loop"; let us also examine some related concepts before providing our working definition of servos.

To understand closed-loop systems we will first examine open-loop systems. In an open-loop system, the output is not measured nor is the information fed back in any way to affect the system operation. A simple automatic dishwasher is an example of an open-loop control system, because it performs a fixed cycle without regard to the degree of cleanness of the dishes. Similarly, a manually-set stove-heating element constitutes an open-loop control system. In a closed-loop system, however, the output parameter is measured and compared with the input command; the difference between the two (the error) is used to make the system correct itself. This introduces the important concept that closed-loop systems are *null-seeking systems*. An example of a closed-loop system is a thermostatically-controlled house heating system.

An important advantage of closed-loop systems over open-loop systems is that they are less affected by disturbances. Disturbances adversely affect the output of a system and can be caused by internal component parts or by external influences. An example of an externally caused disturbance is the opening of an oven door; a closed-loop thermostatically-controlled oven would correct for this disturbance, whereas an oven with manually variable, fixed power-input levels would have a greater resulting temperature variation because of the cooling effect of the open door and the unchanging applied power to the heating elements. An example of a disturbance caused by a component part of a system is the scale buildup around the heating element of an electric hot-water heater; it can be seen that a closed-loop water-temperature control system would tend to correct for this scale buildup by applying the amount of energy necessary to bring the water temperature to the proper value. An open-loop system would *not* compensate for this reduction in efficiency, and over the years the hot water would tend to assume lower and lower temperatures.

A variable autotransformer feeding a rectifier constitutes a variable, open-loop, dc voltage source; a regulated power supply is a closed-loop device. It is clear that the regulated supply controls the dc output voltage more accurately than the open-loop system. Line-voltage variations, load changes, and component aging affect the open-loop system much more than the closed-loop system.

A disadvantage of closed-loop systems is that they may have stability problems, particularly when high performance is required. This introduces the concept that there is a basic conflict in closed-loop systems: gain is increased to reduce errors to a tolerable level, but increasing gain (generally speaking) decreases stability. Therefore there is a limit to performance imposed by stability. Closed-loop systems also tend to respond more rapidly as their gains are increased; thus there is also a limit to speed of response imposed by stability considerations. In general, closed-loop systems must be capable of reducing errors to acceptable levels and must respond to commands or disturbances sufficiently rapidly.

For the purposes of this book, *servomechanisms* will be considered to be closed-loop control systems whose function is to position mechanical loads by means of motors. These servos will use *proportional-control* rather than an on–off ("bang–bang") control (a thermostatically controlled house heating system is an on–off control system). In a proportional-control servo, both the magnitude and the polarity of the difference between the command and the output (the error) are used for control. Servos using electronic instrumentation and electric motors will be the principal subject of discussion, although Chapter 13 will consider the salient aspects of electrohydraulic servos. In the course of using this book, it will be found that there are relatively few basic servo design configurations and relatively few performance criteria.

It is a straightforward matter to select the best configuration for a given application and then predict its performance and finally detail the design.

1-2. basic servo characteritstics

There are four important characteristics of servos:

1. A servo is actuated by an *error*; this error is the difference between the desired output and the actual output.
2. A servo's *output* power is *larger* than that available from the input information; for instance, a potentiometer control knob takes only a finger touch for control, but an antenna weighing many tons may be controlled by this potentiometer as a part of a servo.
3. The power applied to the load is *proportional to* a combination of the error signal, its derivatives, and its integrals. (This represents the linearity assumption which is valid for most servo analyses; there are some exceptions where nonlinearities have to be considered, which will be discussed in this book from the standpoint of the design engineer.)
4. Practical servos are *stable*; it is possible to have unstable servos, but these are not useful devices.

1-3. drive motor selection

In designing servos, certain items must be considered in the very early stages. The most important is that the power to the load must be determined in order to "size" the drive motor. In sizing the motor for a power servo, five characteristics must be known: (1) unbalance (or other relatively steady) load torques, (2) transient torques, (3) the value of load inertia, (4) required load acceleration, and (5) required load velocity.

Power into the load is then determined by considering these parameters. A worst-case load peak power may be calculated by taking the sum of the peak torques and multiplying it by the maximum velocity: this gives a conservative value of peak power to the load. It is possible, however, that the worst-case peak power may be less than that calculated above if the peak torque is *not* required when peak velocity is demanded. Unbalance torques often need not be considered because they are not appreciable in value, but friction torques may demand motor power (e.g., in instrument servos).

An important aspect that must also be considered in sizing the motor(s) to drive the load is the fact that sometimes an appreciable amount of power goes into the motor itself. The motor has inertia, and this inertia has to be accelerated; this takes torque, and the product of this torque times the motor velocity is a real component of power required by the motor that never gets to the load. Therefore, it is the total power delivered by the motor that must be considered in sizing the motor.

Example 1-1. Motor Sizing

Consider a load with the following characteristics:

Steady load torque	$10 \text{ lb} \cdot \text{ft}$
Transient torque	$2 \text{ lb} \cdot \text{ft}$
Load (and motor) inertia*	$4 \text{ slug} \cdot \text{ft}^2$
Load acceleration (max)	$100°/\text{s}^2$
Load velocity (max)	40 rpm

Calculate the worst-case required motor power in (a) horsepower and (b) watts. (See Appendix C for conversion factors.)

solution

(a) Since $4 \text{ slug} \cdot \text{ft}^2 = 4 \text{ lb} \cdot \text{ft} \cdot \text{s}^2$,

$$T_{accel} = 4 \text{ lb} \cdot \text{ft} \cdot \text{s}^2 \times \frac{100°}{\text{s}^2} \times \frac{1 \text{ rad}}{57.3°}$$

$$= 6.98 \text{ lb} \cdot \text{ft} \approx 7 \text{ lb} \cdot \text{ft}$$

$$T_{total} = 10 + 2 + 7 = 19 \text{ lb} \cdot \text{ft}$$

$$P_{max} = T_{max} \Omega_{max}$$

$$= 19 \text{ lb} \cdot \text{ft} \times 40 \frac{\text{rev}}{\text{min}} \times 360 \frac{\text{deg}}{\text{rev}} \times \frac{1 \text{ rad}}{57.3 \text{ deg}} \times \frac{1 \text{ min}}{60 \text{ s}}$$

$$= 79.6 \frac{\text{lb} \cdot \text{ft}}{\text{s}}$$

$$= 79.6 \left(\frac{\text{lb} \cdot \text{ft}}{\text{s}}\right) \times 1 \left(\frac{\text{hp}}{550 \text{ lb} \cdot \text{ft/s}}\right)$$

$$= 0.1445 \text{ hp}$$

(b) $P_{max} = 0.1445 \text{ hp} \times 746 \frac{\text{W}}{\text{hp}} = 108 \text{ W}$

1-4. servo performance

Two basic areas of *performance characteristics* are now considered. The first is the servo's *accuracy* as represented by a number of errors; these errors include those due to command dynamics, errors due to load torques, and errors due to servo components such as motors, tachometers, synchros, electronic components, and so on. The second aspect of performance is the *time* it takes for transients to settle out after a change in command has taken place.

These performance criteria are covered in this book; all of the calculations of these parameters and characteristics are *based on the significant bandwidths of the servo loops* (open- and closed-loop bandwidths).

* For a discussion of moment of inertia, see Section 4-3.

An extremely important fundamental concept is the fact that *loop bandwidths* are often limited by factors beyond the designer's control. It is significant that certain physical realities limit the achievable servo-loop bandwidths, and it is these servo-loop bandwidths that determine the error performance and the settling-time performance of the servomechanism. The loop bandwidths are limited by the *carrier frequency* in ac servo systems; for instance, a 400-Hz servo may have a wider stable bandwidth than a 60-Hz servo. Another effect that limits servo-loop bandwidths is *load structural resonance*; a large antenna system that has a gearbox driving a high-inertia antenna assembly may have a natural mechanical resonant frequency of 2 or 3 Hz due to combined gear-box spring rate and load inertia. This puts an upper limit on the servo loop's bandwidth.

The main emphasis in this book is that servo performance can be calculated from the characteristic servo bandwidths and that these servo bandwidths are readily determined from known limiting characteristics. This technique leads to a simple and direct design approach.

1-5. the standard diagram

System design mathematics is greatly simplified if all loops are reduced to the form shown in Fig. 1-1, which is called the "standard diagram."

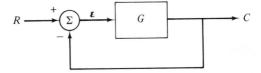

Figure 1-1. The standard diagram.

Equations (1-1) through (1-5) describe the performance of this standard closed-loop system.

$$C = G\epsilon \tag{1-1}$$

$$\epsilon = R - C \tag{1-2}$$

Therefore,

$$C = G(R - C) = GR - GC \tag{1-3}$$

or

$$C + GC = GR, \qquad C(1 + G) = GR \tag{1-4}$$

and

$$\frac{C}{R} = \frac{G}{1 + G} = G' \tag{1-5}$$

The input to the system is R, which stands for the reference variable; the output is C, the controlled variable, and ϵ is the error. It is the error times the loop gain G, that gives the controlled variable output C. Equations (1-1) through (1-5) are quite specific in describing the operation of this loop.

Table 1-1. closed-loop gain as a function of open-loop gain

open-loop gain	closed-loop gain
G	$G' = \dfrac{C}{R} = \dfrac{G}{1 + G}$
> 1	1
< 1	G
≈ 1	$+\frac{1}{2}$ to $-\infty$

Table 1-1 shows the general performance of Eq. (1-5); this table defines the closed-loop gain C/R of the standard diagram in Fig. 1-1 for different values of open-loop gain G. For the magnitude of the open-loop gain $G \gg 1$, the denominator of Eq. (1-5) becomes essentially G, and therefore the closed-loop gain is one; this tells us that *when the open-loop gain is high, the closed-loop gain is unity.* For an open-loop gain $G \ll 1$, the denominator becomes essentially one; therefore *the closed-loop gain is effectively G.* This is shown in Fig. 1-2. Figure 1-2 is a diagram of an assumed gain function which slopes from

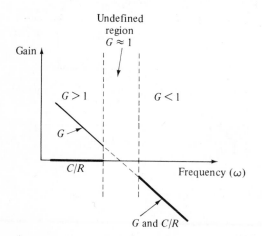

Figure 1-2. Closed-loop gain and open-loop gain (G) versus frequency (ω).

the upper left to the lower right. When the open-loop gain function $G > 1$ (the left part), the closed-loop gain C/R is equal to unity. When the open-loop gain function $G < 1$ (the right part), then the closed-loop gain C/R is essentially the same as the open-loop gain.

The third case in Table 1-1 occurs when the open-loop gain is approximately unity. For the open-loop gain equal to unity, the closed-loop gain is an unknown value ranging from $\frac{1}{2}$ to ∞: if the open-loop phase is zero, then the denominator has a value of 2 and the closed-loop gain is $\frac{1}{2}$; if the open loop phase is 180°, then the denominator is zero and the gain is $-\infty$. It is clear that *only when open-loop gain is near unity is stability of concern*, because as long as the gain is much greater than one the closed-loop gain is close to unity, and as long as the gain is much less than one the closed-loop gain is roughly equal to the gain itself. In neither of these cases can the closed-loop gain become much larger than unity. The only region where instability can possibly occur is where the gain is approximately unity. Recognizing this fact makes the servo stability problem relatively easy to handle.

Another aspect of the "standard diagram" is its *error gain* characteristics. Equations (1-6) through (1-9) describe this error gain performance.

$$\epsilon = \frac{C}{G} \qquad (1\text{-}6)$$

$$C = R\frac{G}{1 + G} \qquad (1\text{-}7)$$

Therefore,

$$\epsilon = R\frac{G}{1 + G} \times \frac{1}{G} = \frac{R}{1 + G} \qquad (1\text{-}8)$$

or

$$\frac{\epsilon}{R} = \frac{1}{1 + G} \qquad (1\text{-}9)$$

The development of these equations is straightforward. Equation (1-6) states that the error is equal to the controlled variable divided by the gain. Equation (1-7) shows that the controlled variable is equal to the reference variable times $G/(1 + G)$ [from Eq. (1-5)]. Combining Eqs. (1-6) and (1-7), Eq. (1-8) is obtained. Equation (1-9) restates this in error gain form.

Table 1-2. error gain as a function of open-loop gain

Open-loop gain	Error gain
G	$\dfrac{\epsilon}{R} = \dfrac{1}{1 + G}$
> 1	$1/G$
< 1	1
≈ 1	$+\frac{1}{2}$ to $+\infty$

Table 1-2 summarizes the characteristics of Eq. (1-9): For the open-loop gain greater than one, the error gain is essentially $1/G$; for the open-loop gain less than one, the denominator becomes essentially unity and so the error gain is unity. For the third case, where the gain is approximately unity, the error gain can range from $\frac{1}{2}$ to ∞. Figure 1-3 demonstrates the characteristics of this error gain expression and of those tabulated in Table 1-2.

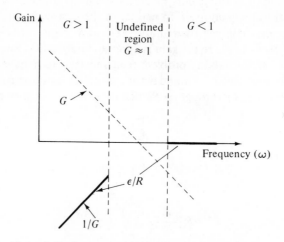

Figure 1-3. Error gain ($\mathcal{E}/R$) and open-loop gain (G) versus frequency (ω).

To get good error performance (small errors), the open-loop gain of a servo should be large. This is indicated in Table 1-2, where it is shown that for G greater than one the error gain is equal to $1/G$; therefore the errors decline as the open-loop gain increases. As the amplifier open-loop gain is increased in a servo, a point is reached where oscillations occur. In general, the performance of a servo is improved by increasing gain, but only to the point where instability becomes intolerable. It will be shown that this *stability gain limit* can be quantified *prior* to detailed design, so that the overall servo system performance may be predicted early in the design process.

Example 1-2. The Standard Diagram

For an open-loop gain of 99, calculate (a) the closed-loop gain G' of a fully fed-back system (standard diagram) and (b) the error gain for this system.

solution

(a) Closed-loop gain $= G' = \dfrac{G}{1 + G} = \dfrac{99}{1 + 99} = 0.99$

(b) $\dfrac{\epsilon}{R} =$ error gain $= \dfrac{1}{1 + G} = \dfrac{1}{1 + 99} = 0.01$

The results indicate that an amplifier having an open-loop gain of 99 with a 1-V input would provide a 0.99-V output, and that the error between the input and the output would be 0.01 V.

Example 1-3. The Standard Diagram

Calculate the closed-loop gain (G') and error gain (ϵ/R) for each of the following open-loop gains: $G_1 = 1 \angle 0°$; $G_2 = 1 \angle -90°$; $G_3 = 1 \angle -175°$; $G_4 = 1 \angle -180°$.

solution

$$G'_1 = \frac{1}{1+1} = 0.5 \angle 0°$$

$$G'_2 = \frac{-j}{1-j} = 0.707 \angle -45°$$

$$G'_3 = \frac{1 \angle -175°}{1 - 0.9962 - j(0.087)} = \frac{1 \angle -175°}{0.0038 - j(0.087)} = \frac{1 \angle -175°}{0.0879 \angle -87.5°}$$
$$= 11.4 \angle -87.5°$$

$$G'_4 = \frac{-1}{1-1} = \frac{-1}{0} = -\infty$$

$$\frac{\epsilon_1}{R} = \frac{1}{1+1} = 0.5 \angle 0°$$

$$\frac{\epsilon_2}{R} = \frac{1}{1-j} = 0.707 \angle +45°$$

$$\frac{\epsilon_3}{R} = \frac{1}{0.088 \angle -87.5°} = 11.4 \angle +87.5°$$

$$\frac{\epsilon_4}{R} = \frac{1}{1-1} = \frac{1}{0} = +\infty$$

1-6. the frequency-response approach

To describe the performance of servos simply and directly, the *frequency-response* point of view is generally used and is the basis of most discussions in this book. Transient performance is presented when it further illuminates the subject.

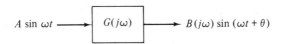

$A \sin \omega t \longrightarrow \boxed{G(j\omega)} \longrightarrow B(j\omega) \sin(\omega t + \theta)$

Figure 1-4. The frequency-response approach.

Figure 1-4 demonstrates the frequency-response approach. An input signal $A \sin \omega t$ is fed into a gain block [described as $G(j\omega)$], and the output of this block is $B(j\omega) \sin(\omega t + \theta)$. In the frequency-response approach, $G(j\omega)$ may be defined as the relationship between the output signal and the input signal (also called the *transfer function*). The *magnitude* of $G(j\omega)$ is $|B(j\omega)/A|$ and the *phase* of $G(j\omega)$ is θ. Therefore $G(j\omega)$ may be described as $|B(j\omega)/A| \angle \theta$, where θ is a function of frequency.

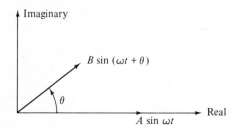

Figure 1-5. The phasor relationship between input and output sine waves.

Figure 1-5 demonstrates the above relationship in phasor representation. The input is $A \sin \omega t$ (along the real axis) and the output is the phasor $B \sin (\omega t + \theta)$ which is counterclockwise from $A \sin \omega t$ by angle θ from the real axis.

1-7. frequency-response testing

Frequency-response testing is accomplished as suggested by Fig. 1-6. The input to an amplifier or servo is a sinusoidal signal. The output of the amplifier or servo is a sine wave of the same frequency, having an amplitude and phase different from the amplitude and phase of the input. The relationship between output and input amplitude and phase defines the gain. In frequency-response analysis it is assumed that the system being tested is *linear*, and thus no harmonics appear at the output. This linearity assumption is satisfactory for practical servos. (Separate design techniques will be developed for situations where nonlinearities do occur.) The second part of Fig. 1-6 shows a servo whose input has a sine wave angle variation. This angle command coming into the servo varies sinusoidally with time and the

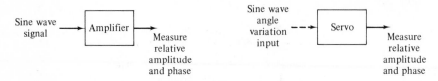

Figure 1-6. Frequency-response tests.

output of the servo therefore also varies sinusoidally with time; the relative amplitude and phase of the two sine waves (output and input) define the gain of the servo.

1-8. the integrator

Figure 1-7 shows a block diagram of an *integrator* that has a sine wave input. This integrator will be examined from a sine wave frequency-response point of view to determine the gain and phase of the output relative to the

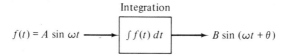

Integration

$$f(t) = A \sin \omega t \longrightarrow \boxed{\int f(t)\, dt} \longrightarrow B \sin (\omega t + \theta)$$

Figure 1-7. Frequency-response test of an integrator.

input. Integrations are very important, because every servo behaves as if it contained an integrator inside the loop. *The best first-order approximation of the open-loop gain of a servo is an integrator.* Because of this, a good deal of emphasis is placed on integrators, and this first development is quite important.

The input to the integrator in Fig. 1-7 is $A \sin \omega t$, and the output is $B \sin(\omega t + \theta)$. A is arbitrary, B is related in amplitude to A, and θ is the phase angle due to the integration, where

$$B \sin(\omega t + \theta) = \int A \sin \omega t \, dt = \frac{-A \cos \omega t}{\omega}$$

$$= \frac{-A \sin(\omega t + 90°)}{\omega}$$

$$= \frac{-A \sin \omega t}{\omega} \angle 90°$$

$$= \frac{A \sin \omega t}{\omega} \angle -90° \tag{1-10}$$

Equation (1-10) develops the relationship between the output and the input and defines the integration process. Using Eq. (1-10), the gain of this integration is expressed in Eq. (1-11).

$$\text{Gain} = \frac{\left(\dfrac{A \sin \omega t}{\omega}\right) \angle -90°}{A \sin \omega t} = \frac{-j}{\omega} = \frac{1}{j\omega} \tag{1-11}$$

Equation (1-11) says that an integrator has the property of causing a 90° phase lag and causing a change in gain inversely proportional to frequency. This is shown in Fig. 1-8, where frequency is plotted as the abscissa and the magnitude of gain is plotted as the ordinate; the lower part of the diagram gives the phase angle (−90°) plotted against frequency.

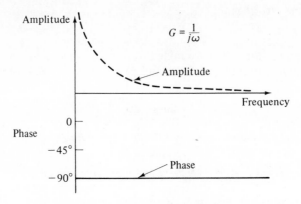

Figure 1-8. Frequency-response plot of an integrator.

1-9. Bode plots

Figure 1-9 shows the Bode plot or logarithmic plot of the gain function for an integrator as expressed in Eq. (1-12).

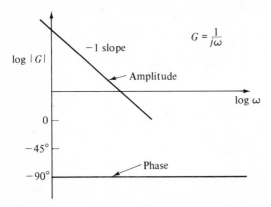

Figure 1-9. Bode plot (logarithmic plot) of an integrator.

$$G = \frac{1}{j\omega} \tag{1-12}$$

Equation (1-13) demonstrates why the Bode plot of an integrator is a straight line.

$$\log |G| = \log \left| \frac{1}{j\omega} \right| = \log \left(\frac{1}{\omega} \right) = 0 - \log \omega \tag{1-13}$$

In Fig. 1-9 the abscissa (horizontal axis) is log ω (the logarithm of the angular frequency in radians per second). The ordinate is the logarithm of the magnitude of the gain function. The Bode plot, therefore, represents the logarithm of the gain function plotted against the logarithm of frequency. The gain function as expressed in Eq. (1-12) shows that the gain magnitude changes according to the reciprocal of frequency. By taking the logarithm of this expression, Eq. (1-13) can be written. Equation (1-14) expresses and summarizes the relationship that the logarithm of the magnitude of the gain is equal to $-\log \omega$.

$$\log |G| = -\log \omega \qquad (1\text{-}14)$$

Now, plotting the logarithm of the gain magnitude against the logarithm of ω, one may see that the plot is $-\log \omega$ versus $\log \omega$. This plot is clearly a straight line with a -1 slope, as shown in Fig. 1-9. The phase plot associated with Fig. 1-9 (which constitutes part of the Bode plot) is shown in the lower part of the figure. It can be seen that the phase is a constant $-90°$.

Figure 1-10 shows asymptotic plots of some of the typical mathematical

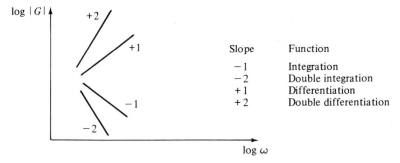

Slope	Function
-1	Integration
-2	Double integration
$+1$	Differentiation
$+2$	Double differentiation

Figure 1-10. Bode gain plots of several functions.

functions encountered in servo design and analysis. These are all straight lines having various slopes. For a double integration, the Bode plot has a -2 slope. In the case of a differentiator, the Bode plot is the function $G = j\omega$, and this has a $+1$ slope. Likewise, a double differentiation has a $+2$ slope. Not shown in Fig. 1-10 are the associated phase characteristics, which are $-90°$ for the single integration, $-180°$ for the double integration, $+90°$ for the differentiation, and $+180°$ for the double differentiation.

1-10. integration in the time domain

The concept of integration is extremely important. A clear understanding of the integration process from several points of view is fundamental to obtaining a physical visualization of the operation of servos. The integration process in the time domain is next considered. Figure 1-11 shows an input signal consisting of two step functions of constant magnitude in sequence. The integrals of these input step function signals are ramps, because

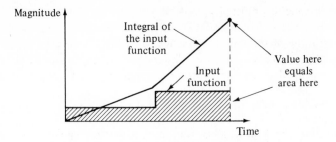

Figure 1-11. Time integral of an input function.

the time integral of a constant value is a time-increasing value. Another way of looking at it is that the total area under any constant function increases linearly with time.

All servomotors and servo drives exhibit the integration characteristic, because a constant command signal input to a motor or drive system results in a constant velocity output. Of course, the output velocity changes as a function of load torques and other disturbances but this does not alter the fact that a motor or drive acts as an integrator. From a first-order-approximation standpoint, *it is valid to consider servo drive devices as simple integrators.* To demonstrate this, consider Fig. 1-12, which shows the torque-speed char-

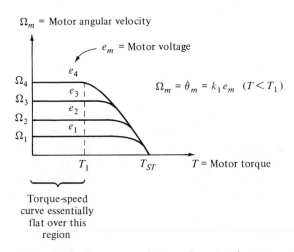

Figure 1-12. Torque-speed curve of an electric motor.

acteristics of a servo drive. This may be a two-phase ac servomotor or a hydraulic servo drive system. Observe that for load torques less than T_1, the velocity of the motor is essentially unaffected by the load torque and is proportional to the input voltage. As the torque required from the motor increases from T_1 to T_{st} (the stall torque), the velocity falls off markedly. If it is assumed that no torque greater than T_1 is demanded of the motor, then the torque-speed characteristic of the drive is essentially flat, as shown in the equation in Fig. 1-12; the motor velocity is directly proportional to the motor voltage.

The fact that the motor shown in Fig. 1-12 may be considered as a position integrator is shown in Fig. 1-13 and by Eqs. (1-15), (1-16), and (1-17). In Fig. 1-13 the potentiometer supplies the voltage e_m to the motor through

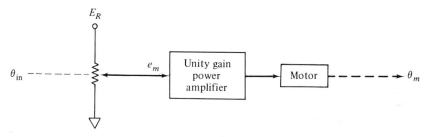

Figure 1-13. An open-loop motor control (integrator).

the power amplifier; the output angle of the motor as a function of the input angle to the potentiometer is now determined as

$$\dot{\theta}_m = \Omega_m = k_1 e_m = \frac{k_1 \theta_{in} E_R}{2\pi} = K\theta_{in} \qquad (1\text{–}15)$$

$$\frac{d\theta_m}{dt} = k\theta_{in} \qquad (1\text{–}16)$$

$$\theta m = k \int \theta_{in}\, dt \qquad (1\text{–}17)$$

Equation (1-15) gives the motor velocity in terms of the motor voltage and in terms of the potentiometer angular setting. It is assumed that the potentiometer in Fig. 1-13 has angular travel of 2π rad (360°). The first and last terms of Eq. (1-15) are expressed in Eq. (1-16). If both sides of this equation are integrated, Eq. (1-17) is obtained; this shows that the motor displacement angle θ_m is equal to a constant k times the *time integral* of θ_{in}. The fact that the output angle is equal to a constant times the integral of the input angle clearly demonstrates the significant point that the motor acts as an *integrator*. This fact is always true; in more comprehensive representations of motor drives other effects will be considered, but this integral characteristic is always the single most important motor characteristic.

Example 1-4. Time-Domain Integration
Find the integral of the time function in Fig. E1-4.

solution   Integral = area = 5(1) + 3(1) + 3(0.5) = 9.5 V·s.

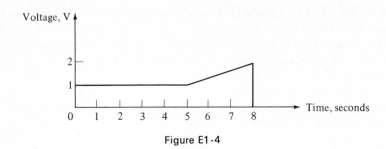

Figure E1-4

1-11. summary

In this first chapter, the standard diagram has been presented as the standard form in which all closed-loop servos are expressed; any closed-loop linear servo may be reduced to this form. The basic characteristics of this standard diagram have been developed. The error characteristics of this simple form were also developed. This error function not only represents the inaccuracy of the servo output C in following the input R, but it also defines the signal ϵ that actuates the system.

The frequency-response technique used throughout this book involves expressing the characteristics of the various parts of a servomechanism as gain functions. These gain functions express the amplitude and phase relationship of output versus input, where the input is always taken to be a sine wave. This frequency-response technique, of course, assumes linearity (a reasonable and safe assumption for most design calculations).

Integration is the most important function in the understanding of servos and the most frequently recurring operation in servos. The magnitude of an integrator's gain changes in proportion to the reciprocal of the radian frequency and the phase of the output lags the input by 90°. The Bode plot for this gain function has a -1 slope (because of the logarithmic characteristic of this Bode plot).

A constant-magnitude input to an integrator causes the output of the integrator to increase at a constant rate; the value of the output is equal to the area under the input signal curve. It has been shown that an "ideal motor" combined with a potentiometer acts as an integrator.

problems

1-1. Calculate the power in horsepower and watts required to drive:
(a) 100 lb·ft at 300 rad/s
(b) 200 lb·ft at 1000 rpm
(c) 80 in·oz at 60°/s

1-2. Calculate the average power required to accelerate a 20-lb·ft·s² (20 slug·ft²) inertia from 0 to 200°/s in 3 s.

1-3. Calculate the power in horsepower and watts for the following cases (see Appendix C for conversion factors):
(a) $T = 10$ lb·ft, $\Omega = 200$ rpm
(b) $T = 1000$ in·lb, $\Omega = 150°/s$
(c) $T = 2000$ in·oz, $\Omega = 30$ rad/s
(d) $T = 13$ ton·yd, $\Omega = 12$ microdegrees/ms
(e) $T = 2.5$ in·oz, $\Omega = 3000$ rpm

1-4. Find the closed-loop gain $G'(j\omega)$ and the error gain $\epsilon(j\omega)/R(j\omega)$ for the following values of $G(j\omega)$:
(a) $100 \angle 0°$
(b) $10 \angle 0°$
(c) $1 \angle 0°$
(d) $0.5 \angle 0°$
(e) $100 \angle -90°$
(f) $10 \angle -90°$
(g) $1 \angle -90°$
(h) $0.5 \angle -90°$
(i) $1 \angle -135°$
(j) $1 \angle -175°$
(k) $1 \angle -180°$

1-5. The open-loop gain of a fully fed-back system is $0.8 \angle -135°$ at the frequency of a 5-V signal. Calculate (a) the system error and (b) the input-to-output phase shift.

1-6. Find the time integrals of the following functions and state the units of the answers:
(a) 7 V from 0 to 3 s
(b) 7 Volts from 8 to 11 s
(c) $8t$ V, where $t = $ time, from 0 to 2 s
(d) $6 \cos 2t$ V from 0 to 0.1 s
(e) $4e^{-5t}$ V from 0 to 0.2 s

2

servomechanism analysis techniques

In this chapter a number of new concepts and techniques are developed. Among them, Laplace transforms are introduced briefly. Near the end of this chapter, a first servo is examined and its characteristic equations analyzed.

2-1. frequency-response analysis

Figure 2-1 shows a voltage source connected to an inductance and a resistance. The simplest way to determine the frequency characteristics of this device is to assume a current i flowing in the circuit and then find the voltage drops across L and R in terms of i. In general, the voltage drop across a circuit element is its impedance times the current i. The magnitude and phase of the impedance are both variables as a function of frequency. Equation (2-1) defines the assumed current flowing in this circuit, $I \sin \omega t$. Equations (2-2) and (2-3) define the voltages across the resistance and the inductor, respectively. Equation (2-4) expresses the sum of these two voltages, which must be equal to the input voltage e.

$$i = I \sin \omega t \qquad (2\text{--}1)$$

$$e_R = RI \sin \omega t \qquad (2\text{--}2)$$

$$e_L = L\frac{di}{dt}(I \sin \omega t) = LI\omega \cos \omega t \qquad (2\text{--}3)$$

$$e = I(R \sin \omega t + L\omega \cos \omega t) \qquad (2\text{--}4)$$

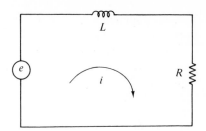

Figure 2-1. Circuit to demonstrate frequency
             response.

Equation (2-5) expresses the relationship between $\cos \omega t$ and $\sin \omega t$. Equation (2-6) restates Eq. (2-4) using Eq. (2-5). In Eq. (2-7), $\sin \omega t$ is factored out; this equation expresses the relationship between the applied voltage e and the resulting current. Impedance is defined as the voltage across an element divided by the current through it; the circuit's impedance is given in Eq. (2-8).

$$\cos \omega t = \sin (\omega t + 90°) = (\sin \omega t)\angle 90° = j \sin \omega t \qquad (2\text{-}5)$$

$$e = I(R \sin \omega t + L\omega \cos \omega t) - I[R \sin \omega t + (jL\omega \sin \omega t)] \qquad (2\text{-}6)$$

$$e = I \sin \omega t(R + j\omega L) \qquad (2\text{-}7)$$

$$Z = \frac{e}{i} = \frac{I \sin \omega t(R + j\omega L)}{I \sin \omega t} = R + j\omega L \qquad (2\text{-}8)$$

In Eq. (2-9) the impedance is separated into magnitude and phase components, where the phase θ is defined by Eq. (2-10).

$$Z = \sqrt{R^2 + (\omega L)^2} \ \angle \theta \qquad (2\text{-}9)$$

$$\theta = \tan^{-1}\left(\frac{\omega L}{R}\right) \qquad (2\text{-}10)$$

Figure 2-2 is a modification of Fig. 2-1 but circuit elements are labeled with

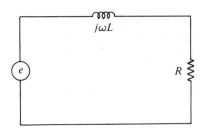

Figure 2-2. Circuit elements labeled with
             frequency-response impedances.

their actual impedance values; it is seen that the impedance expression for a simple ac circuit of this type may be written by inspection. It is this writing of impedance values by inspection that makes the frequency-response technique so easy to use. Naturally, the development that has just been presented via Eqs. (2-1) through (2-10) is *not* necessary when using the technique.

This development is only an informal proof presented as review and summary of the approach to be used.

A more practical way of using the frequency-response technique is to go in the reverse order from the above development, namely, to assume a voltage as given in Eq. (2-11) and then find the current:

$$e = E \sin \omega t \qquad (2\text{--}11)$$

The current is equal to the input voltage divided by the circuit impedance as expressed in Eq. (2-12).

$$i = \frac{e}{Z} = \frac{E \sin \omega t}{\sqrt{R^2 + (\omega L)^2} \angle \theta} = \frac{E \sin (\omega t - \theta)}{\sqrt{R^2 + (\omega L)^2}} \qquad (2\text{--}12)$$

Equation (2-13) expresses the circuit impedance in terms of its two components and then in terms of a magnitude and a phase angle.

$$Z = R + j\omega L = \sqrt{R^2 + (\omega L)^2} \angle \tan^{-1}\left(\frac{\omega L}{R}\right) \qquad (2\text{--}13)$$

The Laplace transform variable s may be substituted directly for $j\omega$, and a valid Laplace transform equation is determined. Equation (2-14), for instance, is the Laplace equivalent for Fig. 2-3 ($j\omega t$ is merely replaced by sL).

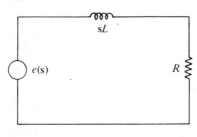

Figure 2-3. Circuit elements labeled with Laplace transform impedances.

$$E(s) = I(s)(R + Ls) \qquad (2\text{--}14)$$

The Laplace-transform approach has advantages which are discussed in Chapter 3; it gives insights into both the frequency response and the transient response of the circuit being analyzed.

Example 2-1. Frequency Response
Find the -3 dB upper break frequency for the network in Fig. E2-1.

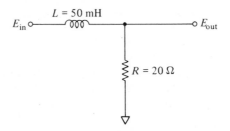

Figure E2-1

solution   The break frequency is such that the inductive reactance (ωL) equals the resistance (R):

$$50 \times 10^{-3}\omega = 20$$

$$\omega = \frac{20}{50 \times 10^{-3}}$$

$$= 400 \text{ rad/s}$$

$$f = \frac{400}{6.28} = 64 \text{ Hz}$$

Example 2-2. Frequency Response
Find the phase shift at 100 Hz for the circuit in Fig. E2-2.

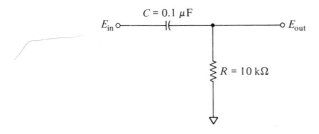

Figure E2-2

solution

$$\tau = RC = 10^4 \times 0.1 \times 10^{-6} = 10^{-3} \text{ s}$$

$$\omega_{\text{break}} = \frac{1}{\tau} = 1000 \text{ rad/s}$$

$$\frac{E_{\text{out}}}{E_{\text{in}}}(j\omega) = \frac{R}{R + 1/j\omega C} = \frac{1}{1 + 1/j\omega RC} = \frac{1}{1 + \omega_B/j\omega} = \frac{1}{1 - j\omega_B/\omega}$$

$$\text{Phase shift} = +\tan^{-1}\frac{\omega_B}{\omega} = +\tan^{-1}\frac{1000}{2\pi \times 100} = +\tan^{-1} 1.59 = +57.8°$$

2-2. *transient analysis*

Figure 2-4 shows a circuit where a constant voltage V is applied to a series combination of a resistor and a capacitor: the initial charge on the

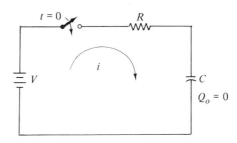

Figure 2-4. Transient response circuit
           example.

capacitor is zero. The integral equation expression for this circuit voltage as a function of current is given in Eq. (2-15).

$$V = iR + \frac{1}{C} \int i\, dt \qquad (2\text{--}15)$$

$$O = R\frac{di}{dt} + \frac{i}{C} \qquad (2\text{--}16)$$

$$\frac{i}{C} = -R\frac{di}{dt} \qquad (2\text{--}17)$$

The integral of the current is charge, and charge divided by capacitance is voltage. By differentiating Eq. (2-15), Eq. (2-16) is obtained; this is rearranged to provide Eq. (2-17). Equation (2-18) is a further rearrangement, and Eq. (2-19) is the integral of Eq. (2-18). Rearranging Eq. (2-19) provides Eq. (2-20). If both sides of Eq. (2-20) are taken as exponents of e, Eq. (2-21) results.

$$-R\frac{di}{i} = \frac{dt}{C} \qquad (2\text{--}18)$$

$$-R \ln i = \frac{t}{C} - k_1 \qquad (2\text{--}19)$$

$$\ln i = -\frac{t}{RC} + \frac{k_1}{R} = -\frac{t}{RC} + k_2 \qquad (2\text{--}20)$$

$$i = (e^{-t/RC})e^{k_2} = k_3 e^{-t/RC} \qquad (2\text{--}21)$$

When t is equal to zero (just after switch closure), the (initial instantaneous) current is the voltage divided by the resistance, because there is no initial voltage on the capacitor and therefore the full applied voltage must appear across the resistor. From Eq. (2-21) it can be seen that when t is zero the current is k_3. Therefore, k_3 is equal to the applied voltage divided by the resistance as expressed in Eq. (2-22); from this the final expression for current in the circuit is given in Eq. (2-23).

$$i(0+) = \frac{V}{R} = k_3 \qquad (2\text{--}22)$$

Therefore,

$$i = \frac{V}{R}e^{-t/RC} \qquad (2\text{--}23)$$

The transient analysis just described is straightforward but cumbersome. To get more insight into circuit operation the Laplace transform technique becomes very desirable, because it reduces differential equations to algebra and further provides simultaneous insight into both transient and frequency-response performance.

Example 2-3. Transient Response
Find the time after switch closure for the capacitor in Fig. E2-3 to charge to 0.5 V.

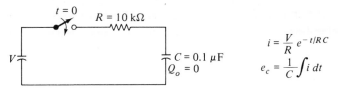

$$i = \frac{V}{R} e^{-t/RC}$$

$$e_c = \frac{1}{C} \int i \, dt$$

Figure E2-3

solution

$$e_c = \frac{1}{C} \int \frac{V}{R} e^{-t/RC} \, dt = -RC \times \frac{1}{C} \times \frac{V}{R} e^{-t/RC} + k$$

$$= -V e^{-t/RC} + k$$

At $t = 0 +$, $e_C = 0$; therefore, $0 = -V + k$ or $k = +V$.

$$e_c = -V e^{-t/RC} + V = V(1 - e^{-t/RC}) = V(1 - e^{-t/\tau})$$

where $\tau = RC = 10 \, k\Omega \times 0.1 \, \mu F = 1$ ms and $0.5 \, V = V(1 - e^{-t/\tau})$. Expressing the ratio t/τ in milliseconds we obtain

$$0.5 \, V = V(1 - e^{-t/1})$$

so that $e^{-t} = 0.5$ and $e^{+t} = 2.0$, and therefore

$$t = 0.694 \text{ ms}$$

2-3. introduction to Laplace transforms

The solution to the circuit shown in Fig. 2-4 will now be found using Laplace transforms. Equation (2-24) expresses the circuit equation in Laplace transform form.

$$\frac{V}{s} = \left(R + \frac{1}{sC}\right) I(s) \tag{2-24}$$

The applied constant input voltage V is divided by s to put it in Laplace transform form (the basis for this is given in Chapter 3). This applied signal is equal to the circuit response signal, which is the impedance times the current [the right side of Eq. (2-24)]. Equation (2-25) solves this for $I(s)$; the denominator of the right-hand expression determines the time character of the transient.

$$I(s) = \frac{V}{s(R + 1/sC)} = \frac{V}{Rs + 1/C} = \frac{V/R}{s + 1/RC} \tag{2-25}$$

$$\mathcal{L}^{-1}[I(s)] = \mathcal{L}^{-1} \frac{V/R}{s + 1/RC} = \frac{V}{R} e^{-t/RC} = i \tag{2-26}$$

Equation (2-26) shows the inverse Laplace transform process which converts the results of Eq. (2-25) into time-domain form. It may be seen that the right-hand part of the denominator becomes the constant k in the expression e^{-kt}; this fact makes it simple to solve transient problems using Laplace transforms. More will be said about Laplace transforms in Chapter 3 to develop further their usefulness as a tool for servo design.

2-4. transfer functions

For linear systems it is possible to use block-diagram algebra; this greatly facilitates the representation and physical visualization of such linear systems. In the frequency domain (or Laplace transform domain), it is possible to find the output of a system by taking the product of the input signal and the system's transfer function; this is shown in Fig. 2-5. Transfer functions

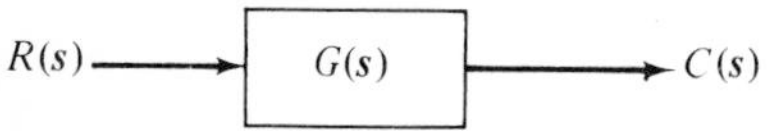

$$R(s) \longrightarrow \boxed{G(s)} \longrightarrow C(s)$$

$$C(s) = R(s)G(s)$$

Figure 2-5. Transfer-function block diagram.

have the property that they do not depend on the input signal or the initial conditions. The transfer-function technique is usable only in the frequency-response or Laplace transform domains, not in the time domain. For instance, for two electric filters in series, it is possible to find their combined characteristic by multiplying together their individual frequency-response characteristics (assuming, of course, that their transfer functions are not altered by mutual loading).

Example 2-4. Transfer Functions
Find the transfer function from E_{in} to E_{out} for the circuit shown in Fig. E2-4a.

solution Solve for the Thévenin equivalent.

$$R_{eq} = \frac{(20\ k\Omega)(100\ k\Omega)}{20\ k\Omega + 100\ k\Omega} = \frac{2000 \times 10^6}{120}\ k\Omega = 16.67\ k\Omega$$

$$E_{eq} = \frac{E_{in} \times 100\ k\Omega}{120\ k\Omega} = 0.833\ E_{in}$$

$$R_{eq}C = (16.67 \times 10^3)(0.001 \times 10^{-6}) = 16.67 \times 10^{-6} = 16.67\ \mu s$$

$$\omega_{RC} = \frac{10^6}{16.67} = 60{,}000\ rad/s$$

$$E_{out} = 0.833\ E_{in} \times \frac{1}{1 + j\omega/(60{,}000)} \times \frac{100}{1 + j\omega/(6280)}$$

$$G(s) = \frac{E_{out}(j\omega)}{E_{in}(j\omega)} = \frac{83.3}{(1 + j\omega/60{,}000)(1 + j\omega/6280)}$$

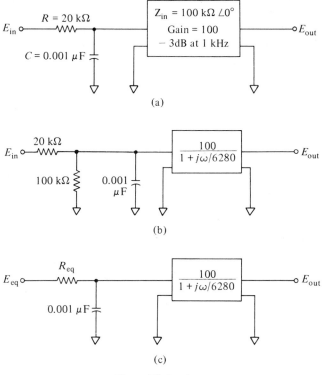

Figure E2-4 a, b, c

2-5. block-diagram algebra

Block-diagram algebra is used to simplify the work of the servo designer; it is an algebra of transfer functions. Figure 1-1 was given as the *standard diagram* of a closed-loop system. In this diagram there is only one gain, the forward loop gain G; the feedback line from the output is a direct connection (unity gain). Practical servo systems are not in the form of Fig. 1-1, and therefore it is necessary to reduce block diagrams of actual systems to this form. These manipulations result in improved insight into the servo's operation and at the same time do not modify the performance of the system.

Block-diagram algebra is a means of manipulating transfer functions; it is an algebra of transfer functions based on the linearity assumption. Input and output loading of the various elements in the system must be considered in writing the individual blocks. Figure 2-6a shows a part of a system where there is an input a coming into a gain A, the output of which is summed with another line that has an input b coming through a gain B and is sub-

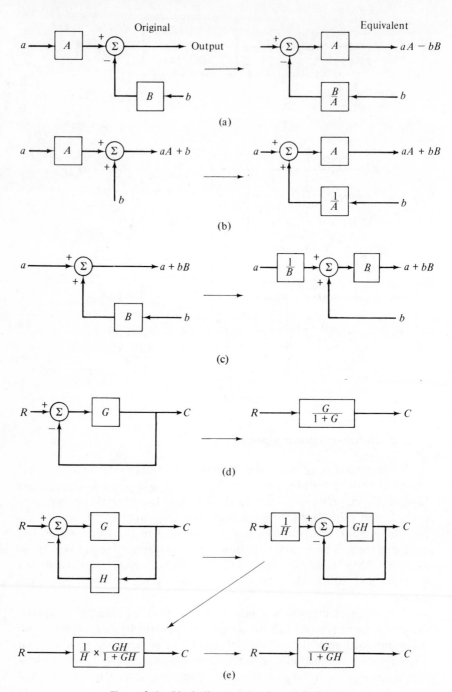

Figure 2-6. Block diagram alegebra equivalents.

tracted at the summing point. Equation (2-27) defines the output of the system of blocks given in Fig. 2-6a.

$$\text{Output} = aA - bB \qquad (2\text{-}27)$$

The second (right-hand) diagram of Fig. 2-6a provides the same output as the first diagram but has been modified to show a new equivalent block configuration. A way to state this block-diagram equivalence as a rule is to say that *the gain block between a and the ouput has moved through the summing point in the direction of signal flow.* Note that to keep the gain from b to the output the same as the original value, *the b-path gain must be divided by A.* This results in a new block diagram shown in Fig. 2-6a, right, but with unity gain between a and the summing point. Figure 2-6b demonstrates this same manipulation for two signals of the same polarity at the summing point. In Fig. 2-6c the gain block B is moved from the feedback path from b; as a result, 1/B appears between a and the summing point. The important aspect of these three situations is that *the gain from any input to the output must be the same before and after the manipulation.* In the case of Fig. 2-6a, the gain from a to the output is A. Likewise, the gain from b to the output is $-B$, and the second part of the diagram shows that this remains true. In both parts of Fig. 2-6b, the gain from a to the output is A and the gain from b to the output is unity. In both parts of Fig. 2-6c, the gain from a to the output is unity and the gain from b to the output is B.

Figure 2-6d is the standard diagram form of a servo; the equations for this configuration are given in Chapter 1. The closed-loop gain of this standard diagram is given in Eq. (1-5) and is repeated in block form in Fig. 2-6d. Figure 2-6e shows a more general form of a closed-loop system, where a constant gain H appears in the feedback path. By applying the manipulation

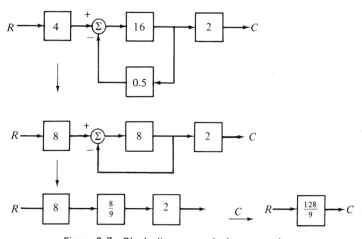

Figure 2-7. Block-diagram equivalent example.

of Fig. 2-6c to the first part of Fig. 2-6e, the second part of Fig. 2-6e is obtained. The part of this diagram to the right of the $1/H$ gain becomes the standard diagram with a forward gain of GH. Figure 2-7 gives an example of block-diagram algebra manipulation in numerical form. The second part is obtained by moving the feedback gain of 0.5 through the summing point as in Fig. 2-6c. The third part of the diagram is determined from Fig. 2-6d. In the fourth part, the three gains are multiplied together to give the final gain indicated in that diagram.

In summary, block-diagram algebra assumes linearity and considers input and output loading; it functions by moving blocks to new locations to give a more desirable system block diagram.

2-6. gain of an integrator

In Chapter 1 it was demonstrated that the overall frequency-response characteristic of an integrator is $1/j\omega$ as given in Eq. (1-11). The general frequency-response shape of this integrator was shown in Fig. 1-9; the gain magnitude changes as the reciprocal of frequency and the phase is a constant 90° lag. Figure 1-9 is a Bode plot which plots the logarithm of the gain magnitude versus the logarithm of the frequency and the phase versus the logarithm of frequency. Figure 2-8 shows this gain characteristic as a -1 slope on a

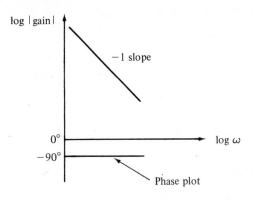

Figure 2-8. Bode plot of an integrator.

log gain versus log frequency curve (Bode plot). Equation (2-28) shows the gain expression for an integrator; included is the gain constant k:

$$G = \frac{k}{j\omega} \tag{2–28}$$

By examination of Eq. (2-28) it can be seen that when the angular frequency ω has the same magnitude as the constant k, the gain magnitude of the integrator is unity. If this integrator is put into a closed-loop system as in Fig.

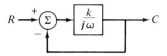

Figure 2-9. Standard form of frequency-response representation of integration in a loop.

2-9, the closed-loop gain can be determined by the use of the standard loop gain formula as given in Eq. (1-5); G' (the closed-loop gain) is equal to $G/(1 + G)$; this expression is worked out in Eq. (2-29).

$$G' = \frac{G}{1 + G} = \frac{k/j\omega}{1 + k/j\omega} = \frac{k}{j\omega + k} = \frac{1}{1 + j\omega/k} \qquad (2\text{-}29)$$

Figure 2-10 shows the closed-loop gain of an integrator plotted as a

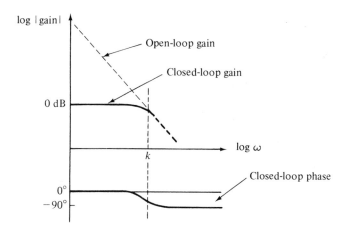

Figure 2-10. Bode plot of closed-loop response of an integrator in a loop.

function of frequency. Equation (2-29) shows that the closed-loop gain behaves as a low-pass filter; this is also demonstrated by Fig. 2-10.

Of significance is the fact that *an open-loop integrator has a gain constant equal to the frequency at which its gain magnitude goes through unity.* A second significant fact is that *if an integrator is closed inside a fully fed-back loop, the gain constant of this integrator (the frequency at which its gain magnitude is unity) becomes the closed-loop break frequency of the resulting low-pass filter.*

Example 2-5. Integrator Gain

An integrator has a gain of 10 at a frequency of 20 Hz. Calculate the gain and phase of a closed-loop system with the integrator output fully fed back to the input (standard diagram) at 100, 200, and 400 Hz.

solution

$$G'(j\omega) = \frac{1}{1 + jf/f_c}$$

$$f_c = \text{unity gain frequency} = 10 \times 20 = 200 \text{ Hz}$$

At $f = 100$ Hz,

$$G'(j2\pi \times 100) = \frac{1}{1 + j\frac{100}{200}} = \frac{1}{1 + j0.5} = \frac{1}{1.118 \angle 26.6°} = 0.895 \angle -26.5°$$

At $f = 200$ Hz,

$$G'(j2\pi \times 200) = \frac{1}{1 + j\frac{200}{200}} = \frac{1}{1 + j1} = 0.707 \angle -45°$$

At $f = 400$ Hz,

$$G'(j2\pi \times 400) = \frac{1}{1 + j\frac{400}{200}} = \frac{1}{1 + j2} = \frac{1}{2.236 \angle +63.4°} = 0.447 \angle -63.4°$$

2-7. frequency-response solution of an integrator in a loop

Figure 2-11 shows the same integrator system inside a closed loop. The gain of this integrator is k. Equations (2-30) through (2-32) give the basic system equations for Fig. 2-11.

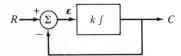

Figure 2-11. Integrator in a loop.

$$C = k \int \epsilon \, dt \qquad (2\text{-}30)$$

$$\epsilon = R - C \qquad (2\text{-}31)$$

$$C = k \int (R - C) \, dt \qquad (2\text{-}32)$$

Equation (2-30) defines the output C as a function of the error signal ϵ. Equation (2-31) shows that the error signal is the difference between the input R and the output C. Equation (2-32) combines Eq. (2-30) and Eq. (2-31). Equation (2-33) expresses Eq. (2-32) in frequency-response form.

In Chapter 1 it was shown that an integrator has a gain that varies as the reciprocal of frequency and has a phase of —90°. This description exactly fits Eq. (2-33). Equations (2-34) and (2-35) are rearrangements of Eq. (2-33). From Eq. (2-35), Eq. (2-36) defines the closed-loop gain. As can be seen, Eq. (2-36) provides the identical closed-loop gain previously developed in Eq. (2-29).

$$C = \frac{k(R - C)}{j\omega} \tag{2-33}$$

$$Cj\omega = kR - kC \tag{2-34}$$

$$(k + j\omega)C = kR \tag{2-35}$$

$$G' = \frac{C}{R} = \frac{k}{k + j\omega} = \frac{1}{1 + j\omega/k} \tag{2-36}$$

Figure 2-12 shows the closed-loop frequency characteristics on a Bode

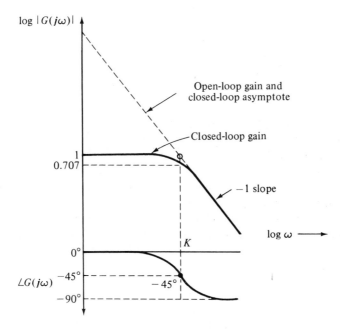

Figure 2-12. Bode plot of an integrator in a loop.

plot of this closed-loop integrator system. It can be seen that at the frequency $\omega = k$, the closed-loop gain is down to 0.707 (or -3 dB), and the phase shift is at $-45°$. On an asymptotic basis, one may consider that the closed-loop gain remains approximately flat to a frequency $\omega = k$ and then declines at a -1 slope for frequencies above $\omega = k$. Further, on an asymptotic basis, it can be assumed that the phase is $0°$ until the frequency approaches $\omega = k$ and then becomes $-90°$ at frequencies well above $\omega = k$, where the gain declines along a -1 slope. This is a convenient approximation; it says that the phase is $90°$ times the frequency derivative of the magnitude in regions of constant gain. The asymptotic approximation for gain is quite accurate when the frequency of interest differs from the break point (k) by a factor greater than 3 or 4; for phase, the approximation must be used with care.

At ten times a break frequency there will be an asymptotic error of slightly less than 6°.

2-8. ideal motor servo

Figure 2-13 again shows the torque-speed characteristic of an "ideal"

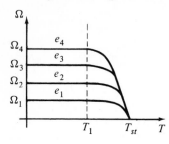

Figure 2-13. Torque-speed characteristic of ideal motor.

motor. This motor is ideal in the sense that over part of its operating characteristic the output velocity is a constant times the applied voltage. This characteristic is true only for demanded torques up to T_1. For torques greater than T_1 the motor velocity declines as the load torque increases. This motor characteristic is not unreasonable; there are practical motors whose performance is quite similar to this characteristic.

To analyze a servo using this ideal motor, it is first necessary to define the gain of the basic elements of the servo. In Fig. 2-14, K_p represents the gain of the potentiometer; Eq. (2-37) defines this gain.

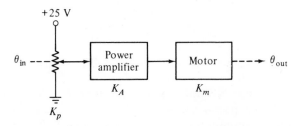

Figure 2-14. An open-loop motor control (integrator).

$$K_p = \frac{25\text{V}}{360°} = 0.0695\frac{\text{V}}{\text{deg}} \times \frac{57.3°}{\text{rad}} = 3.98\frac{\text{V}}{\text{rad}} \qquad (2\text{–}37)$$

K_A, the power amplifier gain in Fig. 2-14, is equal to 100 V/V. The third constant is K_m, which relates the motor output velocity to its applied voltage; this is expressed in Eq. (2-38).

$$K_m = \frac{1200\text{rpm}}{100\text{V}} = \frac{12\text{rpm}}{\text{V}} \times \frac{2\pi\text{ rad}}{\text{rev}} \times \frac{1\text{min}}{60\text{s}} = 1.255\frac{\text{rad/s}}{\text{V}} \qquad (2\text{–}38)$$

The basic gain of this motor is 12 rpm/V, which is equal to 1.255 (rad/s)/V. A closed-loop system may be obtained by adding a second potentiometer (K_p) to the output θ_{out}, and subtracting its output voltage from the input command from θ_{in}; this is shown in Fig. 2-15. The gains of the blocks of

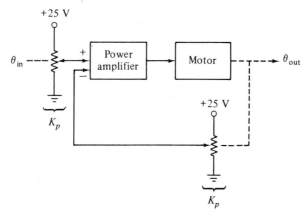

Figure 2-15. A closed-loop positioner (servo).

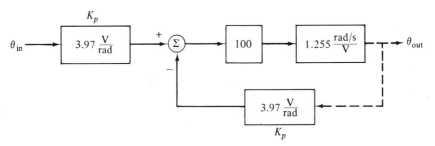

Figure 2-16. Block diagram of servo.

Fig. 2-15 are shown in Fig. 2-16. There is a gain K_p between θ_{in} and the summing point and between θ_{out} and the summing point.

Recalling Fig. 2-6a, it can be seen that the diagram of Fig. 2-16 can be converted directly into Fig. 2-17, which is in the form of the basic standard diagram of Fig. 1-1. By combining these three gains into one constant, Fig. 2-18 is obtained; this gain is G. G is equal to the product of the three constants, K_p, K_A, and K_m, and is shown in Eq. (2-39).

$$G = 3.97 \frac{\text{rad}}{\text{V}} \times 100 \frac{\text{V}}{\text{V}} \times 1.255 \frac{\text{rad/s}}{\text{V}} = 500 \frac{\text{rad/s}}{\text{rad}}$$

$$= 500\text{s}^{-1} \qquad\qquad (2\text{--}39)$$

It is seen that the expression G is equal to 500 rad/s/rad or 500s^{-1}. This result is obtained by multiplying quantities as well as dimensions.

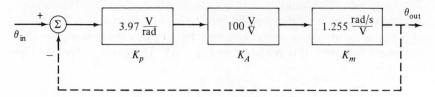

Figure 2-17. Simplified block diagram of servo.

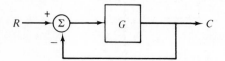

Figure 2-18. Standard form.

What is the meaning of a gain that has dimensions $1/t$? Consider Fig. 2-19 (previously given as Fig. 2-14); the output velocity of $\dot{\theta}_{\text{out}}$ or Ω_{out} is equal to a constant times the input voltage e as shown in Eq. (2-40). Equation

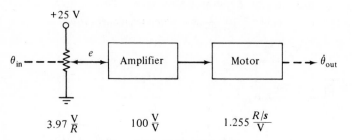

Figure 2-19. Open-loop speed control.

(2-41) combines Eq. (2-40) with K_p, the gain of the potentiometer; it states that the output velocity is equal to a constant times the input angle. Equation (2-42) gives the time integral of Eq. (2-41); the result is that the output angle is equal to a constant times the integral of the input angle. Equation (2-43) expresses Eq. (2-42) in frequency-response form (it was shown previously that an integrator has a frequency characteristic of a constant divided by $j\omega$).

$$\Omega_{\text{out}} = ke = \dot{\theta}_{\text{out}} \tag{2-40}$$

$$\dot{\theta}_{\text{out}} = \frac{d\theta_{\text{out}}}{dt} = kK_p\theta_{\text{in}} = k_1\theta_{\text{in}} \tag{2-41}$$

$$\theta_{\text{out}} = k_1 \int \theta_{\text{in}}\, dt \tag{2-42}$$

$$\theta_{out}(j\omega) = \frac{k_1\theta_{in}(j\omega)}{j\omega} \tag{2-43}$$

$$G(j\omega) = \frac{\theta_{out}(j\omega)}{\theta_{in}(j\omega)} = \frac{k_1}{j\omega} = \frac{500}{j\omega} \tag{2-44}$$

$$G(j\omega) = \frac{500(s^{-1})}{j\omega(s^{-1})} \tag{2-45}$$

The resulting open-loop gain $G(j\omega)$ is expressed in Eq. (2-44). A loop gain must be nondimensional because it expresses the gain from some starting point, around a loop, and back to that starting point. Equation (2-45) shows that the gain is nondimensional. Equation (2-39) gave the dimensions of k as reciprocal seconds; clearly, the dimensions of $j\omega$ are dimensions of frequency or reciprocal seconds. Referring to Fig. 2-18, it may be seen that if output C is subtracted from input R, the difference is an angle. Therefore the input and the output of $G(j\omega)$ are angles dimensionally. Consequently, the gain of $G(j\omega)$ must be nondimensional; to be nondimensional it must consist of 500 s^{-1} divided by a quantity that is also dimensionally reciprocal seconds (frequency); Eqs. (2-44) and (2-45) meet this dimensional requirement perfectly.

It was shown earlier in this chapter that the gain constant of an integrator [k in Eq. (2-44)] is equal to the bandwidth of the closed-loop system. Therefore the servo shown in Figs. 2-17 and 2-18 has a closed-loop bandwidth of 500 rad/s (approximately 80 Hz).

2-9. summary

In this chapter frequency-response analysis was described briefly; this technique involves representing system elements as impedances and determining the overall network impedance by algebra. Transient analysis was introduced; this involves the solution of differential equations considering initial conditions. Laplace transforms were introduced very briefly as a convenient frequency-domain technique that can provide insight into transient performance; Laplace transforms are valuable for servo analysis and design. Block-diagram algebra was described as a useful technique to assist in analysis and design of linear systems. The fact that the gain of an integrator is the same as its unity gain frequency was shown. It was also shown that the break frequency of a low-pass filter (which results from fully feeding back the output of an integrator) is the gain constant of the integrator. Finally, a servo using an ideal motor (one that is relatively insensitive to load torques) was analyzed. This ideal motor also behaves as an integrator.

problems

2-1. Derive the expression for voltage gain in terms of frequency for the following networks:

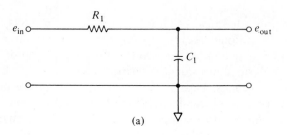

(a)

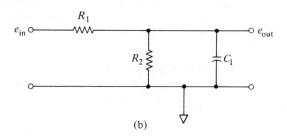

(b)

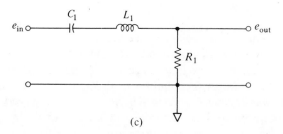

(c)

Figure P2-1 a, b, c

2-2. For $R_1 = 100\ \Omega$, $R_2 = 10\ \Omega$, $C_1 = 10\ \mu F$, and $L_1 = 0.001\ H$, find the significant frequencies for the networks of Problem 2-1.

2-3. For a simple low-pass filter that exhibits a phase lag of 25° at 15 Hz, calculate: (a) the frequencies for phase lags of 45° and 80° and (b) (the magnitude of) its gain at phase lags of 25°, 45°, and 80°.

2-4. For the circuit shown in Fig. P2-4, find e_{out} as a function of time; sketch the output.

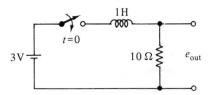

Figure P2-4

2-5. For the circuit shown in Fig. P2-5, find e_{out} as a function of time using Laplace transforms; sketch the output (zero initial conditions).

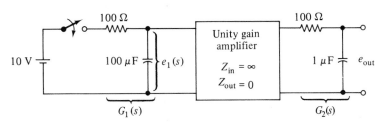

Figure P2-5

2-6. Find the transfer functions (as functions of s) for the three networks of Problem 2-1.

2-7. Find the transfer functions for the networks of (a) Problem 2-4 and (b) Problem 2-5.

2-8. Find the transfer function for the following circuits:

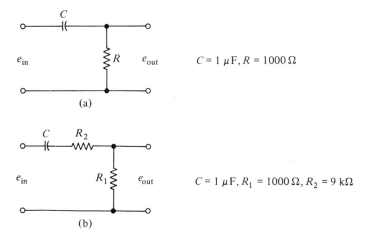

Figure P2-8 a, b

2-9. Reduce the following block diagrams to their simplest form:

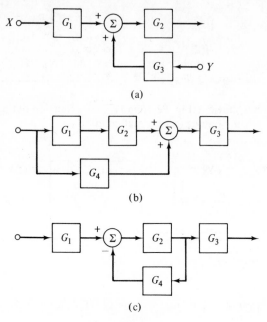

(a)

(b)

(c)

Figure P2-9 a, b, c

2-10. For an integrator with a gain of 100 at 20 Hz, calculate the gain at (a) 10 Hz, (b) 100 Hz, (c) 1000 Hz, and (d) 2000 Hz.

2-11. If the integrator of Problem 2-10 is enclosed in a fully fed-back loop, calculate (a) the −3 dB frequency of the closed-loop response, (b) the frequency when the phase lag is 70°.

2-12. If an integrator has a gain of 10 at 4 rad/s, how much gain should be provided in series to give a closed loop −3 dB bandwidth of 10 Hz?

3

Laplace transforms

The basic properties of practical servos are revealed through the use of linear differential equations with constant coefficients. Laplace transforms are a more convenient tool which provide more information and give the designer some valuable areas of system insight. Laplace transforms convert linear differential equations having constant coefficients into simple algebraic equations. In the design and practical analysis of servos, Laplace transforms give insight into both the transient performance of servos and their frequency-response characteristics. A ready means of transformation of frequency representation into transient performance is made available through the use of Laplace transforms.

3-1. basic properties

An important property of Laplace transforms is the fact that a time function has corresponding to it (and associated with it) a Laplace transform function. This Laplace transform function is essentially a function in the *frequency domain*. The Laplace transform results from an operation on a function of time $f(t)$; this yields $F(s)$, which is a function of the complex variable s (s is typically the term used for the Laplace variable, although p appears in the literature; however, in this book, s is used throughout.)

Equation (3-1) gives the definition of the Laplace transform function $F(s)$ of the original time function $f(t)$.

$$F(s) = \mathcal{L}[f(t)] = \int_0^\infty f(t)e^{-st}\, dt \qquad (3-1)$$

It turns out that often it is not necessary to go through this integration because of the unique correspondence between Laplace functions and real-time functions. Later in this chapter a table is given (Table 3-1) which lists *transform pairs*. The transform pairs given are sufficient to perform most practical servo analysis and design problems.

There are many books that cover Laplace transforms, their development, the rigorous mathematics associated with them, and the complex variable theory which is required for evaluation of some of the inverse transformation integrals. This book is not concerned with a rigorous presentation of Laplace transforms; however, this may be helpful background material for the reader. This chapter is a summary presentation of some of the highlights of Laplace transform theory.

3-2. transform examples

Example 3-1 shows the solution for the determination of the Laplace transform of a *unit step function* defined in Eq. (3-2) and shown in Fig. 3-1.

$$f(t) = 1 \quad \text{for } t > 0 \Big\}$$
$$ = 0 \quad \text{for } t \leq 0 \Big\} \tag{3-2}$$

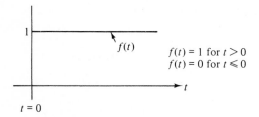

$$f(t) = 1 \text{ for } t > 0$$
$$f(t) = 0 \text{ for } t \leqslant 0$$

$t = 0$

Figure 3-1.   Unit step function.

The development is straightforward; it is the evaluation of the integral given in Eq. (3-1). The unit step function has a value of one over the time range of $t > 0$ to $t = \infty$; therefore its integral becomes the time integral of e^{-st} from zero to ∞. This is evaluated in Eq. (3-3); the answer is $1/s$.

$$\mathcal{L}[f(t)] = \int_0^\infty 1 e^{-st}\, dt = \left[\left(\frac{1}{-s}\right)e^{-st}\right]_0^\infty = \frac{e^{-st}}{-s}\bigg|_0^\infty = 0 - \frac{1}{-s} = \frac{1}{s} \tag{3-3}$$

This result shows that any unit step function applied to a circuit or to a servo may be expressed as the Laplace function K/s, where K is the magnitude of the step. A 7-V step, for instance, is transformed to $7/s$ V in Laplace representation.

Example 3-2 presents the Laplace transform of the simple decaying exponential e^{-at} which is determined in Eq. (3-4). The function e^{-at} is $f(t)$ in this case. The direct evaluation of this integral provides

$$\mathcal{L}[f(t)] = \mathcal{L}[e^{-at}] = \int_0^\infty e^{-at}e^{-st}\,dt = \int_0^\infty e^{-(a+s)t}\,dt$$

$$= \frac{e^{-(a+s)t}}{-(a+s)}\Big|_0^\infty = 0 - \frac{1}{-(a+s)} = \frac{1}{s+a} \qquad (3\text{-}4)$$

yielding $1/(s+a)$ as the Laplace transform of the decaying exponential, e^{-at}.

The transforms determined in Examples 3-1 and 3-2 are used frequently in this book. Step functions (Example 3-1) are widely used as "test inputs" to evaluate servo performance. Decaying exponentials of the form e^{-at} are the time-variable parts of many typical solutions of stable systems.

3-3. the Laplace transform table

The unique correspondence between Laplace functions and time functions is of great importance for the solution of many engineering problems. Table 3-1 gives a number of time functions $f(t)$ and their corresponding Laplace functions $F(s)$. In C, a time ramp (which is the integral of a unit step) is given as $1/s^2$; this introduces the concept of *real-time integration* being accomplished in the Laplace domain by multiplying a given quantity by $1/s$. This is demonstrated in J of Table 3-1, where the integral of $f(t)\,dt$ (with zero

Table 3-1   Laplace transform table

$f(t)$	$F(s)$
A. 1 (unit step)	$1/s$
B. e^{-at}	$\dfrac{1}{s+a}$
C. t (unit ramp)	$\dfrac{1}{s^2}$
D. $\dfrac{1}{a}(1 - e^{-at})$	$\dfrac{1}{s(s+a)}$
E. $\dfrac{1}{\beta}\sin\beta t$	$\dfrac{1}{s^2+\beta^2}$
F. $\cos\beta t$	$\dfrac{s}{s^2+\beta^2}$
G. $\dfrac{1}{\beta}e^{-at}\sin\beta t$	$\dfrac{1}{(s+a)^2+\beta^2}$
H. $e^{-at}\cos\beta t$	$\dfrac{s+a}{(s+a)^2+\beta^2}$
I. $\dfrac{d}{dt}f(t)$ (zero initial conditions)	$sF(s)$
J. $\int f(t)\,dt$ (zero initial conditions)	$\dfrac{F(s)}{s}$
K. $f(t-\tau)$ (time delay or "transport lag")	$e^{-\tau s}$

initial conditions) is $F(s)/s$; therefore, if the integral of $f(t)$ is desired and $F(s)$ is already known, the expression for $F(s)$ is divided by s to obtain the integral. The last transform pair (K) in Table 3-1 is for a pure time delay; the effect is constant gain and a phase lag that increases in proportion to frequency. The other transform pairs are self-explanatory.

Example 3-3.

(a) Find $\mathcal{L}[\sin \omega t]$.

   solution

$$\mathcal{L}[\sin \omega t] = \int_0^\infty [\sin \omega t] e^{-st}\, dt = \int_0^\infty \left[\frac{e^{j\omega t} - e^{-j\omega t}}{2j}\right] e^{-st}\, dt$$

$$= \frac{1}{2j} \int_0^\infty [e^{(j\omega - s)t} - e^{-(j\omega + s)t}]\, dt$$

$$= \frac{1}{2j} \left[\frac{e^{(j\omega - s)t}}{j\omega - s} + \frac{e^{-(j\omega + s)}}{j\omega + s}\right]_0^\infty$$

$$= \frac{1}{2j} \left[\frac{e^{j\omega t} e^{-st}}{j\omega - s} + \frac{e^{-j\omega t} e^{-st}}{j\omega + s}\right]_0^\infty$$

$$= \frac{1}{2j} \left[\frac{-1}{j\omega - s} + \frac{-1}{j\omega + s}\right]$$

$$= \frac{1}{2j} \left[\frac{-j\omega - s - j\omega + s}{-s^2 - \omega^2}\right]$$

$$= \frac{-2j\omega}{2j(-s^2 - \omega^2)}$$

$$= \frac{\omega}{s^2 + \omega^2}$$

(b) Find $\mathcal{L}^{-1}\left[\dfrac{7}{s + 4}\right]$.

   solution

$$\mathcal{L}^{-1}\left[\frac{7}{s + 4}\right] = 7\mathcal{L}^{-1}\left[\frac{1}{s + 4}\right]$$

Using B of Table 3-1,

$$7\mathcal{L}^{-1}\left[\frac{1}{s + 4}\right] = 7e^{-4t}$$

(c) Find $\mathcal{L}^{-1}\left[\dfrac{6}{s^2 + 16}\right] = \mathcal{L}^{-1}\left[\dfrac{6}{s^2 + (4)^2}\right] = 6\mathcal{L}^{-1}\left[\dfrac{1}{s^2 + (4)^2}\right]$.

   solution

   Using E of Table 3-1,

$$6\mathcal{L}^{-1}\left[\frac{1}{s^2 + (4)^2}\right] = \frac{6}{4} \sin 4t = 1.5 \sin 4t$$

(d) Find $\mathcal{L}^{-1}\left[\dfrac{39}{s}\right]$.

solution

$$\mathcal{L}^{-1}\left[\frac{39}{s}\right] = 39\mathcal{L}^{-1}\left[\frac{1}{s}\right]$$

Using A of Table 3-1,

$$39\mathcal{L}^{-1}\left[\frac{1}{s}\right] = 39u(t)$$

where $u(t)$ is a step function defined as zero before $t = 0$ and one after $t = 0$.
(e) Find $\mathcal{L}[3e^{-4t}]$.

solution

$$\mathcal{L}[3e^{-4t}] = 3\mathcal{L}[e^{-4t}] = 3\int_0^\infty e^{-4t}e^{-st}\,dt$$

$$= 3\int_0^\infty e^{(-4-s)t}\,dt = \frac{3}{-4-s}e^{(-4-s)t}\bigg|_0^\infty$$

$$= \frac{3}{-4-s}[0-1] = \frac{3}{s+4}$$

This same result could have been obtained by using B of Table 3-1.
(f) Find $\mathcal{L}[6 \sin 2t]$.

solution

$$\mathcal{L}[6 \sin 2t] = 6\left[\frac{2}{s^2+4}\right] = \frac{12}{s^2+4}$$

This example is a numerical repeat of Example 3-3(a); the result could have been determined from E of Table 3-1.
(g) What is the Laplace transform of a function of time that is equal to 0 V before $t = 0$ and 8 V after $t = 0$?

solution

$$F(s) = \mathcal{L}(8 \text{ V})u(t) = \int_0^\infty 8e^{-st}\,dt$$

$$= \frac{8}{-s}[e^{-\infty} - e^{-0}]$$

$$= \frac{8}{s}\,\text{V}$$

This result is directly obtainable from A of Table 3-1.
(h) Find the time expression for the current in the circuit given in Fig. E3-3.

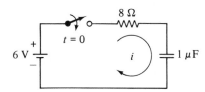

Figure E3-3

solution The transform of the applied voltage is $6/s$ V; this can be equated to the transform of the circuit current:

$$\frac{6}{s} = 8I(s) + \mathcal{L}\left[\frac{1}{C}\int i\,dt\right]$$

Using J of Table 3-1,

$$\frac{6}{s} = 8I(s) + \frac{1}{C}\left[\frac{I(s)}{s}\right]$$

or

$$\frac{6}{s} = \left[8 + \frac{1}{Cs}\right]I(s)$$

Therefore,

$$I(s) = \frac{6/s}{8 + 1/Cs} = \frac{6}{8s + 1/C}$$
$$= \frac{6/8}{s + (^1/_8)/C} = \frac{0.75}{s + 0.125/C}\text{A}$$

Therefore,

$$i(t) = 0.75e^{-0.125t/C} = 0.75e^{-0.125\times10^6 t}\text{ A}$$

The current has a peak value of 0.75 A and decreases exponentially with a time constant of $(0.125 \times 10^6)^{-1}$ s or 0.125 μs.

Example 3-4 derives the transfer function of the circuit given in Fig. 3-2. This is done by transforming the loop equations [Eqs. (3-5) and (3-6)]

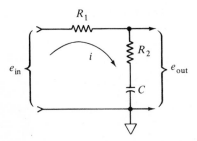

Figure 3-2.   Electrical network.

into their Laplace transform equivalents [Eqs. (3-7) and (3-8)]. Actually, Eqs. (3-5) and (3-6) can be written directly as Laplace "impedance" functions. Equation (3-9) gives the transfer function in Laplace form.

$$e_{\text{in}} = (R_1 + R_2)i + \frac{1}{C}\int i\,dt \qquad (3\text{-}5)$$

$$e_{\text{out}} = iR_2 + \frac{1}{C}\int i\,dt \qquad (3\text{-}6)$$

$$E_{\text{in}}(s) = (R_1 + R_2)I(s) + \frac{1}{Cs}I(s) = \left(R_1 + R_2 + \frac{1}{Cs}\right)I(s) \qquad (3\text{-}7)$$

$$E_{out}(s) = \left(R_2 + \frac{1}{Cs}\right)I(s) \tag{3-8}$$

$$\frac{E_{out}(s)}{E_{in}(s)} = \frac{(R_2 + 1/Cs)I(s)}{(R_1 + R_2 + 1/Cs)I(s)} = \frac{R_2 + 1/Cs}{R_1 + R_2 + 1/Cs}$$

$$= \frac{1 + R_2 Cs}{1 + (R_1 + R_2)Cs} \tag{3-9}$$

3-4. stability

It is also important that system stability may be readily determined from the form of the Laplace transform solution. Consider the time function e^{-at} as shown in Fig. 3-3. The transform of e^{-at} has been shown as $1/(s + a)$; clearly a must be more positive than zero to result in a decaying exponential; a system characterized by a *decaying* exponential is *stable*. Figure 3-4 shows

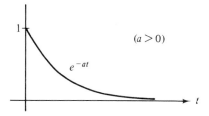

Figure 3-3. Decaying exponential with finite time constant.

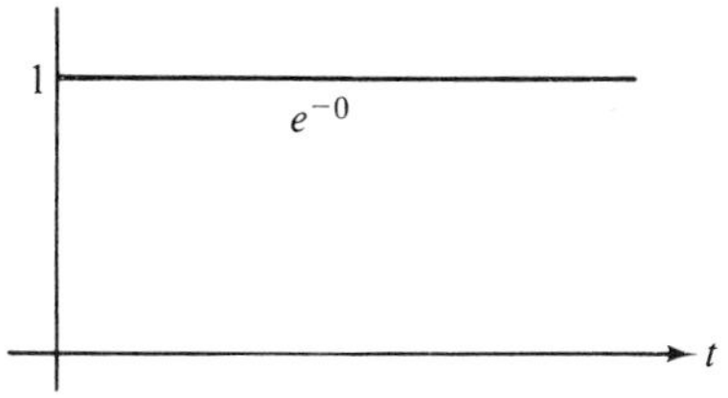

Figure 3-4. Decaying exponential with infinite time constant.

the same decaying exponential, but in this case a is zero. For a equal to zero, the exponential takes an infinitely long time to decay; in other words, the output remains at a constant value. This result is the same as the step function transform which is $1/s$.

For a less than zero ($a = -b$), the result is e^{+bt}, which transforms to $1/(s - b)$; this gives an increasing exponential as shown in Fig. 3-5. This third case shown in Fig. 3-5 is the *unstable* case, because the output keeps climbing until it reaches infinity (circuit or system saturation). Qualitatively

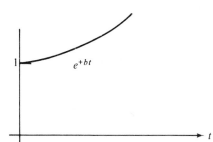

Figure 3-5. Increasing exponential.

speaking, therefore, *denominator* terms of the form $s + a$ are stable, those of the form s are borderline, and those of the form $s - b$ are unstable.

This book is concerned only with the first two cases: $a \geq 0$. By assuming stability, a practical engineering assumption, a lot of complex mathematics is eliminated.

Example 3-5. Find the transfer function of the system shown in Fig. E3-5 for the potentiometer wiper at points a, b, and c.

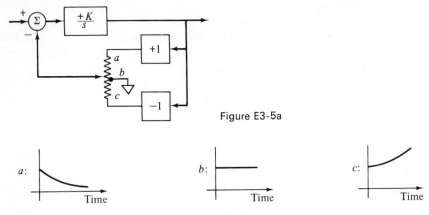

Figure E3-5a

Figure E3-5b

solution

a: $G'(s) = \dfrac{G(s)}{1 + G(s)H(s)} = \dfrac{K/s}{1 + (K/s)(+1)} = \dfrac{K}{s + K}$

b: $G'(s) = \dfrac{K/s}{1 + (K/s)(0)} = \dfrac{K}{s}$

c: $G'(s) = \dfrac{K/s}{1 + (K/s)(-1)} = \dfrac{K}{s - K}$

3-5. the integrator

In Table 3-1 it was noted that the integration process is accomplished by dividing by s. It was shown in Chapter 1 that integration may also be expressed by $1/j\omega$. Therefore, if it is desired to find the performance of the closed-loop system of Fig. 3-6, which has an integrator for $G(s)$, Eqs. (3-10) and (3-11) may be written.

$$G(s) = \frac{\omega_c}{s} \tag{3-10}$$

$$G'(s) = \frac{G(s)}{1 + G(s)} = \frac{\omega_c/s}{1 + \omega_c/s} = \frac{\omega_c}{s + \omega_c} = \frac{1}{1 + s/\omega_c} \tag{3-11}$$

ω_c is used as the gain of this integrator (k was used in Eq. 2-28).

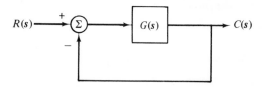

Figure 3-6. Closed-loop system
(standard form).

Equation (3-11) gives the solution for $G'(s)$. The resulting expression for $G'(s)$ is that of a low-pass filter, the same as Eq. (2-29) except that now s is is used rather than $j\omega$.

The fact that *an integrator inside a loop gives a low-pass filter response* is a significant result and will be used throughout the remainder of this book. Because a servo can be approximated as an integration inside a loop, Eq. (3-12) is an excellent first-order approximation of the closed-loop transfer function of a linear servo.

$$G'(j\omega) = \frac{1}{1 + j\omega/\omega_c} \tag{3-12}$$

As can be seen, the result of *an integration inside a loop is a low-pass filter with a bandwidth equal to the gain of the integrator.* Figure 3-6 and Eqs. (3-10), (3-11), and (3-12) are very fundamental to the performance of servos; further study depends on using these basic relationships.

Example 3-6. Find the gain crossover frequency, ω_c for a capacitor driven by a current source as shown in Fig. E3-6, where $C = 0.01\ \mu\text{F}$.

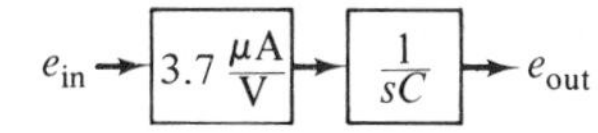

$$e_{in} \rightarrow \boxed{3.7\ \frac{\mu\text{A}}{\text{V}}} \rightarrow \boxed{\frac{1}{sC}} \rightarrow e_{out}$$

Figure E3-6

solution

$$G(s) = \frac{3.7 \times 10^{-6}\ \text{A}}{\text{V}\cdot\text{rad/s}} \times \frac{1}{0.01 \times 10^{-6}\ \text{F}} = \frac{370\ \text{V/s}}{\text{V}\cdot\text{rad/s}} = \frac{370\ \text{rad/s}}{s\ (\text{rad/s})}$$

Therefore,

$$\omega_c = 370\ \text{rad/s}$$

Example 3-7. Integration in Loop

Calculate the break frequency of closed-loop response in the system shown in Fig. E3-7.

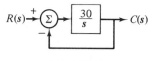

Figure E3-7

solution

$$G = \frac{30}{s}$$

$$G' = \frac{30/s}{1 + 30/s} = \frac{30}{s + 30} = \frac{1}{1 + s/30}$$

Therefore the break frequency is 30 rad/s.

3-6. a simple servomechanism

In Fig. 3-7 consider the same simple servo with a bandwidth of ω_c; apply to it F_{in}, a step function of unity magnitude. Equation (3-13) expresses

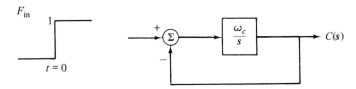

Figure 3-7.   Integrator in a loop (standard form).

the output-controlled variable $C(s)$ in terms of the input function and the closed-loop transfer function of the servo. Equation (3-14) describes the terms of Eq. (3-13).

$$C(s) = F_{in}(s)G'(s) \tag{3-13}$$

$$\text{Output transform} = \text{Input transform} \times \text{Transfer function} \tag{3-14}$$

The transform of the input function F_{in} is given in Eq. (3-15). The transfer function for $G'(s)$ was given in Eq. (3-11) and is restated in Eq. (3-16). By taking the product of the right sides of Eqs. (3-15) and (3-16), the transform of the output signal $C(s)$ is determined in Eq. (3-17).

$$F_{in}(s) = \frac{1}{s} \tag{3-15}$$

$$G'(s) = \frac{\omega_c}{s + \omega_c} \tag{3-16}$$

Therefore,

$$C(s) = \frac{1}{s} \times \frac{\omega_c}{s + \omega_c} \tag{3-17}$$

The system time response (transient response) can now be determined by taking the inverse transform of $C(s)$. The controlled variable in Laplace transform form is given in Eq. (3-17). This result is restated in Eq. (3-18) in "partial fraction" form. It is necessary here to break the transform into two parts to use the previously listed simple transform pairs to obtain the transient solution.

$$\frac{1}{s} \times \frac{\omega_c}{s + \omega_c} = \frac{A}{s} + \frac{B}{s + \omega_c} \tag{3-18}$$

A partial fraction solution may be obtained by finding values of A and B that satisfy Eq. (3-18) for all values of s. To do this, the left and right sides of Eq. (3-18) are multiplied by s; this gives Eq. (3-19).

$$\frac{\omega_c}{s + \omega_c} = A + \frac{Bs}{s + \omega_c} \qquad (3\text{-}19)$$

By letting s go to zero, the value of A is immediately determined as 1. This is a valid procedure because Eq. (3-18) must hold for all values of s. Similarly, Eq. (3-18) may be multiplied by $s + \omega_c$ to provide Eq. (3-20)

$$\frac{\omega_c}{s} = \frac{A(s + \omega_c)}{s} + B \qquad (3\text{-}20)$$

$$\frac{1}{s} \times \frac{\omega_c}{s + \omega_c} = \frac{1}{s} - \frac{1}{s + \omega_c} = C(s) \qquad (3\text{-}21)$$

By substituting $s = -\omega_c$, it is found that B is equal to -1. The result of substituting the values of A and B gives Eq. (3-21); this is the equivalent of Eq. (3-18) but with the proper values of A and B. It is now possible to take the inverse transform of the two parts of Eq. (3-21); this is given in Eq. (3-22). This inverse transform gives the output as a function of time; the time plot is shown in Fig. 3-8.

$$C(t) = 1 - e^{-\omega_c t} \qquad (3\text{-}22)$$

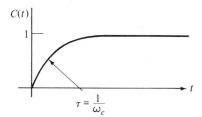

Figure 3-8.   Step-function response of integrator in a loop.

The above solution was relatively straightforward and simple; the important results are (1) that a servo acts as a low-pass filter and (2) that the output rise time due to a step-function input is $1/\omega_c$, where ω_c is the gain of the integrator (i.e., bandwidth of the servo).

Example 3-8. Using partial fractions and Table 3-1, find the expression for the output time response of the system in Fig. E3-8.

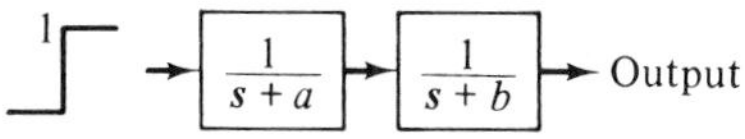

$$\boxed{\frac{1}{s+a}} \longrightarrow \boxed{\frac{1}{s+b}} \longrightarrow \text{Output}$$

Figure E3-8

solution

$$\text{Output} = \frac{1}{s} \times \frac{1}{s+a} \times \frac{1}{s+b} = \frac{1}{s(s+a)(s+b)}$$

$$= \frac{A}{s} + \frac{B}{s+a} + \frac{C}{s+b}$$

where

$$A = \frac{1}{ab}$$

$$B = \frac{1}{-a(-a+b)} = \frac{1}{a^2 - ab}$$

and

$$C = \frac{1}{-b(-b+a)} = \frac{1}{b^2 - ab}$$

Then

$$\text{Output} = \frac{1/ab}{s} + \frac{1/(a^2 - ab)}{s+a} + \frac{1/(b^2 - ab)}{s+b}$$

or

$$0(t) = \frac{1}{ab} + \frac{1}{a^2 - ab}e^{-at} + \frac{1}{b^2 - ab}e^{-bt}$$

Example 3-9. Find the response of Example 3-7 to a unit step function.

$$R(s) = \frac{1}{s} \qquad C(s) = ? \qquad C(t) = ?$$

solution

$$C(s) = \frac{30}{s(s+30)} = \frac{A}{s} + \frac{B}{s+30}$$

where

$$A = \left[s \frac{30}{s(s+30)}\right]_{s=0} = \frac{30}{0+30} = +1$$

and

$$B = \left[(s+30)\frac{30}{s(s+30)}\right]_{s=-30} = \frac{30}{-30} = -1$$

$$C(s) = \frac{1}{s} - \frac{1}{s+30}$$

$$C(t) = \mathcal{L}^{-1}\left[\frac{1}{s} - \frac{1}{s+30}\right] = 1 - e^{-30t}$$

3-7. summary

Basic properties of Laplace transforms have been introduced. There is a unique correspondence between a time function and a Laplace transform function; therefore changing from the Laplace domain to the time domain can be readily accomplished through the use of a Laplace transform table and some algebraic manipulations. To find a system's response to an input function, the transforms of the input and of the system transfer function are multiplied together to obtain the transform of the output. To obtain the output time function, the inverse transformation can be taken by using partial fractions and the Laplace transform table. The integrator has been reexamined using Laplace transforms, and finally a simple servo (a pure integrator in a loop) has been examined to shown that it has a bandwidth of ω_c and a step-function response time constant of $1/\omega_c$.

problems

3-1. Find $\mathcal{L}[\sin \omega t]$.

3-2. Find the transfer function of the circuit in Fig. P3-2. Let $R_1 C_1 = \tau_1$, $R_2/(R_1 + R_2) = k$.

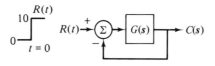

Figure P3-2

3-3. For $G(s) = 18/s$, and the step input shown in Fig. P3-3, evaluate:

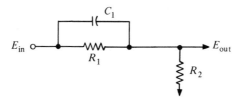

Figure P3-3

(a) ω_c
(b) $R(s)$
(c) $G'(s)$
(d) $C(t)$
(e) $G'(j18)$, closed-loop gain at 18 rad/s

3-4. Given Fig. P3-4, find:

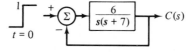

Figure P3-4

(a) ω_c
(b) $C(t)$

3-5. Given Fig. P3-5, find $C(t)$.

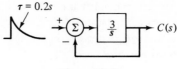

Figure P3-5

4

simple servo performance

The velocity constant K_v is discussed; K_v for a simple servo will be found equal to ω_{cp}, the open-loop gain crossover frequency (frequency of unity gain). ω_{cp}, which was introduced in Chapter 3 as ω_c, is the most basic servo constant; ω_{cp} will be discussed further in this chapter and throughout the remainder of this book. It is now designated as ω_{cp} rather than as ω_c to indicate that it relates to the *position* loop. The physical characteristics of springs, dampers, and inertias are examined, and reflection of inertias through gear trains is discussed.

4-1. velocity constant

The velocity constant (K_v) of a servo may be defined as the ratio between the steady-state constant input velocity and the resulting angular error. Consider Fig. 4-1. According to the previous definition, ω_{cp} is 5.1 rad/s, since this is the gain of the integrator (or ideal motor). Consider now an input ramp as shown in Fig. 4-2, where the input angle θ equals At. The servo error ε approaches a constant because this provides a ramp at the output, C.* The output rate is the same as the input rate; this resulting output is shown in Fig. 4-3. If the output C is equal to A rad/s (which it must be for a constant angular error), then the error is equal to C rad/s divided by ω_{cp} (which is 5.1). Therefore the ratio between the output C and the error ε is ω_{cp}, ω_{cp} is 5.1, and this is (equal to) the velocity constant K_v.

* If the error were a ramp, the output would be a parabola; if the error were zero, the output would be a constant; therefore the error must be constant in order to satisfy the system equation, $R - C = \varepsilon$.

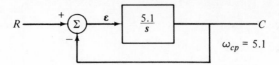

Figure 4-1.   Integration in a loop: A simple servo.

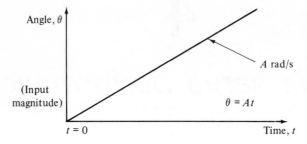

Figure 4-2.   A ramp function starting at $t = 0$.

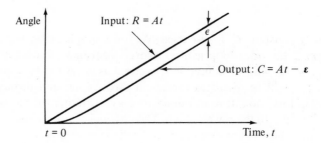

Figure 4-3.   Input and response of a simple servo to a ramp
function.

In summary, to provide a steadily increasing output, the system error
must be a constant; for the error to be a constant, the output C must lag
behind the input R. The K_v of this simple system of Fig. 4-1 is ω_{cp}.

Now let us consider K_v by the *final value theorem*, which will now be
introduced. Equation (4-1) states the final value theorem: A function of time
as time approaches infinity is equal to s times the Laplace transform of the
function as s approaches zero.

$$f(t) = sF(s) \qquad (4\text{-}1)$$
$$\scriptstyle t\to\infty \qquad s\to 0$$

Equation (4-2) is the transform expression for the error. $R(s)$ is $1/s^2$ because
this is the transform of a ramp (Table 3-1c); this is given in Eq. (4-3). The
Laplace expression for the error is given in Eq. (4-4).

$$\varepsilon(s) = R(s)\frac{1}{1 + G(s)} = \frac{R(s)}{1 + 5.1/s} = \frac{sR(s)}{s + 5.1} \qquad (4\text{-}2)$$

$$R(s) = \frac{1}{s^2} \qquad \text{(ramp transform)} \qquad (4\text{-}3)$$

$$\varepsilon(s) = \frac{s}{s^2(s + 5.1)} = \frac{1}{s(s + 5.1)} \tag{4-4}$$

To find the error as t approaches infinity, $\varepsilon(s)$ is used for $F(s)$ in Eq. (4-1); this is given in Eq. (4-5). K_v, which is the input divided by the steady-state error, is 5.1 as shown in Eq. (4-6); this agrees with the previous conclusion that K_v is ω_{cp}.

$$\varepsilon(t)\Big|_{t \to \infty} = s\,\varepsilon(s)\Big|_{s \to 0} = \frac{s}{s(s + 5.1)}\Big|_{s \to 0} = \frac{1}{s + 5.1}\Big|_{s \to 0} = \frac{1}{5.1} \tag{4-5}$$

$$K_v = \frac{\text{input}}{\text{error}}\Big|_{t \to \infty} = \frac{1}{1/5.1} = 5.1 = \omega_{cp} \tag{4-6}$$

Example 4-1. Given $K_v = 60 \text{ s}^{-1}$, find the servo error in degrees for a $10°/\text{s}$ input.

solution

$$\text{Error} = \frac{\text{input rate}}{K_v} = \frac{10°/\text{s}}{60 \text{ s}^{-1}} = \tfrac{1}{6}°$$

Example 4-2. Given $\omega_{cp} = 20 \text{ rad/s}$, and $\dot\theta = 20 \text{ rpm}$, find the error in degrees.

solution

$$K_v = \omega_{cp} = 20 \text{ s}^{-1}$$

$$\dot\theta = 20\frac{\text{rev}}{\text{min}} \times \frac{360°}{\text{rev}} \times \frac{1 \text{ min}}{60 \text{ s}} = 120°/\text{s}$$

$$\text{Error} = \frac{120°/\text{s}}{20 \text{ s}^{-1}} = 6°$$

4-2. first-order approximation of a servo

Let us now consider the first-order approximation of a servo as given in Fig. 4-4. As has been seen previously, Fig. 4-4 behaves as a low-pass filter.

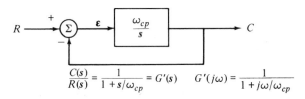

$$\frac{C(s)}{R(s)} = \frac{1}{1 + s/\omega_{cp}} = G'(s) \qquad G'(j\omega) = \frac{1}{1 + j\omega/\omega_{cp}}$$

Figure 4-4.   Simple servo: First-order approximation of any servo.

This is stated both in Laplace form and in frequency-response form under Fig. 4-4. Figure 4-5 shows the asymptotic frequency behavior of a simple servo. The open-loop characteristic is a -1 slope with unity gain at ω_{cp} rad/s.

Asymptotically, the closed loop gives a flat response out to ω_{cp} and then

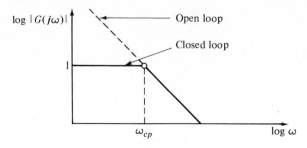

Figure 4-5. Asymptotic frequency response of a simple servo.

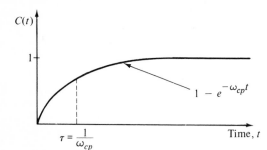

Figure 4-6. Step response of a simple servo.

the gain slopes off at a -1 slope. The step response, as solved in Section 3-6, is given in Fig. 4-6. The time constant of the transient is $1/\omega_{cp}$. The error response to a step function is shown in Fig. 4-7. In all the cases given in Figs. 4-4 through 4-7 the expression ω_{cp} is used; since ω_{cp} and K_v are identical for this simple servo, K_v could just as well have been used.

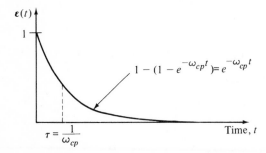

Figure 4-7. Error response to a step function for a simple servo.

K_v has been a very popular constant in servo literature and justifiably so. In this book, however, K_v is considered secondary relative to ω_{cp} because ω_{cp} is the fundamental constant of servo performance from both a frequency-response and transient-response standpoint. Therefore, servo parameters and performance characteristics are expressed in terms of this basic constant, ω_{cp}.

Example 4-3. Given an integrator $G(s) = 16/s$ in series with a constant gain of 5: find K_v and the error in degrees for an input rate of 10 rpm.

solution

$$\omega_{cp} = 16 \times 5 = 80 \text{ s}^{-1} = K_v$$

$$\dot{\theta} = 10 \text{ rpm} \times \frac{6°/\text{s}}{\text{rpm}} = 60°/\text{s}$$

$$\text{Error} = \frac{60°/\text{s}}{80 \text{ s}^{-1}} = 0.75°$$

Example 4-4. For the system shown in Fig. E4-4, determine the output due to a step input.

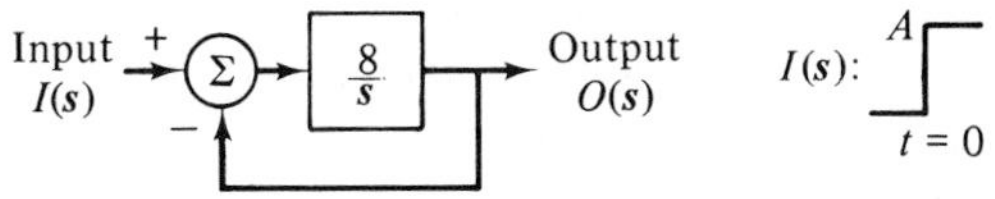

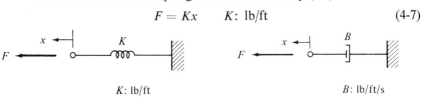

Figure E4-4

solution

$$G(s) = \frac{8}{s}$$

$$G'(s) = \frac{G(s)}{1 + G(s)} = \frac{8/s}{1 + 8/s} = \frac{8}{8 + s}$$

For step:

$$O(s) = I(s)G'(s) = \frac{A}{s} \times \frac{8}{s + 8} = \frac{M}{s} + \frac{N}{s + 8}$$

$$M = A \qquad N = -A$$

$$O(s) = \frac{A}{s} - \frac{A}{s + 8}$$

$$O(t) = A - Ae^{-8t} = A(1 - e^{-8t})$$

4-3. linear mechanical elements

There are three basic linear mechanical elements; these can be described in either translational or rotational terms. In translational terms, Figs. 4-8, 4-9, and 4-10 show the spring, dashpot, and mass elements. These three elements are the only components of any linear mechanical dynamic system. The characteristics of these mechanical systems may be determined through the investigation of the differential equations which describe their motion.

The characteristics of a spring are described in Eq. (4-7).

$$F = Kx \qquad K: \text{lb/ft} \tag{4-7}$$

$K:$ lb/ft

Figure 4-8. The spring element.

$B:$ lb/ft/s

Figure 4-9. The viscous friction or dashpot element.

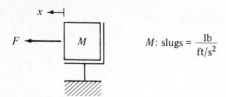

Figure 4-10.   The mass element.

The spring provides a retarding force in proportion to the amount that it is stretched (or compressed). The force is F and the amount of stretch is x. In the case of a dashpot which provides a viscous friction effect, the amount of force is proportional to the *velocity* of motion or $\dot{x}$ (the first time derivative of the position x). The three proportionality constants for the spring, dashpot, and mass are K, B, and M, and these are used in Eqs. (4-7), (4-8), and (4-9).

$$F = B\dot{x} \qquad B: \text{lb/ft/s} \tag{4-8}$$

$$F = M\ddot{x} \tag{4-9}$$

It is important to recognize that mass and weight are not the same physical quantity. Equation (4-10) defines the relationship between mass and weight.

$$W = Mg$$
$$\text{lb} = \text{slugs} \cdot \text{ft/s}^2 \tag{4-10}$$

Weight is mass times gravitational acceleration; the result is that a certain mass will have a particular weight on the earth, but the same mass will have a lower weight on the moon where the gravitational acceleration, g, is less. The dimensions of Eq. (4-10) are shown below it; weight is expressed in pounds, mass is expressed in slugs, and gravity is 32.2 ft/s² in the English system. A useful relationship to recognize is the one written as part of Fig. 4-10: Slugs are the same as pound seconds squared per foot (lb·s²/ft). This may be determined by transposing Eq. (4-11). Of importance is the fact that Eq. (4-9) is valid for M equal to mass, not weight; if the weight is known, it can be converted to mass using Eq. (4-10).

$$32.2 \text{ lb} = 1 \text{ slug} \times 32.2 \text{ ft/s}^2 \tag{4-11}$$

In a rotational system the same three mechanical components appear, but torques are used instead of forces, and angular rotation is used instead of translational motion. Figure 4-11 demonstrates the relationship between a

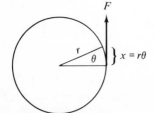

Figure 4-11.   Relationship between rotational and translational motion.

translation x and a rotation θ for a radius arm r moving about a center C. It may be seen that for small angles the translation x is equal to the radius r times θ.

It is known that torque is force times distance, in this case F times r. Torque in English system units is expressed in pound feet. In the case of a spring rotational system as shown in Fig. 4-12, the equation is essentially the

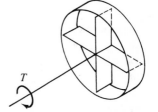

Figure 4-12.   Rotational spring element.

same as Eq. (4-7) except that torque is used instead of force; this is shown in Eq. (4-13). The rotational spring constant in this case is shown in Eq. (4-14) and is torque per unit angle rather than force per unit distance.

$$T = \text{torque} = Fr \qquad (4\text{-}12)$$

$$T = k\theta \qquad (4\text{-}13)$$

$$K = \frac{T}{\theta} \qquad K: \frac{\text{lb} \cdot \text{ft}}{\text{rad}} \qquad (4\text{-}14)$$

The dimensions of this constant K are pound feet per radian in the English system. In the case of viscous friction, Fig. 4-13 suggests a rotational dashpot.

Figure 4-13.   Rotational viscous friction element (rotational dashpot).

A rotational dashpot provides a back or counter torque proportional to angular velocity. This is defined in Eq. (4-15), where the torque is equal to a constant B times the angular rotation rate; the rotational rate is expressed as $\dot{\theta}$ or as Ω.

$$T = B\dot{\theta} = B\Omega \qquad B: \frac{\text{lb} \cdot \text{ft}}{\text{rad/s}} \qquad (4\text{-}15)$$

Example 4-5. Find the expression for the output velocity for the system shown in Fig. E4-5.

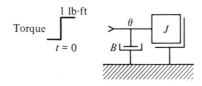

Figure E4-5.   For $B = \dfrac{2 \text{ lb} \cdot \text{ft}}{\text{rad/s}}$; $J = 8$ slug$\cdot$ft^2

solution

$$T(s) = (Bs + Js^2)\theta(s) = (B + Js)\Omega(s)$$

$$\Omega(s) = \frac{T(s)}{Js + B} = \frac{1/s}{8s + 2} = \frac{1}{s(8s + 2)}$$

$$= \frac{0.125}{s(s + 0.25)} = \frac{A}{s} + \frac{B}{s + 0.25}$$

$$A = 0.5 \qquad B = -0.5$$

$$\Omega(s) = \frac{0.5}{s} - \frac{0.5}{s + 0.25}$$

$$\Omega(t) = 0.5(1 - e^{-0.25t}) \text{ rad/s}$$

Example 4-6. For a 10-lb step input, find $x(t)$ for the systems in Fig. E4-6.

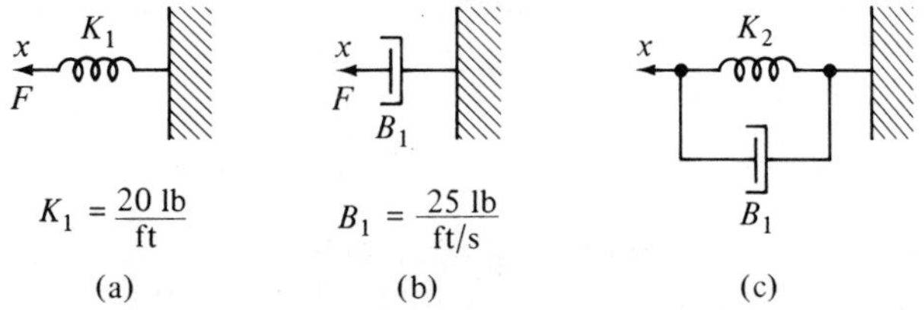

$$K_1 = \frac{20 \text{ lb}}{\text{ft}}$$

(a)

$$B_1 = \frac{25 \text{ lb}}{\text{ft/s}}$$

(b)

$$B_1$$

(c)

Figure E4-6

solution

(a) $F = K_1 x$

$$x = \frac{F}{K_1} = \frac{10 \text{ lb}}{20 \text{ lb/ft}} = 0.5 \text{ ft}$$

(b) $F(s) = B_1 sx(s)$ or $x(s) = \frac{F(s)}{B_1 s} = \frac{10 \text{ lb/s}}{B_1 s} = \frac{10 \text{ lb}}{(25 \text{ lb/ft/s})s^2} = \frac{0.4}{s^2} \text{ ft/s} = 0.4t \text{ ft}$

(c) $F(s) = B_1 sx(s) + K_1 x(s) = (K_1 + B_1 s)x(s)$

$$F(s) = (K_1 + B_1 s)x(s) \quad \text{or} \quad x(s) = \frac{F(s)}{K_1 + B_1 s}$$

$$x(s) = \frac{10/s}{20 + 25s}$$

$$x(s) = \frac{10}{s(25s + 20)} = \frac{0.4}{s(s + 0.8)} = \frac{A}{s} + \frac{B}{s + 0.8}$$

$$A = \frac{0.4}{0.8} = 0.5 \qquad B = \frac{0.4}{-0.8} = -0.5$$

$$x(s) = \frac{0.5}{s} - \frac{0.5}{s + 0.8}$$

$$x(t) = 0.5(1 - e^{-0.8t}) \text{ ft}$$

Figure 4-14 may assist the explanation of moment of inertia. If at the

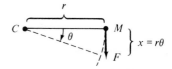

Figure 4-14. Point mass at the end of a radius arm
(to develop moment of inertia).

end of a weightless radius arm r which is rotating about a center C is placed a point mass M, then the force required to accelerate the mass is defined in Eq. (4-16), the mass times the second derivative of the position x.

$$F = M\ddot{x} \tag{4-16}$$

It has been shown using Fig. 4-11 that x is equal to $r\theta$ and so $\ddot{x}$ is equal to $r\ddot{\theta}$; therefore the force is equal to $mr\ddot{\theta}$ as given in Eq. (4-17). But the torque is equal to the radius times the force, and this gives the result $mr^2\ddot{\theta}$ as in Eq. (4-18).

$$F = Mr\ddot{\theta} \tag{4-17}$$

$$T = rF = Mr^2\ddot{\theta} \tag{4-18}$$

It is common to define the quantity mr^2 as the moment of inertia; this, naturally, is true only for a point mass on a weightless arm as shown in Fig. 4-14. For a more general mass, the inertia is the sum of *all* the point masses times the square of their individual radii from the center of rotation, or the integral of $r^2\,dm$ as in Eq. (4-19). The result is that Eq. (4-18) may be restated as Eq. (4-20): it can then be redefined in Laplace variable terms as Eq. (4-21).

$$J = \sum Mr^2 = \int r^2\,dM \tag{4-19}$$

$$T = J\ddot{\theta} = J\dot{\Omega} \tag{4-20}$$

$$T(s) = Js^2\theta(s) \tag{4-21}$$

Moment of inertia has dimensions of slug feet squared in the English system; and as shown in Section 4-3 and in Appendix C, a slug is also 1 lb·s²/ft. The result is that moment of inertia in the English system is also pound feet seconds squared (lb·ft·s²).

Example 4-7. Find the moment of inertia J of a 10-lb mass at a 2-ft radius.

solution

$$J = Mr^2 \qquad M = \frac{10\text{ lb}}{32.2\text{ ft/s}^2} = 0.31\,\frac{\text{lb}\cdot\text{s}^2}{\text{ft}}$$

$$J = 0.31\,\frac{\text{lb}\cdot\text{s}^2}{\text{ft}} \times 4\text{ ft}^2 = 1.24\text{ lb}\cdot\text{ft}\cdot\text{s}^2$$

$$= 1.24\text{ slug}\cdot\text{ft}^2$$

Example 4-8. Find the moments of inertia of the following (see Appendix D):

(a) a solid right-circular cylinder weighing 4 lb with a diameter of 2 in.; about its axis.

(b) a solid sphere weighing 4 lb about a diameter; the diameter is 6 in.

(c) a 28-lb, 2-ft diameter disk about its axis.

   solution

(a) $J = \dfrac{Mr^2}{2}$ $M = \dfrac{4\ lb}{32.2\ ft/s^2}$ $r = 1\ in. = \frac{1}{12}\ ft$

$J = \dfrac{1}{2} \times \dfrac{4}{32.2} \times \dfrac{1}{(12)^2} lb \cdot ft \cdot s^2 = 0.000431\ lb \cdot ft \cdot s^2$

(b) $J = \dfrac{2Mr^2}{5} = \dfrac{2}{5} \times \dfrac{4}{32.2} \times \left(\dfrac{1}{4}\right)^2 = 0.0031\ lb \cdot ft \cdot s^2$

(c) $J = \dfrac{Mr^2}{2} = \dfrac{28}{32.2} \times \dfrac{1}{2} = 0.435\ lb \cdot ft \cdot s^2$

Inertia is very important in the analysis of servos because it is normally an accurate representation of a servo load; the inertial forces acting on the system usually far exceed the friction forces. In most servos there is no spring-like restraining force. The practical analysis and design approach pursued in this book considers the load to be an inertia and uses this model to examine the stability and dynamic performance. Friction forces are considered separately as perturbations causing predictable system errors.

4-4. reflected inertia

An easy way to determine how inertias reflect through gear trains is to consider the kinetic energy of various different gears in a system. Equation (4-22) gives kinetic energy in its normal rectalinear form: $\frac{1}{2}MV^2$. To convert to a rotating system, consider the point mass at the end of a weightless radius arm r shown in Fig. 4-15; the linear velocity is $r\Omega$ and therefore the kinetic

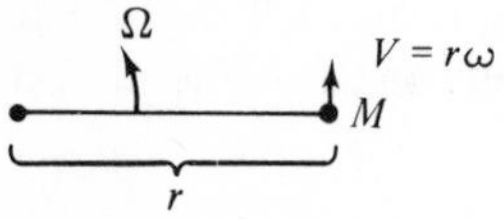

Figure 4-15.   Point mass at radius r (to develop kinetic energy).

energy is $\frac{1}{2}Mr^2\Omega^2$ as shown in Eq. (4-23). The moment of inertia is Mr^2; therefore the kinetic energy can be restated as $\frac{1}{2}J\Omega^2$ as given in Eq. (4-24). This is quite similar to the original kinetic-energy expression of $\frac{1}{2}MV^2$.

$$\text{Kinetic energy} = \tfrac{1}{2}MV^2 \qquad (4\text{-}22)$$

$$= \tfrac{1}{2}Mr^2\Omega^2 \qquad (4\text{-}23)$$

$$= \tfrac{1}{2}J\Omega^2 \qquad (4\text{-}24)$$

This development was restricted to a point mass; however the same relationship is true for *any* shaped mass as long as the moment of inertia about the

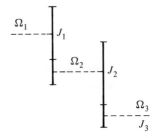

Figure 4-16. Three-pass gear system (to develop reflected inertia ratios).

shaft of interest is known. Figure 4-16 shows three gears which have inertias J_1, J_2, and J_3. Actually, the gear train is a "three-pass" system where the total inertia on shaft 1 is J_1, the total inertia on shaft 2 is J_2, and the total inertia on shaft 3 is J_3. Using Eq. (4-24), the kinetic energy of the whole system can be written as given in Eq. (4-25). The angular velocity of any different part of the system is related to the number of gear teeth on the various gears; defining N_m as a gear ratio from Ω_1 to Ω_m, Eq. (4-26) restates Eq. (4-25) using the appropriate gear ratios.

$$\text{Kinetic energy} = \tfrac{1}{2}J_1\Omega_1^2 + \tfrac{1}{2}J_2\Omega_2^2 + \tfrac{1}{2}J_3\Omega_3^2 + \cdots \qquad (4\text{-}25)$$
$$= \tfrac{1}{2}(J_1\Omega_1^2 + J_2\Omega_1^2 N_2^2 + J_3\Omega_1^2 N_3^2)$$
$$= \tfrac{1}{2}\Omega_1^2(J_1 + J_2 N_2^2 + J_3 N_3^2 + \cdots)$$
$$\text{where } \Omega_m = N_m\Omega_1 \qquad (4\text{-}26)$$
$$J_{eq} = J_1 + J_2 N_2^2 + J_3 N_3^2 + \cdots \qquad (4\text{-}27)$$

This demonstrates that the total kinetic energy is $\tfrac{1}{2}\Omega_1^2$ times several different inertia expressions: $J_1, J_2 N_2^2$, and $J_3 N_3^2$. The original kinetic-energy expression as given in Eq. (4-24) is of the form $\tfrac{1}{2}J\Omega^2$; therefore the equivalent inertia of the system at Ω_1 is $J_1 + J_2 N_2^2 + J_3 N_3^2$, and the total equivalent inertia reflected to the Ω_1 axis is as given in Eq. (4-27). In general, *any* inertia at a gear ratio N_m reflects as N_m^2.

Example 4-9. Find the moment of inertia of (a) 20 lb at 3 ft radius, (b) of (a) through a 10:1 gear ratio (low speed at inertia).

  solution

(a) $J = \dfrac{20}{32.2}(3)^2 \text{ lb·ft·s}^2 = 5.58 \text{ lb·ft·s}^2$
$$= 5.58 \text{ slug·ft}^2$$

(b) $J_{reflected} = \dfrac{5.58 \text{ slug·ft}^2}{N^2} = \dfrac{5.58 \text{ slug·ft}^2}{100}$
$$= 0.0558 \text{ slug·ft}^2$$

Example 4-10. Given the system of Fig. E4-10a.
(a) Determine the transfer function for each block.
(b) Draw the diagram in block/transfer-function form. Reduce to standard form.

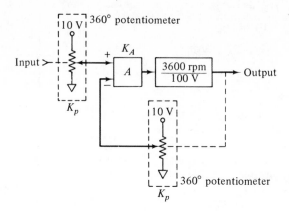

Figure E4-10a

(c) What is the expression for ω_{cp}?
(d) What value should K_A have to give a steady-state error of 0.1° for a 10°/s input rate (ramp)?

solution

(a) $K_p = \dfrac{10\ \text{V}}{2\pi\ \text{rad}} = 1.59\dfrac{\text{V}}{\text{rad}}$

$K_A = A\dfrac{\text{V}}{\text{V}}$

$K_{\text{motor}} = \dfrac{1}{s} \times 3600\dfrac{\text{rev}}{\text{min}} \times \dfrac{1}{100\ \text{V}} \times \dfrac{2\pi\ \text{rad}}{\text{rev}} \times \dfrac{1\ \text{min}}{60\ \text{s}}$

$= \dfrac{1}{s} \times \dfrac{6 \times 2\pi\ \text{rad/s}}{10}\dfrac{}{\text{V}} = \dfrac{3.76\ \text{rad/s}}{s}\dfrac{}{\text{V}}$

(b)

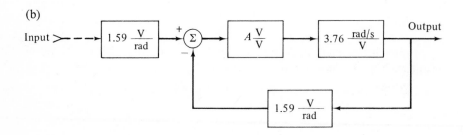

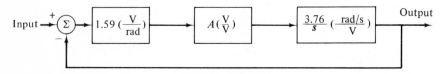

Figure E4-10b

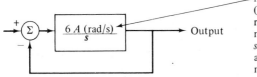

Note that dimensions (units) of numerator are radians per second; this must be the case since s has like dimensions and the net loop gain must be nondimensional.

Figure E4-10b (cont.)

(c) $\omega_{cp} = 6A$ rad/s

(d) $K_v = \dfrac{10(°/s)}{0.1(°)} = 100\left(\dfrac{1}{s}\right) = \omega_{cp} = 6A$

$6A = 100$

$A = 16.67\dfrac{V}{V}$

4-5. summary

The concept of the velocity constant K_v was introduced. The more fundamental constant, ω_{cp}, which is the frequency of unity gain of an integrator, was discussed. The spring, dashpot, and inertia were introduced; these are the three mechanical components found in linear dynamic systems. The forces required to move these three components are significant in the study and design of servos. In particular, inertia is used realistically as the standard servo mechanical load for stability and dynamic analysis; friction and other perturbating forces will be considered in the analysis of servo errors. Finally, the way in which inertias reflect through gear trains was developed.

problems

4-1. For $K_v = 20$, calculate the error in degrees for a 10-rpm input.

4-2. An integrator with a gain of 15 at 4 Hz is enclosed in a fully fed-back loop. Calculate the error in degrees for a 6-rpm input.

4-3. To have an error of 0.1°, what gain must be added in series with an integrator with a gain of 3 at 2 Hz if it is in a fully fed-back loop, and the input is 10°/s?

4-4. For the mechanical system shown in Fig. P4-4, find $x(t)$ for a force step of $F = 9$ lb.

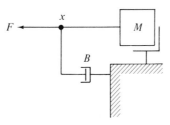

Figure P4-4

4-5. Find the moment of inertia of the following:
(a) A 6-lb point mass at a radius of 2 ft
(b) Repeat (a) but at the low-speed end of a 3:1 gear train
(c) An 8-lb disk about an axis through its center (diameter = 3 ft)

4-6. Find the time expression for $\Omega_1(t)$ and $\Omega_2(t)$ for the system in Fig. P4-6, where J is a 4-ft diameter disk weighing 7 lb, and B is 6 lb·ft/rad/s.

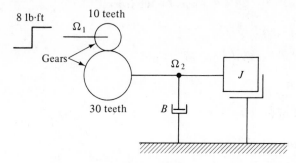

8 lb·ft   10 teeth
Ω_1
Gears
Ω_2
J
30 teeth B

Figure P4-6

4-7. Given the system shown in Fig. P4-7.

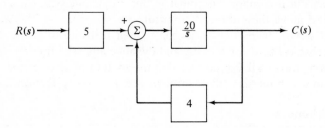

$R(s) \longrightarrow \boxed{5} \longrightarrow \overset{+}{\underset{-}{\Sigma}} \longrightarrow \boxed{\dfrac{20}{s}} \longrightarrow C(s)$

$\boxed{4}$

Figure P4-7

(a) Reduce the system to standard form.
(b) Calculate ω_{cp}
(c) Find $C(s)/R(s)$.
(d) Calculate C/R at a frequency of 10 Hz.

4-8. Given the system shown in Fig. P4-8, calculate:

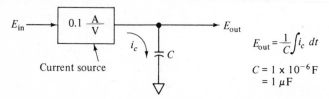

$E_{in} \longrightarrow \boxed{0.1 \dfrac{A}{V}} \longrightarrow E_{out}$

$i_c \downarrow \quad \overline{\overline{}} C$

Current source

$E_{out} = \dfrac{1}{C}\int i_c \, dt$

$C = 1 \times 10^{-6} F$
$= 1 \,\mu F$

Figure P4-8

(a) $(E_{\text{out}}/E_{\text{in}})(s)$

(b) ω_{cp}

(c) the open-loop gain $(E_{\text{out}}/E_{\text{in}})$ at 10 kHz

4-9.

(a) Plot the error response for a "simple servo" (Bode).

(b) Solve the transient-error response for a unit step input.

5

servo motors

In this chapter some basic characteristics of dc servo motors are developed. The important *conceptual loop* technique is introduced and is used for the basic dc servo with and without armature inductance. A generally valuable technique of servo constant subscripts is presented.

Figure 5-1a shows the torque-speed characteristic of a dc servo motor. This servo motor supplies increasing torque for increasing voltage as indicated on the ordinate and gives increasing angular velocity for increasing applied voltage as shown on the abscissa. An expression for torque is given in this figure; this torque expression is nothing more than an equation for the family of torque-speed curves labeled e_1, e_2, e_3, and e_4, respectively. The form of this equation is of interest; it indicates that torque is proportional to a constant times the applied voltage and that the torque varies inversely as speed. The second part of this expression accounts for the decrease in speed; the effect is similar to a viscous friction force as defined in Chapter 4. Figure 5-1b shows these two components of the torque equation; the upper half of Fig. 5-1b shows torque as a constant times the applied voltage; the torque remains constant as the angular velocity increases: this is the $K_T e_{in}$ portion. The lower part of the lower diagram shows the viscous friction part of the motor characteristic. It may be seen that the graphical sum of these two components provides the actual resultant motor characteristic.

5-1. dc servo motor characteristics

Figure 5-2 is a pictorial diagram of an armature-controlled dc motor; a constant-field flux is provided by means of a constant current i_f passing

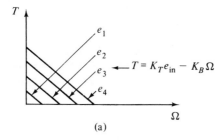

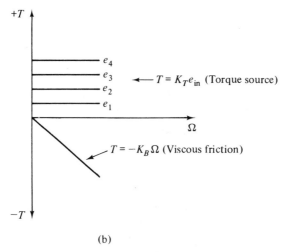

(a)

(b)

Figure 5-1. Torque-speed characteristic of servo motor:
normal form and in parts.

through the field coils. Two equations relating torque to current are given
to the right of Fig. 5-2. The performance of this motor may be analyzed using
the equivalent diagram shown in Fig. 5-3. This figure is useful because its
dynamic behavior is the same as the measured performance of dc servo
motors. The applied voltage to the armature is e_{in}, the armature current is
i_m, and J_m is the combined motor and load moment of inertia. It will be noted
that the motor is shown also as an armature generator which generates a
back emf, $e_{mv\Omega}$. Equation (5-1) defines this back emf voltage, $e_{mv\Omega}$; the constant $K_{mv\Omega}$ is proportional to field flux and thus to i_f.

$$e_{mv\Omega} = N\frac{d\Phi}{dt} = K_{mv\Omega}\Omega_m = K_{mv\Omega}\dot{\theta}_m \longrightarrow K_{mv\Omega}s\theta_m(s) \qquad (5\text{-}1)$$

$$\text{Torque} = T_m = K_{mTI}i_m = J_m\frac{d^2\theta_m}{dt^2} \longrightarrow J_ms^2\theta_m(s) \qquad (5\text{-}2)$$

$$E_{in}(s) = R_mI_m(s) + E_{mv\Omega}(s) = R_mI_m(s) + K_{mv\Omega}s\theta_m(s) \qquad (5\text{-}3)$$

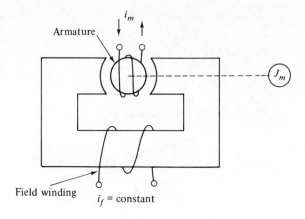

$T = Bli_m$ = torque

B = constant due to fixed field

l = constant due to winding configuration

$T = K_{mTI}i_m$ where $K_{mTI} = Bl$

Figure 5-2. Armature-controlled dc servo motor.

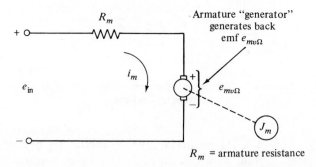

R_m = armature resistance

Figure 5-3. Equivalent diagram of armature-controlled dc servo motor without armature inductance.

The motor torque is used to accelerate the inertia J_m, as stated in Eq. (5-2) (friction and other load torques need not be considered at this time). Equation (5-3) equates the applied voltage $E_{in}(s)$ to the motor voltage (the armature resistance drop plus the back emf voltage).

$$I_m(s) = \frac{E_{in}(s) - K_{mv\Omega}s\theta_m(s)}{R_m} \tag{5-4}$$

$$T(s) = K_{mTI}I_m(s) = J_m s^2 \theta_m(s) = K_{mTI}\left[\frac{E_{in}(s) - K_{mv\Omega}\theta_m(s)}{R_m}\right] \tag{5-5}$$

$$J_m s^2 \theta_m(s) + \frac{K_{mTI}K_{mv\Omega}s\theta_m(s)}{R_m} = \frac{K_{mTI}E_{in}(s)}{R_m} \tag{5-6}$$

$$\left(J_m s^2 + \frac{K_{mTI}K_{mv\Omega}}{R_m}s\right)\theta_m(s) = \frac{K_{mTI}}{R_m}E_{in}(s) \tag{5-7}$$

Equation (5-4) defines the armature current in terms of the applied voltage and the angular velocity of the motor. Equation (5-5) restates Eq. (5-2) using Eq. (5-4). The last two terms of this equation constitute an equation in two variables, the motor angle, $\theta_m(s)$ and the applied voltage $E_{in}(s)$. The variables are separated in Eqs. (5-6) and (5-7). The transfer function relating the output angle to the input voltage is given in Eq. (5-8).

$$\frac{\theta_m(s)}{E_{in}(s)} = \frac{K_{mTI}/R_m}{J_m s^2 + (K_{mTI}K_{mv\Omega}/R_m)s} = \frac{K_{mTI}/R_m J_m}{s(s + K_{mTI}K_{mv\Omega}/R_m J_m)} \tag{5-8}$$

$$\frac{K_{mTI}K_{mv\Omega}}{R_m J_m} = \omega_m = \frac{1}{\tau_m} \tag{5-9}$$

$$\frac{\theta_m(s)}{E_{in}(s)} = \frac{\omega_m/K_{mv\Omega}}{s(s + \omega_m)} = \frac{1/K_{mv\Omega}}{s(1 + s/\omega_m)} \tag{5-10}$$

$$\frac{\Omega_m(s)}{E_{in}(s)} = \frac{1/K_{mv\Omega}}{1 + s/\omega_m} \tag{5-11}$$

The characteristic frequency associated with the motor is ω_m, which is equal to the reciprocal of the motor time constant as stated in Eq. (5-9). Equation (5-10) restates Eq. (5-8) in terms of ω_m.

Equations (5-9) and (5-10) are valuable because they offer a convenient tool for visualizing motor operation. For instance, for zero motor inertia, ω_m must be infinitely large, the motor must have an infinitely wide bandwidth, and Eq. (5-10) is reduced to a constant over s (the characteristic of a pure integrator). As motor inertia J_m increases, the motor exhibits an increasing time constant (lowering of ω_m) and the performance becomes more sluggish; this is born out by physical measurements. Equation (5-11) presents this motor characteristic in a slightly different form; the motor angular velocity is given as the output instead of the motor angle.

Figure 5-4 shows the development of the "conceptual-loop" representa-

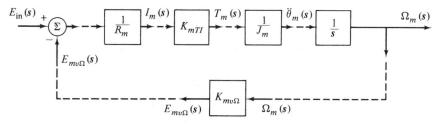

Figure 5-4.   Development of conceptual loop of armature-controlled dc servo motor without armature inductance.

tion of a dc motor. The basis of this conceptual-loop approach is that the various equations of motor performance are represented by blocks in a block diagram. As a result, the block diagram for the motor and its transfer function can be derived directly using block-diagram algebra. From Fig. 5-3 it may be seen that the current flowing into the motor, i_m, is equal to the difference between the applied voltage e_{in} and the back emf voltage $e_{mv\Omega}$ divided by R_m. These two voltages are subtracted in the block diagram (Fig. 5-4) and then a block to divide by R_m is included to give i_m. The current i_m is multiplied by K_{mTI}, giving the motor torque, T_m. Dividing this torque by motor inertia gives motor acceleration $\ddot{\theta}_m$. Integrating $\ddot{\theta}_m$ by means of a $1/s$ block gives motor velocity, Ω_m. To obtain the back emf voltage, $e_{mv\Omega}$, the motor angular velocity Ω_m is multiplied by $K_{mv\Omega}$.

In Fig. 5-5 this diagram is drawn in its more complete form; Eq. (5-12)

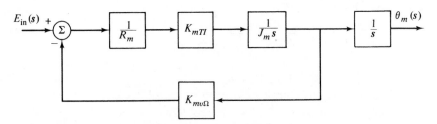

Figure 5-5.   Completed conceptual loop of dc servo motor (fixed field; $L_m = 0$).

solves this final motor block diagram and provides the same answer as Eq. (5-8)

$$\frac{\theta_m(s)}{E_{in}(s)} = \frac{1}{s}\left[\frac{(1/R_m)(K_{mTI})(1/J_m s)}{1 + K_{mv\Omega}(1/R_m)K_{mTI}(1/J_m s)}\right] = \frac{1}{s}\left(\frac{K_{mTI}/R_m J_m s}{1 + K_{mv\Omega}K_{mTI}/R_m J_m s}\right)$$

$$= \frac{1}{s}\left(\frac{K_{mTI}/R_m J_m}{s + K_{mv\Omega}K_{mTI}/R_m J_m}\right) = \frac{K_{mTI}/R_m J_m}{s(s + K_{mv\Omega}K_{mTI}/R_m J_m)} \qquad (5\text{-}12)$$

Example 5-1. Calculate ω_m for a motor having the following constants:

$$K_{mTI} = 3\frac{\text{lb}\cdot\text{ft}}{\text{A}} \qquad K_{mv\Omega} = 18\frac{\text{V}}{\text{rad/s}}$$

$$R_m = 10\,\Omega \qquad J_m = 2\,\text{slug}\cdot\text{ft}^2$$

solution From Eq. (5-9),

$$\omega_m = \frac{K_{mTI}K_{mv\Omega}}{R_m J_m} = \frac{3\,\text{lb}\cdot\text{ft/A} \times 18\,\text{V}\cdot\text{s/rad}}{10\,\text{V/A} \times 2\,\text{lb}\cdot\text{ft}\cdot\text{s}^2}$$

$$= 2.7\,\text{rad/s}$$

Example 5-2. Find the analytical expression for $\Omega_m(t)$ in degrees per second for the motor of Example 5-1, given a step input of 9 V.

$$e_m \longrightarrow \boxed{\dfrac{1/K_{mv\Omega}}{1 + s/\omega_m}} \longrightarrow \Omega_m \qquad \dfrac{\Omega_m(s)}{E_m(s)} = \dfrac{(\tfrac{1}{18})\text{rad/s/V}}{1 + s/2.7}$$

solution

$$\Omega_m(s) = \frac{9}{s} \times \frac{2.7 \times \tfrac{1}{18}}{s + 2.7} = \frac{1.35}{s(s + 2.7)} = \frac{A}{s} - \frac{A}{s + 2.7}$$

$$A = 0.5$$

$$\Omega_m(t) = 0.5(1 - e^{-2.7t}) \text{ rad/s}$$
$$= 28.65(1 - e^{-2.7t}) \,°/s$$

Example 5-3. A dc motor is running at no load at 1000 rpm; the field current is quickly reduced by one-half (assuming no field flux saturation). (a) How does the no-load velocity change? (b) How does the motor's torque capability change?

solution

(a) $\Omega = \dfrac{E_{\text{arm}}}{K_{mv\Omega}}$

$$K_{mv\Omega} = K_1\phi_f = K_2 I_f$$

then the original velocity,

$$\Omega_1 = \frac{E_{\text{arm}}}{K_2 I_{f1}}$$

$$\Omega_2 = \frac{E_{\text{arm}}}{K_2 I_{f2}}$$

$$\frac{\Omega_2}{\Omega_1} = \frac{E_{\text{arm}}}{K_2 I_{f2}} \times \frac{K_2 I_{f1}}{E_{\text{arm}}} = \frac{I_{f1}}{I_{f2}} = 2$$

Therefore reducing I_f by one-half doubles the speed.

(b) $T_{\max} = I_{\max} K_{mTI}$; $K_{mTI} = K_3\phi_f = K_4 I_f$. Therefore the maximum torque drops to one-half the original torque.

5-2. dimensions of ω_m

Equation (5-13) is a restatement of Eq. (5-9). The definition of the terms and their dimensions are given in Eqs. (5-14) through (5-17). Note that radians are nondimensional in Eq. (5-15).

$$\frac{K_{mTI}K_{mv\Omega}}{R_m J_m} = \omega_m \tag{5-13}$$

Motor torque constant: $\quad K_{mTI} = \dfrac{\text{oz·in}}{\text{A}} = \dfrac{EI}{I} \tag{5-14}$

Motor back emf constant: $\quad K_{mv\Omega} = \dfrac{\text{V}}{\text{rad/s}} = ET \tag{5-15}$

Motor armature resistance: $\quad R_m = \dfrac{E}{I} \tag{5-16}$

Motor armature moment of inertia:

$$J_m = ML^2 = \frac{F}{g}L^2 = \frac{FL^2}{L/T^2} = FLT^2 \qquad (5\text{-}17)$$

$$\omega_m = \frac{(FL/I)ET}{(E/I)FLT^2} = \frac{1}{T} \qquad (5\text{-}18)$$

Note that dimensions are multiplied together in Eq. (5-18) to give $1/T$, which is correct for angular frequency (radian frequency), verifying the previous equations by dimensional analysis.

For small servo motors, the motor constants are usually given as: volts per radian per second for $K_{mv\Omega}$; ounce inches per ampere for K_{mTI}; ohms for R_m; and gram centimeters squared for J_m. If these constants are multiplied together as in Eq. (5-19), the dimensions of ω_m are found to be ounce inches seconds per gram centimeter squared.

$$\omega_m = \frac{K_{mv\Omega}(\text{V}\cdot\text{s/rad})K_{mTI}(\text{oz}\cdot\text{in/A})}{R_m(\text{V/A})J_m(\text{g}\cdot\text{cm}^2)} = \frac{K_{mv\Omega}K_{mTI}}{R_m J_m}\left(\frac{\text{oz}\cdot\text{in}\cdot\text{s}}{\text{g}\cdot\text{cm}^2}\right) \qquad (5\text{-}19)$$

$$1\text{ slug} = 1.459 \times 10^4 \text{ g}; \quad \frac{1.459 \times 10^4 \text{ g}}{1\text{ slug}} = 1 \qquad (5\text{-}20)$$

$$\omega_m = \frac{K_{mv\Omega}K_{mTI}(\text{oz}\cdot\text{in}\cdot\text{s})}{R_m J_m(\text{g}\cdot\text{m}^2)} \times \frac{1.459 \times 10^4 \text{ g}}{\text{slug}}$$

$$\times \frac{(2.54)^2 \text{ cm}^2}{\text{in}^2} \times \frac{144 \text{ in}^2}{\text{ft}^2}$$

$$= \frac{K_{mv\Omega}K_{mTI}}{R_m J_m} \times 1.459 \times 10^4 \times (2.54)^2 \times 144 \frac{\text{oz}\cdot\text{in}\cdot\text{s}}{\text{slug}\cdot\text{ft}^2} \qquad (5\text{-}21)$$

Equation (5-19) has to be resolved so that the units finally emerge as reciprocal seconds. To accomplish this, the final expression of Eq. (5-19) is multiplied by various factors that equal unity. Consider Eq. (5-20): because 1 slug equals 14,590 g (see Appendix C), the right part of Eq. (5-20) may be written as a ratio identical to unity. This unity factor may now be multiplied by Eq. (5-19) to alter the dimensions. Equation (5-21) includes unity factors relating grams and slugs, centimeters squared and inches squared, and inches squared and feet squared. By cancelling out the appropriate dimensions, the last part of Eq. (5-21) is obtained; but this is still not in the desired form. The fact that a slug foot squared is the same as a pound foot second squared will now be developed (see Section 4-3); this equality makes it possible to get Eq. (5-21) in its proper form.

Equation (5-22) relates mass to weight and gravitational acceleration; this is stated in numerical terms in Eq. (5-23). Equations (5-24) and (5-25) restate this result.

$$M = \frac{F}{A} = \frac{W}{g}\left(\frac{\text{force on mass at earth's surface}}{\text{gravitational acceleration at earth's surface}}\right)$$

$$(5\text{-}22)$$

$$1 \text{ slug} = \frac{32.2 \text{ lb}}{32.2 \text{ ft/s}^2} = \frac{1 \text{ lb}}{1 \text{ ft/s}^2} \tag{5-23}$$

$$1 \text{ slug·ft} = 1 \text{ lb·s}^2 \tag{5-24}$$

$$1 \text{ slug·ft}^2 = 1 \text{ lb·ft·s}^2 \tag{5-25}$$

Now Eq. (5-21) is multiplied by a unity factor derived from Eq. (5-25): this is given in Eq. (5-26). In Eq. (5-27) two final unit conversions are made to give the final desired units of reciprocal seconds (or radians per second).

$$\omega_m = \frac{K_{mv\Omega}K_{mTI}}{R_m J_m} \times 1.459 \times 10^4 \times (2.54)^2 \times 144 \frac{\text{oz·in·s}}{\text{slug·ft}^2} \times \frac{1 \text{ slug·ft}^2}{\text{lb·ft·s}^2}$$

$$= \frac{K_{mv\Omega}K_{mTI}}{R_m J_m} \times 1.459 \times 10^4 \times (2.54)^2 \times 144 \frac{\text{oz·in·s}}{\text{lb·ft·s}^2}$$

$$\times \frac{\text{lb}}{16 \text{ oz}} \times \frac{\text{ft}}{12 \text{ in}} \tag{5-26}$$

$$= \frac{K_{mv\Omega}K_{mTI}}{R_m J_m} \times 70{,}600 \text{ s}^{-1} \approx \frac{K_{mv\Omega}K_{mTI}}{R_m J_m} \times 70{,}000 \text{ s}^{-1} \tag{5-27}$$

Note that using $K_{mv\Omega}$, K_{mTI}, R_m, and J_m in the stated units of Eq. (5-19) requires a factor of approximately 70,000 to convert to radians per second. Equation (5-28) defines this constant; it is restated in Eq. (5-29).

$$70{,}000 \text{ s}^{-1} = \frac{\text{oz·in·s}}{\text{g·cm}^2} \tag{5-28}$$

$$70{,}000 \frac{\text{rad}}{\text{s}^2} = \frac{1 \text{ oz·in}}{\text{g·cm}^2} \tag{5-29}$$

Small servo motors usually have their torque specified in ounce inches and motor inertia in gram centimeters squared. By taking the ratio of a motor's stall torque to its inertia, the theoretical acceleration at stall can be calculated. The equation as stated will have units of ounce inches per gram centimeter squared; if this expression is multiplied by the right side of Eq. (5-30), the theoretical acceleration in radians per second squared is determined.

$$1 = \frac{70{,}000 \text{ rad/s}^2}{1 \text{ oz·in/g·cm}} \tag{5-30}$$

Example 5-4. Find ω_m of an instrument servo motor with the following characteristics.

$$K_{mTI} = 4 \text{ in·oz/A}$$
$$K_{mv\Omega} = 0.0028 \text{ V/rpm}$$
$$J_m = 30 \text{ g·cm}^2$$
$$R_m = 100 \text{ }\Omega$$

solution

$$\omega_m = \frac{K_{mTI}K_{mv\Omega}}{R_m J_m}$$

$$K_{mv\Omega} = 0.0028 \frac{V \cdot min}{rev} \times \frac{rev}{2\pi \ rad} \times \frac{60 \ s}{min} = 0.0267 \frac{V}{rad/s}$$

$$\omega_m = \left[\frac{(4 \ in \cdot oz/A) \times 0.0267 \ V \cdot s/rad}{100 \ V/A \times 30 \ g \cdot cm^2} \right]$$

$$= 0.356 \times 10^{-4} \frac{in \cdot oz \cdot s}{g \cdot cm^2} \times 70{,}000 \frac{rad/s^2}{in \cdot oz/g \cdot cm^2}$$

$$= 2.49 \ rad/s$$

Example 5-5. Find the maximum acceleration (acceleration at stall) of the motor of Example 5-4 if $T_{max} = 5$ in·oz.

solution

$$\ddot{\theta}_{max} = \frac{T_{max}}{J} = \frac{5 \ in \cdot oz}{30 \ g \cdot cm^2} \times \frac{70{,}000 \ rad/s^2}{in \cdot oz/g \cdot cm^2}$$

$$= 11{,}650 \ rad/s^2$$

Example 5-6. If a dc motor with an input armature voltage of 28 V has a no-load speed of 10,000 rpm, a stall torque of 5 in·oz, and an armature resistance of 20 Ω, calculate the no-load speed and maximum torque if the motor is driven from a source with an impedance of 10 Ω and a maximum voltage of 35 V.

solution: Neglecting friction effects, the new no-load speed is independent of armature circuit resistance.

$$\Omega_{35V} = 10{,}000 \ rpm \times \frac{35}{28} = 12{,}500 \ rpm$$

$$T_{max} \ (new) = 5 \ in \cdot oz \times \frac{35}{28} \times \frac{20 \ \Omega}{30 \ \Omega} = 4.17 \ in \cdot oz$$

5-3. effect of drive amplifier impedance on ω_m

Figure 5-6 shows a drive amplifier with a drive source resistance, R_{AO}. The amplifier drives the motor, which has armature resistance R_m, and de-

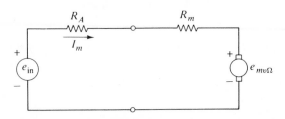

Figure 5-6.   Equivalent diagram of a dc servo motor driven by an amplifier with source resistance R_{AO}.

velops a back emf $e_{mv\Omega}$. The current flowing in this circuit i_m is defined in Eq. (5-31); the conceptual loop for this motor is shown in Fig. 5-7.

$$i_m = \frac{e_{in} - e_{mv\Omega}}{R_{AO} + R_m} \tag{5-31}$$

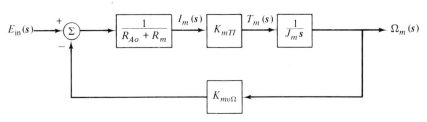

Figure 5-7. Conceptual loop of a dc servo motor driven by an amplifier with source resistance R_{AO}.

The motor break frequency ω_m is given in Eq. (5-32). This is the same as the expression previously used, except that the resistance is now in two parts: the motor armature resistance and the drive resistance R_{AO}.

$$\omega_m = \frac{K_{mTI}K_{mv\Omega}}{J_m(R_{AO} + R_m)} = \frac{B}{J_m} \tag{5-32}$$

$$B = \frac{K_{mTI}K_{mv\Omega}}{R_{AO} + R_m} = \frac{(\text{torque/current})(\text{volts/velocity})}{\text{volts/current}} = \frac{\text{torque}}{\text{velocity}} \tag{5-33}$$

An equivalent viscous damping constant is given in Eq. (5-33); dimensionally, this is torque divided by velocity. From Eq. (5-32) it can be seen that as the amplifier resistance R_{AO} approaches infinity, ω_m approaches zero. This means that a current source (a very high resistance source) driving a motor makes the motor act like a double integrator; the second integration comes from the fact that a $1/s$ term is needed to obtain θ_m from ω_m. (Actually, double integrators are never really fully realized this way; but inertially loaded "torque motors" often *approach* this type of characteristic.) The Magnetic Technology 1937-

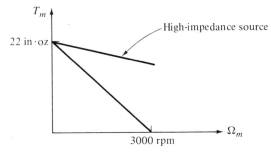

Figure 5-8. Magnetic Technology 1937–050 torque motor torque-speed characteristics.

050 torque motor characteristics are shown in Fig. 5-8; the low-impedance drive curve is the one that intersects the angular velocity axis at 3000 rpm. The high-impedance source curve shows less torque reduction as the angular velocity increases. This high-impedance source curve would have to be perfectly horizontal in order for ω_m to be zero. As a practical matter, therefore, ω_ms are finite but can become very small; thus dc servo motors may become, in effect, very much like double integrators.

5-4. armature inductance

Figure 5-9 shows the conceptual loop for a dc servo motor which has armature inductance L_M. It may be observed that this diagram is identical to the conceptual loop of the basic motor, with the exception that the conversion from voltage to current is done through the armature impedance $R + sL_M$ instead of through just R. Using the block-diagram algebra equivalent of Fig. 2-6e, Fig. 5-9 is reduced to its transfer function in Eq. (5-34).

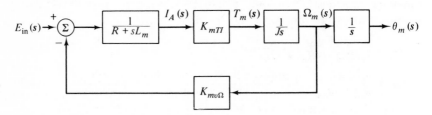

Figure 5-9. Conceptual loop of an armature-controlled dc motor with armature inductance.

Introducing ω_e, the electric break frequency, Eq. (5-35) is written.

$$\frac{\theta_m(s)}{E_{in}(s)} = \frac{1}{s} \times \frac{K_{mTI}/(R + sL_m)Js}{1 + K_{mTI}K_{mv\Omega}/(R + sL_m)Js}$$

$$= \frac{1}{s} \times \frac{K_{mTI}}{(R + sL_m)Js + K_{mTI}K_{mv\Omega}}$$

$$= \frac{K_{mTI}}{s(s^2 JL_m + sJR + K_{mTI}K_{mv\Omega})}$$

$$= \frac{1}{sK_{mv\Omega}\left(\dfrac{s^2}{K_{mTI}K_{mv\Omega}/JL_m} + \dfrac{s}{K_{mTI}K_{mv\Omega}/JR} + 1\right)} \tag{5-34}$$

$$= \frac{1/K_{mv\Omega}}{s[(s^2/\omega_m\omega_e) + (s/\omega_m) + 1]} \tag{5-35}$$

for
$$\omega_m = \frac{K_{mTI}K_{mv\Omega}}{JR}$$

$$\omega_e = \frac{R}{L_m}$$

$$\omega_m \omega_e = \frac{K_{mTI} K_{mv\Omega}}{JL_m}$$

Although Eq. (5-35) is a straightforward result, an effort to simplify Eq. (5-35) further is now made.

In Eq. (5-36) the denominator portion of Eq. (5-35) is rearranged and then factored into two assumed terms, $s + a$ and $s + b$; Eq. (5-37) defines these two assumed terms. Let us assume that $a = \omega_m$ and $b = \omega_e - \omega_m$ and then examine the accuracy of this assumption.

$$\frac{1}{(s^2/\omega_m \omega_e) + (s/\omega_m) + 1} = \frac{\omega_m \omega_e}{s^2 + \omega_e s + \omega_m \omega_e} = \frac{\omega_m \omega_e}{(s + a)(s + b)} \qquad (5\text{-}36)$$

$$(s + a)(s + b) = s^2 + \omega_e s + \omega_m \omega_e \qquad (5\text{-}37)$$

By multiplying these two terms Eq. (5-38) is obtained; the error in the result is equal to $-(\omega_m)^2$. For this error to be negligible, ω_e must be much greater than ω_m, and then $\omega_e - \omega_m$ is essentially equal to ω_e.

$$(s + \omega_m)(s + \omega_e - \omega_m) = s^2 + \omega_e s + \omega_m \omega_e - (\omega_m)^2 \qquad (5\text{-}38)$$

$$(s + \omega_m)(s + \omega_e - \omega_m) \approx s^2 + \omega_e s + \omega_m \omega_e$$
$$\text{for } \omega_e \gg \omega_m \ [\omega_m \omega_e \gg (\omega_m)^2] \qquad (5\text{-}39)$$

$$\frac{\theta_m(s)}{E_{in}(s)} = \frac{1/K_{mv\Omega}}{s[(s^2/\omega_m \omega_e) + (s/\omega_m) + 1]} = \frac{\omega_m \omega_e/K_{mv\Omega}}{s(s^2 + \omega_e s + \omega_m \omega_e)}$$

$$\approx \frac{\omega_m \omega_e/K_{mv\Omega}}{s(s + \omega_m)(s + \omega_e - \omega_m)} \approx \frac{\omega_m \omega_e/K_{mv\Omega}}{s(s + \omega_m)(s + \omega_e)}$$

$$= \frac{1/K_{mv\Omega}}{s(1 + s/\omega_m)(1 + s/\omega_e)} \qquad (5\text{-}40)$$

In most cases, ω_e is much greater than ω_m and the approximations of Eqs. (5-39) and (5-40) are more than accurate enough for design purposes.

To examine the accuracy for some typical values, assume ω_m to be 10 rad/s and the electrical break frequency to be 1000 rad/s. Equation (5-41) restates Eq. (5-35) using these assumed motor constants. Equation (5-42) gives the simplified approximate solution. Equation (5-43) actually solves the denominator of Eq. (5-41) using the quadratic formula; the exact values (to one decimal place) for the two poles are 989.9 rad/s and 10.1 rad/s.

$$\frac{\Omega_m(s)}{E_{in}(s)} = \frac{1}{K_{mv\Omega}} \left(\frac{\omega_m \omega_e}{s^2 + \omega_e s + \omega_m \omega_e} \right) = \frac{1}{K_{mv\Omega}} \left(\frac{10{,}000}{s^2 + 1000s + 10{,}000} \right)$$
$$(5\text{-}41)$$

$$\approx \frac{1}{K_{mv\Omega}} \left[\frac{10{,}000}{(s + 10)(s + 990)} \right] = \frac{1}{K_{mv\Omega}} \left[\frac{10{,}000}{(s + \omega_m)(s + \omega_e - \omega_m)} \right]$$
$$(5\text{-}42)$$

$$S_{a,b} = \frac{-1000 \pm \sqrt{1,000,000 - 40,000}}{2} = \frac{-1000 \pm 1000\sqrt{1 - 0.04}}{2}$$

$$= \frac{-1000 \pm 1000 \times 0.9798}{2} = \frac{-1000 \pm 979.8}{2}$$

$$= \frac{-1979.8}{2}, \frac{-20.2}{2} = -989.9, -10.1 \tag{5-43}$$

The lower pole error is approximately 1 per cent and the upper pole error is 0.01 per cent; it can be clearly seen that for engineering design purposes this approximation is more than adequate for this ratio of ω_e to ω_m. If the $\omega_e - \omega_m$ term is assumed to be at ω_e, both errors will be approximately 1 per cent; this again is perfectly adequate for engineering design purposes. The conclusion is that unless the electrical break frequency is quite close to the motor break frequency, the characteristic poles can be considered to be at these two break frequencies. The farther apart they are, the more accurate this approximation becomes; the error due to the approximation is equal to the ratio of the smaller pole to the larger pole.

Example 5-7. Find the transfer function of an Inland T-1352 torque motor with the following characteristics:

T_{max}	20 oz·in
Ω_{max}	400 rad/s
R_{arm}	11.3 Ω
K_{mTI}	8.7 oz·in/A
$K_{mv\Omega}$	0.06 V/rad/s
L	4.0 mH
J_{motor}	8.8×10^{-4} oz·in·s²

solution

$$\omega_m = \frac{0.06 \text{ V·s}}{\text{rad}} \times \frac{8.7 \text{ oz·in}}{A} \times \frac{1 \text{ A}}{8.8 \text{ oz·in·s}^2 \times 11.3 \text{ V} \times 10^{-4}} = 52.5 \text{ rad/s}$$

$$\omega_e = \frac{R}{L} = \frac{11.3 \text{ Ω}}{4 \times 10^{-3} H} = 2825 \text{ rad/s}$$

$$\frac{\theta_m(s)}{E_{in}(s)} = \frac{1/K_{mv\Omega}}{s[(s^2/\omega_m\omega_e) + (s/\omega_m) + 1]} = \frac{(1/0.06) \text{ rad/s/V}}{s[(s^2/52.5 \times 2825) + (s/52.5) + 1]}$$

$$= \frac{16.7 \text{ rad/s/V}}{s[(s^2/148,500) + (s/52.5) + 1]} = \frac{2.48 \times 10^6 \text{ rad/s}^3/V}{s(s^2 + 2825s + 148,500)}$$

Example 5-8. Find the exact and approximate pole locations for the transfer function of Example 5-7.

solution Approximate: $P_1 = -52.5$; $P_2 = -2825$. Exact:

$$\frac{-2825 \pm \sqrt{7.99 \times 10^6 - 0.595 \times 10^6}}{2} = \frac{-2825 \pm 2717.8}{2}$$

$$= \frac{-107.2}{2}, \frac{-5542.8}{2}$$

$$= -53.6, -2771.4$$

5-5. servo constants

Table 5-1 is a list of standardized servo constants. The first subletter indicates the type of device, the second subletter indicates the output para-

Table 5-1. servo constants

K = gain constant
$K_{(1)(2)(3)}$:

(1)	= device type:	m = motor
		G = generator
		A = amplifier
(2)	= output parameter:	
		T = torque
		v = voltage
(3)	= input parameter:	
		E = voltage
		I = current
		Ω = velocity

K_{mTI} = motor torque (per unit) current
K_{mTE} = motor torque (per unit) voltage
$K_{G E\Omega}$ = generator voltage (per unit) velocity
$K_{mv\Omega}$ = motor voltage (per unit) velocity (back emf constant)
R_m = resistance, motor
J_m = inertia, motor
J_{Tm} = inertia, total (reflected to) motor
J_{TL} = inertia, total (reflected to) load
J_L = inertia, load
I_m = current, motor (armature)

---

meter, and the third subletter indicates the input parameter. In the case of K_{mTI}, for instance, this is a constant of motor output torque per unit input current. In Fig. 5-10 these constants are used for a dc motor with no armature inductance. Figure 5-11 is the same as Fig. 5-10, except that a new constant K_{mTE} is used. K_{mTE} is a constant of motor output torque per unit input voltage; it must be borne in mind in using this constant K_{mTE} that a motor pro-

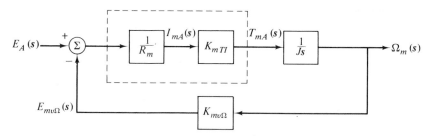

Figure 5-10.   Conceptual loop of an armature-controlled dc motor.

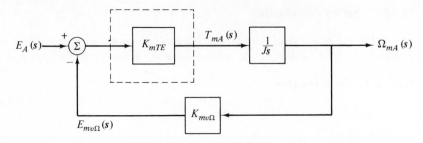

Figure 5-11. Modified conceptual loop of armature-controlled dc motor using K_{mTE}.

vides torque only for applied current through the armature: applied voltage is not directly relatable to torque. Therefore K_{mTE} is a constant that will be convenient for certain purposes but is not a basic constant of the motor; K_{mTI} is the basic motor torque constant.

5-6. relationship between K_{mTE} and K_{mTI}

Equations (5-44) and (5-45) state the relationships between K_{mTE} and K_{mTI} that are implied by Figs. 5-10 and 5-11.

$$K_{mTE} = \frac{K_{mTI}}{R_m} \tag{5-44}$$

$$R_m = \frac{K_{mTI}}{K_{mTE}} \tag{5-45}$$

An informal proof of Eq. (5-45) is given in Eqs. (5-46), (5-47), and (5-48).

$$K_{mTE} = \left.\frac{T_{\max}}{E_{\max}}\right|_{\Omega=0} \tag{5-46}$$

$$K_{mTI} = \frac{T_{\max}}{I_{\max}} \tag{5-47}$$

$$\frac{K_{mTI}}{K_{mTE}} = \frac{T_{\max}/I_{\max}}{T_{\max}/E_{\max}} = \frac{E_{\max}}{T_{\max}} = R_m \tag{5-48}$$

Equation (5-49), which is the basic analytical statement of ω_m, is modified using Eq. (5-44) to give the useful relationship of Eq. (5-50).

$$\omega_m = \frac{K_{mTI}K_{mv\Omega}}{J_{Tm}R_m} \tag{5-49}$$

$$= \frac{K_{mTE}K_{mv\Omega}}{J_{Tm}} \tag{5-50}$$

Figure 5-12 shows the torque-speed characteristic of a particular dc servo motor; Eqs. (5-51) and (5-52) are expressions for the constants K_{mTE} and $K_{mv\Omega}$.

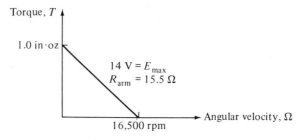

Figure 5-12.   Torque-speed curve of C.P.P.C. 08-DM-☐-2 dc motor.

$$K_{mTE} = \left.\frac{T_{max}}{E_{max}}\right|_{\Omega=0} = \frac{1.0 \text{ in}\cdot\text{oz}}{14 \text{ V}} = 0.0714 \frac{\text{in}\cdot\text{oz}}{\text{V}} \qquad (5\text{-}51)$$

$$K_{mv\Omega} = \left.\frac{E_{max}}{\Omega_{max}}\right|_{T=0} \qquad (5\text{-}52)$$

$$\omega_m = \frac{K_{mTE}K_{mv\Omega}}{J_{Tm}} = \left(\left.\frac{T_{max}}{E_{max}}\right|_{\Omega=0}\right)\frac{E_{max}}{\Omega_{max}}\frac{1}{J_{Tm}} = \frac{T_{max}}{\Omega_{max}J_{Tm}} \qquad (5\text{-}53)$$

Equation (5-53) restates the motor break frequency ω_m using Eqs. (5-51) and (5-52). The result is that ω_m can be determined directly from the maximum torque, the maximum velocity, and the motor inertia; it is partially because of this convenient result that K_{mTE} is introduced.

Example 5-9. For a total inertia of 38 g·cm², $T_{max} = 15$ in·oz, and Ω_{max} is 4000 rpm, Calculate ω_m.

solution $J_{total} = 38$ g·cm²; $T_{max} = 15$ in·oz; $\Omega_{max} = 4000$ rpm.

$$\Omega_{max} = 4000 \frac{\text{rev}}{\text{min}} \times \frac{2\pi \text{ rad}}{\text{rev}} \times 1\frac{\text{min}}{60 \text{ s}} = 419 \frac{\text{rad}}{\text{s}}$$

$$\omega_m = \frac{T_{max}}{J_{total}\Omega_{max}} = \frac{15 \text{ in}\cdot\text{oz}}{38 \text{ g}\cdot\text{cm}^2 \times 419 \text{ rad/s}} \times \frac{70{,}000 \text{ rad/s}^2}{\text{oz}\cdot\text{in/g}\cdot\text{cm}^2}$$

$$= 66 \text{ rad/s}$$

5-7. the effect of high-value poles

The effect of a high-value pole (such as ω_e) is examined further by means of Eqs. (5-54) through (5-60). The approximate transfer function of input voltage E_{in} to output angle θ_m is given in Eq. (5-54).

$$\frac{\theta_m(s)}{E_{in}(s)} = \frac{1/K_{mv\Omega}}{s(1 + s/\omega_m)(1 + s/\omega_e)} \qquad (5\text{-}54)$$

$$\frac{\Omega_m(s)}{E_{in}(s)} = \frac{1/K_{mv\Omega}}{(1 + s/\omega_m)(1 + s/\omega_e)} = \frac{\omega_m\omega_e/K_{mv\Omega}}{(s + \omega_m)(s + \omega_e)} \qquad (5\text{-}55)$$

Equation (5-55) gives the angular velocity transfer function. Equation (5-56) gives the transform of the output angular velocity for an applied unit step input.

$$\Omega_m(s) = \frac{\omega_m \omega_e / K_{mv\Omega}}{s(s + \omega_m)(s + \omega_e)} = \frac{1}{K_{mv\Omega}}\left[\frac{\omega_m \omega_e}{s(s + \omega_m)(s + \omega_e)}\right]$$

(5-56)

$$\frac{\omega_m \omega_e}{s(s + \omega_m)(s + \omega_e)} = \frac{A}{s} + \frac{B}{s + \omega_m} + \frac{C}{s + \omega_e}$$

(5-57)

The bracketed part of this equation represents the dynamics of motion; this is reexpressed in Eq. (5-57), where it is separated into partial fractions.

Equations (5-58), (5-59), and (5-60) solve for the constants A, B, and C using the partial fraction technique and making further approximations based on the fact that ω_m is assumed to be much smaller than ω_e.

$$A = \frac{\omega_m \omega_e}{\omega_m \omega_e} = 1$$

(5-58)

$$B = \frac{\omega_m \omega_e}{(-\omega_m)(-\omega_m + \omega_e)} = \frac{\omega_e}{\omega_m - \omega_e} = \frac{-1}{1 - \omega_m/\omega_e}$$

$$\approx -\left(1 + \frac{\omega_m}{\omega_e}\right)$$

(5-59)

$$C = \frac{\omega_m \omega_e}{(-\omega_e)(\omega_m - \omega_e)} = \frac{\omega_m}{\omega_e - \omega_m} = \frac{\omega_m/\omega_e}{1 - \omega_m/\omega_e} \approx \frac{\omega_m}{\omega_e}$$

(5-60)

Substitutions for ω_m and ω_e are made and the final expression for the output velocity versus the input step for the two break frequencies of 10 and 1000 rad/s is given in Eq. (5-61).

$$\Omega_m(t) = \frac{1}{K_{mv\Omega}}(1 - 1.01e^{-10t} + 0.01e^{-1000t})$$

(5-61)

The significance of Eq. (5-61) is that there are two poles, which result in two transient terms; one is a transient that has a time constant of $\frac{1}{10}$ s and the second has a time constant of $\frac{1}{1000}$ s. It will be noticed that the magnitudes of these transient terms are inversely proportional to the break frequencies (or directly proportional to the time constants). Of importance is the fact that *high-value poles have small-magnitude transients;* therefore it is often possible to neglect poles that are much higher in frequency than the predominant ones.

5-8. dc motor maximum power point

The relationship between maximum motor power and the velocity at which this takes place is developed in Eqs. (5-62) through (5-68); Fig. 5-13 gives the torque-speed curve. First torque is expressed in terms of velocity in Eq. (5-62). By substituting the end values of Eqs. (5-63) and (5-64), Eq. (5-65) is obtained. The power expression is given in Eq. (5-66).

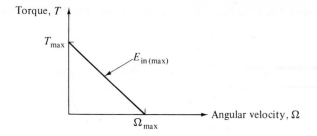

Figure 5-13.   dc motor torque-speed curve.

$$T = A + B\Omega \tag{5-62}$$

$$\Omega = \Omega_{max} \qquad \text{at } T = 0 \tag{5-63}$$

$$\Omega = 0 \qquad \text{at } T = T_{max} \tag{5-64}$$

$$T = T_{max}(1 - \Omega/\Omega_{max}) \tag{5-65}$$

$$\text{Power} = T_{max}(1 - \Omega/\Omega_{max})\Omega \tag{5-66}$$

By taking the derivative with respect to Ω of Eq. (5-66) and letting the result go to zero, the condition for maximum power is obtained; this is stated in Eq. (5-67). Equation (5-68) uses this result to determine the maximum power velocity, Ω_{mp}.

$$\frac{dP}{d\Omega} = \frac{d}{d\Omega}\left(T_{max}\Omega - \frac{T_{max}\Omega^2}{\Omega_{max}}\right) = T_{max} - \frac{2T_{max}\Omega}{\Omega_{max}} \longrightarrow 0 \tag{5-67}$$

$$\Omega_{mp} = \frac{\Omega_{max}}{2} \tag{5-68}$$

$$P_{max} = T_{max}\left(\frac{\Omega_{max}}{2}\right)\left(1 - \frac{1}{2}\right) = \frac{T_{max}\Omega_{max}}{4} \tag{5-69}$$

The value of power at this angular velocity is given in Eq. (5-69); it is one-fourth the (theoretical) power represented by the maximum velocity times the maximum torque. Figure 5-14 shows the curve of power versus angular velocity.

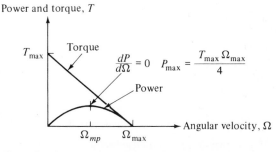

Figure 5-14.   dc motor power and torque-speed curves.

Example 5-10. Find the maximum output power for the motors of Examples 5-7 and 5-9.

solution

$$P_7 = \frac{T_{max}\Omega_{max}}{4} = \frac{(20 \text{ oz} \cdot \text{in})(400 \text{ rad/s})}{4} \times \frac{1 \text{ b} \cdot \text{ft}}{192 \text{ oz} \cdot \text{in}}$$

$$= 10.4 \text{ lb} \cdot \text{ft/s} \times 1.818 \times 10^{-3} \frac{\text{hp}}{\text{lb} \cdot \text{ft/s}} = 0.0189 \text{ hp}$$

$$P_9 = \frac{15 \text{ in} \cdot \text{oz} \times 4000 \text{ rev/min}}{4} \times \frac{\text{lb} \cdot \text{ft}}{192 \text{ oz} \cdot \text{in}} \times \frac{2\pi \text{ rad}}{\text{rev}} \times \frac{\text{min}}{60 \text{ s}}$$

$$= 8.18 \text{ lb} \cdot \text{ft/s} \times 1.818 \times 10^{-3} \frac{\text{hp}}{\text{lb} \cdot \text{ft/s}} = 0.01485 \text{ hp}$$

5-9. summary

The characteristics of a dc servo motor were developed. The more direct "conceptual-loop" technique was used to develop the servo motor characteristics. It was shown analytically that ω_m has dimensions or radians per second and that 70,000 rad/s² (equal to 1 oz·in/g·cm²) is a useful quantity when working with small electric servo motors. It was shown that increasing drive-amplifier impedance affects a dc servo motor by making it appear more like a "torque source" and by decreasing ω_m. The conceptual loop for a fixed-field, armature-controlled motor with armature inductance was given, and the exact transfer function was obtained. A convenient method of labeling servo constants was introduced, and the relationship between K_{mTI} and K_{mTE} was explored. The important fact that high-value poles have a relatively small effect on transient performance was shown. Finally, the dc motor maximum power point was found.

problems

5-1. Find ω_m for motors with the following constants:
(a) $K_{mTI} = 2 \text{ in} \cdot \text{oz/A}$
   $K_{mv\Omega} = 0.04 \text{ V/rpm}$
   $R_m = 6 \Omega$
   $J_m = 13 \text{ g} \cdot \text{cm}^2$
(b) $K_{mTI} = 3 \text{ lb} \cdot \text{ft/A}$
   $K_{mv\Omega} = 40 \text{ V/rad/s}$
   $R_m = 6 \Omega$
   $J_m = 2 \text{ slug} \cdot \text{ft}^2$

5-2. Give the transfer functions for the two motors of Problem 5-1(a) and (b).

5-3. Write the time expression for motor velocity for the two motors of Problem 5-1 for a 40-V step input to the armature.

5-4. Assuming that the two motors of Problem 5-1 have a field winding, solve Problem 5-2 for one-half the field current of Problem 5-1, for each motor, respectively.

5-5. Solve Problem 5-3 for one-half the field current.

5-6. What maximum motor power can the motors of Problem 5-1 provide for 40 V to the armature?

5-7. Find the exact transfer function for motor (b) of Problem 5-1 if the armature inductance is 4.0 mH. How much do the poles differ from ω_m and ω_e?

5-8. Find ω_m for the following two motors:
(a) T_{max} = 10 lb·ft
    Ω_{max} = 40 rpm
    J_{total} = 12 slug·ft²
(b) T_{max} = 10 oz·in
    Ω_{max} = 9600 rpm
    J_{total} = 13 g·cm²

elementary servo design;
torque stiffness

To introduce certain elementary techniques of design, a simple servo is designed using a series of calculations. Table 6-1 gives the characteristics of the Clifton Precision 13-DM dc servo motor, which is used in the calculations. In the later part of this chapter, torque stiffness in general is discussed, and the concept of "direct design" is introduced.

Table 6-1.   clifton precision 13-dm dc servo motor

$L_m = 4.6 \times 10^{-3}$ H
electrical drive output impedance = 0 Ω
$J_m = 11.5$ g·cm²
$R_m = 15.5$ Ω
maximum angular velocity = 10,000 rpm
stall torque = 5 in·oz
maximum input voltage to armature = 14 V

6-1. electrical break frequency

A Clifton Precision 13-DM dc motor (see Table 6-1) is used to calculate the electrical break frequency, ω_e [see Eq. (5-35)]. Equation (6-1) shows this calculation; the resulting value of ω_e is 3,370 rad/s.

$$\omega_e = \frac{R_m}{L_m} = \frac{15.5 \ \Omega}{4.6 \times 10^{-3} \ \text{H}} = 3370 \frac{\text{rad}}{\text{s}} \approx 540 \ \text{Hz} \qquad (6\text{-}1)$$

6-2. gear ratio at maximum power point

This calculation determines the gear ratio between this motor and a load with a required maximum velocity of 50 rpm for an assumed motor maximum speed of 5000 rpm, the maximum power speed.

$$N = \frac{5000 \text{ rpm}}{50 \text{ rpm}} = 100 \tag{6-2}$$

6-3. motor break frequency, ω_m

The motor break frequency ω_m is calculated for a load inertia of 100,000 g·cm². It was previously developed (in Section 4-4) that the load inertia will reflect to the motor axis according to the square of the gear ratio; the reflected inertia, therefore, is $10^5/(10^2)^2$ or 10 g·cm², and the total inertia is the sum of the motor inertia and the load inertia, which is 21.5 g·cm² as given in Eq. (6-3). From Eq. (5-50), Eq. (6-4) calculates ω_m from T_{max}, ω_{max}, and J_{Tm}, the total inertia reflected to the motor axis.

$$J_{Tm} = J_m + J_{Lm} = (11.5 + 10) \text{ g·cm}^2 = 21.5 \text{ g·cm}^2 \tag{6-3}$$

$$\omega_m = \frac{K_{mTE}K_{mv\Omega}}{J_{Tm}} = \frac{(T_{max}/E_{max})(E_{max}/\Omega_{max})}{J_{Tm}}$$

$$= \frac{T_{max}}{\Omega_{max}J_{Tm}} = \frac{5.0 \text{ in·oz}}{10,000 \text{ rpm} \times 21.5 \text{ g·cm}^2} \times \frac{1 \text{ rpm}}{[0.104 \text{ rad/s}]}$$

$$= \frac{5}{22,400} \frac{\text{in·oz·s}}{\text{g·cm}^2} \left[\frac{70,000 \text{ rad/s}^2}{\text{in·oz/g·cm}^2} \right] = 15.6 \frac{\text{rad}}{\text{s}} \tag{6-4}$$

Two bracketed terms, each of which are unity, are used to convert the units to the desired form for ω_m in units of radians per second.

6-4. closing the loop; ω_{cp}

This motor is used as part of a position servo where the input angle is θ_{in} and the output angle is θ_L. In Fig. 6-1, the block connected to θ_{in} with a

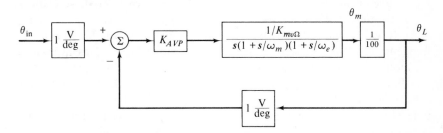

Figure 6-1.   Position servo.

gain of 1 v/deg represents the input transducer; a similar device is used to measure θ_L. A power amplifier is provided which has a voltage gain of K_{AVP}. The output of the K_{AVP} amplifier drives the motor. The motor output is attached to the gear reducer, the output of which is the load angle, θ_L. The output of the load angle transducer is compared with the input angle at the summing point.

Figure 6-2 is obtained by means of a block-diagram algebra equality reduction. Equation (6-5) defines the loop gain of the diagram given in Fig. 6-2.

$$G(s) = \frac{57.3 \, K_{AVP}}{100 \, K_{mv\Omega}} \frac{1}{s(1 + s/\omega_m)(1 + s/\omega_e)} = \frac{k_1}{s(1 + s/\omega_m)(1 + s/\omega_e)} \quad (6\text{-}5)$$

$$\text{where } k_1 = \text{gain constant}$$

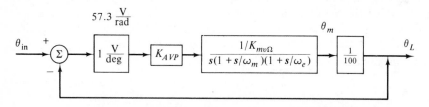

Figure 6-2.   Standard-form reduction of Figure 6-1.

Loop gain is defined as the gain starting from any point in the loop and going all the way around to the starting point. For instance, starting at the input to K_{AVP}, the loop gain is given in Eq. (6-5). The numerical constant associated with this equation is designated k_1 in the second part of Eq. (6-5).

Equation (6-6) states that the gain magnitude is unity at the *gain crossover frequency* of the loop, ω_{cp}.

$$1 \approx \left| \frac{k_1}{j\omega_{cp}(1 + j\omega_{cp}/\omega_m)(1 + j\omega_{cp}/\omega_e)} \right| \quad (6\text{-}6)$$

Actually, ω_{cp} is the *asymptotic* gain crossover frequency, and will be slightly different from the *actual* frequency at which the gain is unity. The significant aspect of Eq. (6-6) is that it is a truism; it states the fact that the magnitude of the gain expression is essentially unity when $j\omega_{cp}$ is substituted for s. Figure 6-3 shows the Bode plot of the gain expression given in Eq. (6-5). It will be noticed that this asymptotic plot has a -1 slope up to the frequency ω_m. This -1 slope is due to the $1/s$ term which is present because the motor acts as an integrator.

For the frequency ω_m (when s is set equal to $j\omega_m$, the first parenthetical denominator term becomes $1 + j1$: at frequencies above ω_m, the magnitude of the j part of this term becomes increasingly larger than unity. As a consequence, the overall gain expression will diminish in magnitude at close to a -2 slope on a Bode plot until a frequency ω_e is approached. The Bode plot changes to a -3 slope at frequencies above ω_e.

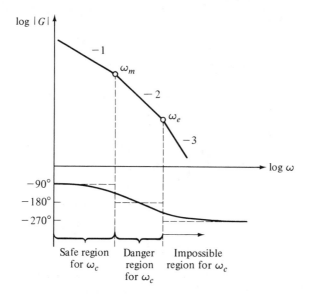

Figure 6-3. Bode plot of open-loop gain of servo of
Figure 6-2.

In summary, each frequency-variable term in the denominator has a distinct frequency (*break point*) at which it starts to alter the shape of the Bode plot significantly. The pure s term starts acting at zero frequency, resulting in a -1 slope at the far left of the curve. The $1 + s/\omega_m$ term starts having an effect on the gain magnitude when s approaches $j\omega_m$. The next term starts to act when the frequency variable approaches $j\omega_e$. Naturally, there is some effect on the gain magnitude for frequencies below these so-called "break" frequencies; the effect, however, is insignificant unless the frequency is within a factor of 2 or 3 of the break frequency.

Example 6-1. Consider the transfer function $G(s) = (s + 2)/s(s + 7)(s + 31)$. Figure E6-1 plots the logarithm of the gain magnitude in decibels against the logarithm of frequency. The figure shows that the denominator s term causes a -1 slope up to a frequency of 2 rad/s, whereupon the numerator term comes into play and causes the gain to remain constant as the frequency increases. Starting at 7 rad/s, the gain again tends to decline at a -1 slope up to 31 rad/s, above which the gain slope approaches -2.

Now, returning to the design of Figs. 6-1 and 6-2, which has the Bode plot of Fig. 6-3, it may also be seen that the phase angle changes from $-90°$ at zero frequency to the region of $-180°$ and then to $-270°$. As long as the gain slope is -1, the phase lag is approximately 90°. Near the break frequency ω_m, the phase becomes minus 135°, and above ω_m the phase approaches 180°; above ω_e it approaches 270°. From a stability standpoint, a safe cri-

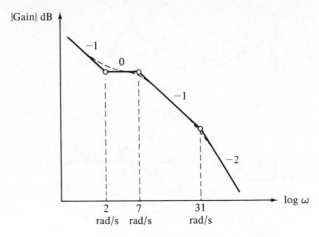

Figure E6-1

terion for system operation is to assure that the phase lag is less than 180°
when the gain falls to unity (crossover). If the gain is unity at a phase lag of
180°, the conditions required for creating oscillation are satisfied. Therefore,
a general rule may be stated: *The gain crossover (unity gain) frequency cannot occur at a frequency where the phase lag is 180°.* In Fig. 6-3 the phase lag
at ω_m is 135°; *this 135° is a reasonable maximum for phase lag at the gain
crossover (unity gain) frequency.* (Chapter 8, which is concerned with stability, estabilshes this fact quantitatively.) For this criterion, the gain crossover
frequency ω_{cp} may occur at any frequency up to ω_m. For frequencies larger
than ω_m, there is an increasing danger of oscillation.

Example 6-2. Consider a servo which uses a motor, amplifier, and other devices
all of which in combination have an open-loop gain function consisting of a pure
integration, a lag due to ω_m at 10 rad/s, and a controllable gain crossover frequency,
ω_{cp}:

$$G(j\omega) = \frac{\omega_{cp}}{j\omega(1 + j\omega/10)}$$

Determine the open- and closed-loop gains at ω_{cp} for ω_{cp} equal to 1, 5, and
10 rad/s.

solution For $\omega_{cp} = 1$,

$$G_1(j\omega) = \frac{1}{j\omega(1 + j\omega/10)}$$

$$G_1(j1) = \frac{1}{j(1 + 0.1j)} = 0 \text{ dB} \angle -95.6°$$

$$G_1'(j1) = \frac{1/j(1 + 0.1j)}{1 + 1/j(1 + 0.1j)} = \frac{1}{j - 0.1 + 1} = \frac{1}{0.9 + j}$$

$$= \frac{1}{1.345 \angle 48°} = -2.6 \text{ dB} \angle -48°$$

For $\omega_{cp} = 5$,

$$G_5(j\omega) = \frac{5}{j\omega(1 + j\omega/10)}$$

$$G_5(j5) = \frac{5}{j5(1 + j0.5)} = \frac{1}{j(1 + j0.5)} = -1\text{ dB}\angle -116.6°$$

$$G'_1(j5) = \frac{1/j(1 + j0.5)}{1 + 1/(j(1 + j0.5))} = \frac{1}{j - 0.5 + 1} = \frac{1}{0.5 + j}$$

$$= \frac{1}{1.12\angle 63.4°} = -1\text{ dB}\angle -63°$$

For $\omega_{cp} = 10$,

$$G_{10}(j\omega) = \frac{10}{j\omega(1 + j\omega/10)}$$

$$G_{10}(j10) = \frac{10}{j10(1 + j)} = \frac{1}{j(1 + j)} = -3\text{ dB}\angle -135°$$

$$G'_{10}(j10) = \frac{1/j(1 + j)}{1 + 1/j(1 + j)} = \frac{1}{j - 1 + 1} = \frac{1}{j} = 0\text{ dB}\angle -90°$$

From the results of this example it can be seen that the closed-loop gain at ω_{cp} increases as ω_{cp} is increased up to ω_m, where the open-loop phase lag is 135°. For ω_{cp} equal to ω_m (10 rad/s), $G'(j\omega_{cp})$ is still stable. For higher values of ω_{cp}, the system will continue to become more unstable.

When the upper limit of the gain crossover frequency ω_{cp} is discussed, this is the same as discussing the amount of gain in the loop. By varying the gain in the loop, the gain crossover frequency ω_{cp} is varied. For the present design example, ω_{cp} will be made equal to or less than ω_m to assure a stable system. For the present design, we let ω_{cp} equal ω_m; this value is substituted in Eq. (6-7). Equation (6-8) is a simplification of Eq. (6-7) based on the fact that ω_e (3370 rad/s) is much greater than ω_m (15.6 rad/s).

$$G(j\omega_m) = \frac{k_1}{j\omega_m(1 + j\omega_m/\omega_m)(1 + j\omega_m/\omega_e)} \tag{6-7}$$

$$\approx \frac{k_1}{j\omega_m(1 + j)} \tag{6-8}$$

$$|G(j\omega_m)| \approx 1 \tag{6-9}$$

Equation (6-9) states that the gain crossover frequency is ω_m, and that at that frequency the magnitude of the loop gain is approximately unity.

$$1 \approx \left|\frac{k_1}{j\omega_m(1 + j)}\right| \approx \left|\frac{k_1}{j\omega_m}\right| = \frac{k_1}{\omega_m} \tag{6-10}$$

$$k_1 \approx \omega_m = \omega_{cp} \tag{6-11}$$

In Equation (6-10), the details of the simplification are given; this gives the result that k_1 over ω_m is essentially unity. The fact that $1 + j1$ is approximated as unity results in approximately a 3 dB error. This is normally the maximum possible error due to the asymptotic assumption that a low-pass filter has unity gain up to and including its break frequency. The error is usually less for practical cases where there are more poles and zeros in the loop gain expression. The great simplicity in system calculating resulting from the use of the asymptotic gain crossover frequency ω_{cp} more than offsets the fact that there is some error inherent in the asymptotic assumption. Equation (6-11) follows from Eq. (6-10) and makes the statement that the gain constant k_1 is equal to the motor break frequency ω_m, which in turn is equal to the gain crossover frequency ω_{cp}. Using this result, Eq. (6-12) gives the open-loop gain expression using ω_{cp} as the asymptotic gain crossover frequency and neglecting ω_m.

$$G(s) \approx \omega_{cp}/s \qquad (6-12)$$

Figures 6-4 and 6-5 show the relationships between ω_m and two assumed

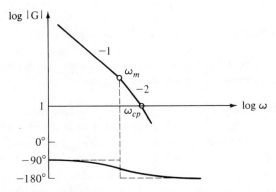

Figure 6-4.   Unsafe   gain   crossover   frequency, ω_{cp}
(above ω_m).

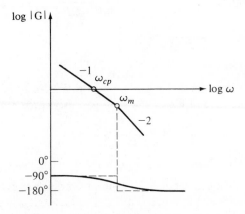

Figure 6-5.   Safe gain crossover frequency, ω_{cp} (below
ω_m).

values of ω_{cp}. If ω_{cp} is above the motor break frequency ω_m as in Fig. 6-4, the system has a tendency to be unstable because the phase lag exceeds 135° and therefore is an unsafe situation. For ω_{cp} below ω_m as shown in Fig. 6-5, the system stability is assured because the phase lag is less than 135°. This comparison leads to a simple criterion for gain adjustment: *The open-loop gain must fall below unity before the open-loop phase lag reaches 135°.* Equation (6-13) is the open-loop gain expression for a servo using a dc motor having armature inductance; the second part of Eq. (6-13) is a simplified version neglecting the electrical break frequency ω_e (it will be recalled from Section 5-7 that higher-order poles, if they are quite high compared to the low-frequency poles, may be neglected because the transient amplitude terms associated with them are relatively small).

$$G(s) = \frac{\omega_{cp}}{s(1 + s/\omega_m)(1 + s/\omega_e)} \approx \frac{\omega_{cp}}{s(1 + s/\omega_m)} \tag{6-13}$$

Equation (6-14) states the important fact that k_1 (of Eq. 6-5) equals the gain crossover frequency ω_{cp}, which equals the literal expression on the right.

$$k_1 = \omega_{cp} = \frac{57.3 K_{AVP}}{100 K_{mv\Omega}} = \frac{57.3 K_{AVP}}{N K_{mv\Omega}} \tag{6-14}$$

$$\frac{1}{K_{mv\Omega}} = \frac{10{,}000 \text{ rpm}}{14 \text{ V}} \times \frac{0.104 \text{ rad/s}}{\text{rpm}} = 74.2 \frac{\text{rad/s}}{\text{V}} \tag{6-15}$$

Equation (6-15) calculates the value of $1/K_{mv\Omega}$ based on the known characteristics of the servomotor. Equation (6-16) states the numerical expression for the gain crossover frequency ω_{cp} which is 42.6 times the voltage amplifier gain, K_{AVP}.

$$\omega_{cp} = 0.573 \times 74.2 K_{AVP} \left(\frac{\text{V}}{\text{rad}}\right)\left(\frac{\text{rad/s}}{\text{V}}\right) = 42.6 K_{AVP}(\text{s}^{-1}) \tag{6-16}$$

$$K_{AVP} = \frac{\omega_{cp}}{42.6} \tag{6-17}$$

Equation (6-17) inverts this expression giving the voltage amplifier gain K_{AVP} in terms of the gain crossover frequency ω_{cp}. Equation (6-17) is the desired result, giving the voltage amplifier gain directly in terms of ω_{cp}; the upper limit on ω_{cp} has been established as ω_m, and therefore it is now possible to calculate K_{AVP}.

6-5. calculating amplifier gain

For a reasonably stable system, the gain crossover frequency ω_{cp} will be equal to ω_m, the motor break frequency (as developed in Section 6-4); therefore K_{AVP} is determined in Eq. (6-18) from Eq. (6-17).

$$K_{AVP} = \frac{15.6}{42.6} = 0.365 \frac{\text{V}}{\text{V}} \tag{6-18}$$

$$G(s) = \frac{57.3 \times 0.365 \times 74.2 \times \frac{1}{100}}{s(1 + s/15.6)(1 + s/3370)} = \frac{15.6}{s(1 + s/15.6)(1 + s/3370)}$$

$$\approx \frac{15.6}{s(1 + s/15.6)} = \frac{243}{s(s + 15.6)} \qquad (6\text{-}19)$$

In Fig. 6-6, the gain constants are given in the various blocks. The overall

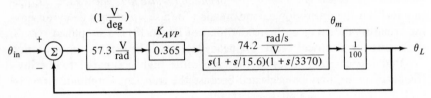

Figure 6-6.   Servo diagram with actual gains.

approximate open-loop gain expression is given in Eq. (6-19); this neglects the electrical break frequency which is high enough to be negligible. $G'(s)$, the closed-loop gain expression is given in Eq. (6-20).

$$G'(s) = \frac{G(s)}{1 + G(s)} = \frac{243/s(s + 15.6)}{1 + (243/s(s + 15.6))} = \frac{243}{s^2 + 15.6s + 243} \qquad (6\text{-}20)$$

$$= \frac{\omega_n^2}{s^2 + 2\zeta\omega_n s + \omega_n^2} \qquad \text{where } \omega_n^2 = 243, \ \omega_n = 15.6$$

$$\zeta = \frac{15.6}{2\omega_n} = \frac{15.6}{2 \times 15.6} = 0.5$$

$$(6.21)$$

The *standard quadratic form** is given in Eq. (6-21). From this the natural frequency ω_n is found to be 15.6 rad/s, and the *damping coefficient* ζ is 0.5. A damping coefficient of 0.5 corresponds to a step response with a 16 per cent overshoot†; for a 1° step into the servo, the output would overshoot by 0.16°. Based on standard quadratic characteristics, the frequency response of this servo exhibits a 1-dB peak at a frequency of about 0.7 of the natural frequency of the loop (0.7 of 15.6 rad/s), approximately 11 rad/s.

In Eq. (6-22), the closed-loop response at ω_{cp} (15.6 rad/s) is calculated.

$$G'(j15.6) = \frac{243}{-243 + j243 + 243} = \frac{1}{j} = 1 \angle -90° \qquad (6\text{-}22)$$

$$|G'(j0.7 \times 15.6)| \approx \left| \frac{243}{-0.5 \times 243 + j0.7 \times 243 + 243} \right|$$

$$= \left| \frac{1}{0.5 + j0.7} \right| = \frac{1}{0.868} = 1.15 \qquad (6\text{-}23)$$

The result is that the closed-loop gain at ω_{cp} is unity and the closed-loop phase lag is 90°, as shown by Eq. (6-22), assuring stablity. The closed-

* See Section 8-4.

† In Section 8-3, it will be shown that a quadiatic system with ζ = 0.5 has a transient response overshoot of 16 per cent; Eqs. 8-32 through 8-39 demonstrate this.

loop response at $0.7\,\omega_{cp}$ is calculated in Eq. (6-23); there is a peaking of 15 per cent (about 1.2 dB) as predicted from the standard quadratic curves. The conclusion is that a reasonable gain crossover frequency was chosen, as demonstrated by well-behaved transient and frequency responses.

6-6. velocity constant

Chapter 4 developed the concept of K_v, the velocity constant; now the motor voltage required to support an assumed load velocity of 50 rpm is used to calculate K_v. This motor voltage emerges as 7 V from Eq. (6-24). With 7 V at the amplifier output, the amplifier input must be 19.2 V (or e_m/K_{AVP}), where $K_{AVP} = 0.365$.

$$e_m = \frac{14\ \text{V}}{10{,}000\ \text{rpm}} \times 50\ \text{rpm} \times \overset{\text{N}}{100} = 7\ \text{V} \qquad (6\text{-}24)$$

$$\text{Error} = \frac{19.2\ \text{V}}{1\ \text{V}/^\circ} = 19.2^\circ \qquad (6\text{-}25)$$

$$K_v = \frac{50\ \text{rpm}}{19.2^\circ}\left(\frac{360^\circ}{1\ \text{rev}}\right)\left(\frac{1\ \text{min}}{60\ \text{s}}\right) = 15.6\ \text{s}^{-1} \qquad (6\text{-}26)$$

For a 19.2-V input, the error must be 19.2° [Eq. (6-25)]. K_v is defined as the velocity divided by the error angle and is calculated in Eq. (6-26) to be 15.6 rad/s. (This value for K_v was already known because K_v and ω_{cp} are equal in this simple servo). The method just used to calculate K_v is an alternative approach using physical reasoning.

6-7. torque stiffness

A load torque of 1 lb·ft is assumed and the resulting steady-state error will be calculated assuming that the servo is at stall. This is a straightforward problem because if the load torque is known and there is no steady-state load motion, the motor constant K_{mTE} may be used to determine the input motor voltage to support that torque.

First the torque referred to the motor shaft must be determined; this is found to be (1 lb·ft × 12 in/ft × 16 oz/lb × $\frac{1}{100}$) or 1.92 in·oz at the motor as shown in Fig. 6-7. This torque divided by K_{mTE} results in 5.38 V at

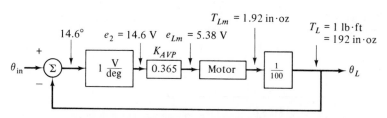

Figure 6-7.   Error due to a steady load torque.

the motor terminal as given by Eq. (6-27) and shown in Fig. 6-7. The error voltage e_2 is determined to be 14.6 V from Eq. (6-28).

$$e_{Lm} = \frac{1.92 \text{ in} \cdot \text{oz}}{K_{mTE}} = \frac{1.92 \text{ in} \cdot \text{oz}}{5.0 \text{ in} \cdot \text{oz}/14 \text{ V}} = 5.38 \text{ V} \qquad (6\text{-}27)$$

$$e_2 = \frac{5.38 \text{ V}}{0.365} = 14.6 \text{ V} \longrightarrow 14.6° \qquad (6\text{-}28)$$

From Fig. 6-6, it is known that the amplifier gain K_{AVP} is 0.365, which is used in Eq. (6-28) to find the error voltage of 14.6 V. This voltage is equivalent to a servo error of 14.6°. It has been determined for the servo of Figs. 6-6 and 6-7 that to support a load torque of 1 lb·ft, an error of 14.6° is required. To state this differently, if the servo is sitting at rest with zero error and a (disturbance) torque of 1 lb·ft is applied to the motor load, the output shaft will deflect 14.6° (see Fig. 6-7).

It is interesting to note that the higher the output force the greater the error; it can be seen therefore, that the servo acts like a spring. This is an important way to visualize a servo; the so-called "stiffness" of the servo is similar to the stiffness of a spring.

6-8. torque disturbances

Figure 6-8 is essentially the same as Fig. 6-2. The bandwidth ω_{cp} of this servo is equal to the quantity indicated in Eq. (6-29), which is a restatement of Eq. (6-14). Equation (6-30) modifies Eq. (6-29), allowing the redrawing of Fig. 6-8 to give Fig. 6-9; in this figure the electrical break frequency ω_e is neglected.

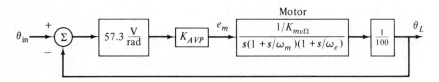

Figure 6-8.   Position servo block diagram.

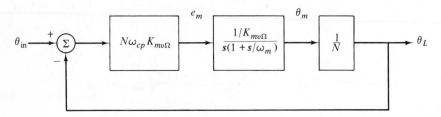

Figure 6-9.   Modified block diagram of position servo.

$$\frac{57.3K_{AVP}}{NK_{mv\Omega}} = \omega_{cp} \tag{6-29}$$

$$N\omega_{cp}K_{mv\Omega} = 57.3K_{AVP} \tag{6-30}$$

In Fig. 6-10 the same block diagram is expressed again by returning the

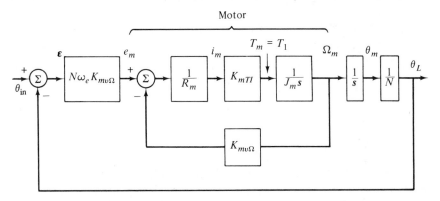

Figure 6-10.   Servo diagram with motor in conceptual loop form.

motor to its original "conceptual-loop" form; this allows examination of some particular variables within the loop that are of interest. In particular, the motor torque T_m is of interest. An externally applied torque T_1 is assumed, and this will be equated to T_m for equilibrium; this is done to determine the servo error which occurs due to this applied load torque.

In Fig. 6-10, for the motor at stall and $T_m = T_1$, the motor voltage e_m is equal to the torque T_1 divided by K_{mTI}/R_m; this is stated in Eq. (6-31). Equation (6-32) states that the servo error is equal to the motor voltage divided by the gain in front of it; in the second part of this equation, e_m is substituted using the results of Eq. (6-31).

$$e_m = \frac{T_1}{K_{mTI}/R_m} \tag{6-31}$$

$$\epsilon = \frac{e_m}{N\omega_{cp}K_{mv\Omega}} = \frac{T_1}{N\omega_{cp}K_{mv\Omega}(K_{mTI}/R_m)} \tag{6-32}$$

If a torque is applied to a servo, for the servo to develop an equal counter torque an error must be present. When the error becomes large enough, adequate torque is developed to equal the applied load torque. This final equilibrium condition has been calculated in Eq. (6-32); the value of this error is that quantity necessary to support the load torque at the motor shaft.

Equation (6-33) is a restatement of Eq. (5-9), giving the motor break frequency ω_m. Equation (6-34) is a modification of Eq. (6-33) and is used to simplify Eq. (6-32) to give the servo error, Eq. (6-35).

$$\omega_m = \frac{K_{mv\Omega}K_{mTI}}{R_m J_m} \tag{6-33}$$

$$J_m \omega_m = \frac{K_{mv\Omega}K_{mTI}}{R_m} \tag{6-34}$$

$$\epsilon = \frac{T_1}{N\omega_{cp}J_m\omega_m} \tag{6-35}$$

The torque at the motor T_1 is equal to the torque applied at the load divided by the gear ratio; this is stated in Eq. (6-36).

$$T_1 = \frac{T_{load}}{N} \tag{6-36}$$

$$\epsilon = \frac{T_{load}}{N^2 J_m \omega_{cp}\omega_m} \tag{6-37}$$

$$\epsilon_{KT} = \frac{T_{load}}{K_T} \tag{6-38}$$

Equation (6-37) states the servo error in terms of the load torque, T_{load}. The term $N^2 J_m$ is the motor inertia reflected to the load (in general this is the total inertia reflected to the load). The general form of Eq. (6-37) is of great interest; it states that the servo error due to steady torque disturbance is equal to that torque divided by the reflected inertia times two frequency terms. This is the general form for the magnitude of all servo errors due to torque disturbances. The torque constant K_T (or stiffness) is introduced in Eq. (6-38); the denominator of Eq. (6-37) is the torque constant K_T for a simple servo. K_T has dimensions of torque.

Equation (6-39) restates Eq. (6-37); and Eq. (6-40) shows that K_T is dimensionally torque and that the error is nondimensional.

$$\epsilon_{KT} = \frac{T_{TL}}{N^2 J_{Tm}\omega_{cp}\omega_m} = \frac{T_{TL}}{J_{TL}\omega_{cp}\omega_m} \tag{6-39}$$

$$= \frac{lb \cdot ft}{lb \cdot ft \cdot s^2 \cdot s^{-1} \cdot s^{-1}} = \text{nondimentional} \tag{6-40}$$

This result is to be expected, because the error should be in radians and radians are nondimensional. This answer can be converted into degrees (by multiplying by 57.3 deg/rad and cancelling units). Thus, Eq. (6-41) recalculates the servo error for the servo design example; the calculated error agrees with the previous calculation.

$$\epsilon_{KT} = \frac{192 \ in \cdot oz}{10,000(21.5 \ g \cdot cm^2)(15.6)^2 s^{-2}} \times \frac{70,000 \ rad/s^2}{1 \ in \cdot oz/g \cdot in^2} \tag{6-41}$$
$$= 0.256 \ rad = 14.7°$$

Example 6-3. Design a servo with a transient overshoot of approximately 16 per cent (see Section 6-5) using the specified amplifier, transducers, motor and driving the specified load; find gains, significant characteristics, and errors for a 40-rpm input and a 0.004 lb·ft load torque.

Motor: Magnetic Technology, Inc., type 1937–063.

> Peak torque: 30 oz·in
> Current at peak torque: 1.5 A
> Motor voltage at maximum velocity: 45 V
> Electrical time constant: 0.0003 s (τ)
> dc resistance: 30 Ω
> No-load maximum velocity: 2700 rpm
> Armature inertia: 0.0012 oz·in·s²

Power amplifier: Voltage gain $= 0.4$; $E_{out(max)} = 40$ V; $I_{out(max)} = 1.2$ A; $R_{out} = 5\ \Omega$.

Load: a 0.625-in diameter thin cylinder weighing 8 oz.

Input and output error sensors: 0.01 V/deg.

solution Load inertia: Since the mass of 8 oz is concentrated at a radius of 0.3125 in, the load inertia can be calculated as Mr^2.

$$J_{load} = \frac{8\ oz(1\ lb)}{16\ oz} \frac{1}{32.2\ ft/s^2} \left(\frac{0.3125\ in}{12\ in/ft}\right)^2$$

$$= \frac{0.5\ lb}{32.2\ ft/s^2} \left(\frac{0.3125}{12}\right)^2 ft^2$$

$$= \frac{0.5 \times 0.0975}{32.2 \times 144} lb \cdot ft \cdot s^2 = \frac{0.5 \times 0.0975 \times 192}{32.2 \times 144} oz \cdot in \cdot s^2$$

$$= 0.00202\ oz \cdot in \cdot s^2$$

$$J_T = J_L + J_m$$

$$J_{total} = 0.00202 + 0.0012 = 0.00322\ oz \cdot in \cdot s^2$$

$$\tau_e = \frac{1}{\omega_e}\ 0.0003\ s = \frac{L_{motor}}{R_{motor}} \quad and \quad L_{motor} = \tau_e R_{motor}$$

$$= 0.0003 \times 30 = 0.009\ H$$

$$\omega_e = \frac{R_{motor} + R_{ampl}}{L_{motor}} = \frac{(30 + 5)\ \Omega}{L_{motor}}$$

[See Section 5-4 and Eq. (5-35); the expression here is the electrical break frequency of the motor-amplifier combination.]

$$\omega_e = \frac{35\ \Omega}{0.009\ H} = 3890\ rad/s$$

$$\omega_m = \frac{K_{mTI} K_{mv\Omega}}{R_{total} J_{total}}$$

See Eq. (5-9), where individual terms are as follows:

$$K_{mTI} = \frac{30\ oz \cdot in}{1.5\ A} = 20\ \frac{oz \cdot in}{A} \quad (see\ Table\ 5\text{-}1)$$

$$K_{mv\Omega} = \frac{45\ V}{2700\ rev/min} \times \frac{rev}{2\pi\ rad} \times \frac{60\ s}{min} = 0.159\ \frac{V}{rad/s} \quad (see\ Table\ 5\text{-}1)$$

$$R_{total} = 35$$

$$J_{total} = 0.00322\ oz \cdot in \cdot s^2$$

then,

$$\omega_m = \frac{20 \text{ oz}\cdot\text{in}/A \times 0.159 \text{ V/rad/s}}{35 \text{ V/A} \times 0.00322 \text{ oz}\cdot\text{in}\cdot\text{s}^2} = 28.2 \text{ rad/s}$$

Motor transfer function:

$$\frac{\Omega_m(s)}{E_m(s)} = \frac{1/K_{mv\Omega}}{(s^2/\omega_m\omega_e) + (s/\omega_m) + 1} \approx \frac{1/K_{mv\Omega}}{(1 + s/\omega_m)(1 + s/\omega_e)}$$

$$= \frac{1/(0.159 \text{ V/rad/s})}{(1 + s/28.2)(1 + s/3890)}$$

$$= \frac{6.28 \text{ rad/s/V}}{(1 + s/28.2)(1 + s/3890)} \qquad [\text{see Eq. (5-35)}]$$

System block diagram:

$$\text{Error sensor gain} = 0.01 \frac{V}{\text{deg}} = 0.573 \frac{V}{\text{rad}}$$

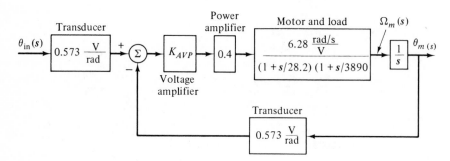

Figure E6-3a

Modified system block diagram, standard form:

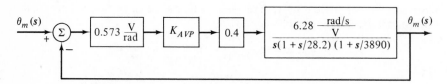

Figure E6-3b

$$G(s) = \frac{0.573 \times 0.4 \times 6.28 K_{AVP}}{s(1 + s/28.2)(1 + s/3890)} = \frac{1.44 K_{AVP}}{s(1 + s/28.2)(1 + s/3890)}$$

$$\approx \frac{1.44 K_{AVP}}{s(1 + s/28.2)} = \frac{\omega_{cp}}{s(1 + s/28.2)}$$

From Eqs. (6-19), (6-20), and (6-21) it was found that for $\omega_{cp} = \omega_m$, $\zeta = 0.5$, and there is a 16 per cent overshoot. Therefore $\omega_{cp} = 1.44K_{AVP} = 28.2$; $K_{AVP} = 19.6$ V/V.

Final diagram:

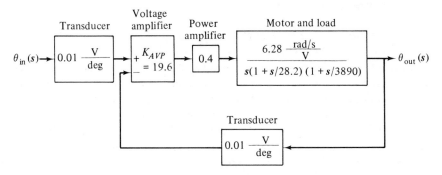

Figure E6-3c

$K_v = \omega_{cp} = 28.2 \text{ s}^{-1}$

($K_v = \omega_{cp}$ for a simple servo, which is the type considered in this example.)

$$\text{Velocity error} = \frac{40 \text{ rev/min}}{28.2 \text{ s}^{-1}} \times \frac{360°}{\text{rev}} \times \frac{\text{min}}{60 \text{ s}}$$

$$= \frac{40 \times 360}{28.2 \times 60} \text{ deg} = 8.51°$$

$$\text{To check}: 8.51° \times \frac{0.01 \text{ V}}{\text{deg}} \times 19.6 \times 0.4 \times 6.28 \frac{\text{rad/s}}{\text{V}}$$

$$= 4.2 \frac{\text{rad}}{\text{s}} \times \frac{2\pi \text{ rad}}{\text{rev}} \times \frac{60 \text{ s}}{\text{min}} = 40 \text{ rpm}$$

$$\text{Stiffness} = J\omega_m\omega_{cp} = 0.00322 \text{ oz} \cdot \text{in} \cdot \text{s}^2 \times (28.2)^2 \text{s}^{-2}$$

$$= 2.55 \text{ oz} \cdot \text{in/rad}$$

[see the discussion related to Eq. (6-37)].

$$\text{Stiffness error} = \frac{T_{\text{load}}}{J\omega_m\omega_{cp}} = \frac{0.004 \text{ lb} \cdot \text{ft}}{2.55 \text{ oz} \cdot \text{in/rad}} \times \frac{192 \text{ in} \cdot \text{oz}}{\text{lb} \cdot \text{ft}}$$

$$= 0.301 \text{ rad} = 17.3°$$

$$\text{To check}: 17.3° \times \frac{0.01 \text{ V}}{\text{deg}} \times 19.6 \times 0.4 \times \frac{20 \text{ oz} \cdot \text{in}}{\text{A}} \times \frac{1}{35 \Omega}$$

$$= 0.774 \text{ oz} \cdot \text{in} = \frac{0.774}{192} \text{ lb} \cdot \text{ft} = 0.004 \text{ lb} \cdot \text{ft}$$

$$\Omega_{\text{max}} = E_{PA(\text{max})} K_{mv\Omega} = \frac{40 \text{ V}}{6.28 \text{ rad/s/V}} = 6.37 \frac{\text{rad}}{\text{s}} \times \frac{\text{rpm}}{0.105 \text{ rad/s}} = 60.6 \text{ rpm}$$

$$T_{\text{max}} = I_{PA(\text{max})} K_{mTI} = 1.2 \text{ A} \times 20 \frac{\text{oz} \cdot \text{in}}{\text{A}} = 24 \text{ oz} \cdot \text{in.} = 0.125 \text{ lb} \cdot \text{ft}$$

6-9. linearity

In the preceding development of torque disturbances it was assumed that the motor was at stall. This assumption is actually unnecessary, because the system is (assumed) linear. The servo could be running at some velocity (less than maximum) and working against the assumed torque and the resulting error required to support that torque would still be 14.7° (some additional error is also required to support the output velocity). A type 1 system (the usual servo type having a single integration) has a finite velocity constant; the velocity constant is defined as the ratio between a constant angular velocity and the error necessary to support that velocity. It is very important to recognize in servos that an error is required to support a torque or a velocity: these errors are a significant and very real part of servo operation.

Another point that should be borne in mind in regard to the linearity assumption is that some motor characteristics do *not* remain constant (an ac motor torque constant varies more with velocity changes than a dc motor torque constant); this causes some destabilizing effects. A motor whose torque constant varies exhibits a motor break frequency that changes; the relatively straightforward relation given in Eq. (6-39) includes ω_m, which in the case of an ac motor varies within a restricted range depending on load speed and torque. To calculate the worst-case errors, one may determine the variation in ω_m and from this compute the actual errors for the conditions of interest.

6-10. direct design

It is possible to calculate many of the characteristics of servos before amplifier gains are calculated and before most electronic components are selected. If the factors that limit the performance of the servo are known, ω_{cp} and other important frequencies may then be determined, and the servo's performance may be predicted accurately. Consider the following example.

Example 6-4. Consider a servo in which $\omega_m = 10$ rad/s and $J_{Tm} = 1$ slug·ft². Calculate the error for the servo operating at 2 rpm against a load of 3 lb·ft.

solution   It is safe (and reasonably conservative) to assume that $\omega_{cp} = \omega_m$ and that $K_v = \omega_{cp} = \omega_m = 10$ rad/s. Therefore

$$\epsilon_{k_v} = \frac{\Omega_{\text{load}}}{K_v} = \frac{2 \text{ rpm}}{10 \text{ rad/s}} = \frac{12°/\text{s}}{10 \text{ rad/s}} = 1.2°$$

Using the expression for K_T which was determined in Section 6-7, the torque error is calculated as follows:

$$\epsilon_{K_T} = \frac{T_{TL}}{K_T} = \frac{T_{TL}}{J_{Tm}\omega_m\omega_{cp}} = \frac{3 \text{ lb} \cdot \text{ft}}{(1 \text{ lb} \cdot \text{ft} \cdot \text{s}^2)(100 \text{ s}^{-2})}$$

$$= \frac{3 \text{ lb} \cdot \text{ft}}{100 \text{ lb} \cdot \text{ft}} = 0.03 \text{ rad} = 1.72°$$

The total worst-case error is the sum of ϵ_{K_v} and ϵ_{K_T}, which is approximately 2.9°.

It can be seen from this example that performance of a simple servo can be predicted if only the total inertia and the motor break frequency ω_m are known. Later in this book it will be shown that the performance of more advanced servo configurations can also be predicted with knowledge of only a few system parameters (see section 10-5, chapter 12, Table 14-3, and section 14-6).

Example 6-5. Design a simple servo to drive a 33,000 g·cm² load using a Kearfott T110-36 400-Hz two-phase servomotor (see specifications below); define its characteristics for a design that will provide maximum load acceleration. Assume a 350° potentiometer excited by 24 V rms for input and output transducers and a power amplifier with a voltage gain of 0.9 to drive phase 2 of the motor.

Kearfott T110-36 400-Hz, two-phase servo characteristic
Phase 1: 115 V, 0.11 A
Phase 2 (control winding): 18 V (two windings in parallel), 0.692 A
Rotor inertia: 3.3 g·cm²
Stall torque: 1.53 oz·in
No-load speed: 5300 rpm
Torque at P_{max}: 0.85 oz·in
Speed at P_{max}: 2800 rpm
Time constant: 0.0169 s

Calculate the errors for a load velocity of 28 rpm and a load torque of 50 in·oz.

solution　Maximum load acceleration results when the reflected load inertia is equal to the motor inertia:

$$N = \sqrt{\frac{33,000}{3.3}} = \sqrt{10,000} = 100$$

The time constant is $1/\omega_m$; therefore unloaded $\omega_m = 1/0.0169 = 59.1$ rad/s. To check this:

$$\omega_m \approx \frac{T_{max}}{\Omega_{max}J_m}$$

$$= \frac{1.53 \text{ in} \cdot \text{oz}}{5300 \text{ rev/min} \times 3.3 \text{ g} \cdot \text{cm}^2} \times \frac{\text{rpm}}{0.105 \text{ rad/s}} \times \frac{70,000 \text{ rad/s}^2}{\text{in} \cdot \text{oz/g} \cdot \text{cm}^2}$$

$$= \frac{1.53 \times 70,000}{5300 \times 3.3 \times 0.105} \text{ s}^{-1} = 58.4 \text{ rad/s}$$

This checks quite well with ω_m (unloaded) above. Therefore loaded $\omega_m = 58.4/2 = 29.2$ rad/s, because the inertia is doubled.

$$K_{\text{transducer}} = \frac{24 \text{ V}}{350 \text{ deg}} \times \frac{57.3°}{\text{rad}} = 3.92 \frac{\text{V}}{\text{rad}}$$

Motor Transfer Function: Because two-phase ac servomotors exhibit saturation in the relationship between speed and control phase voltage (phase 2 voltage), it is necessary to use an approximate figure for $K_{mv\Omega}$. Up to 50 per cent of maximum speed, the curve is quite straight and has a slope of 3.6 V for 2500 rpm.

$$K_{mv\Omega} = \frac{3.6 \text{ V}}{2500 \text{ rpm}} \times \frac{1 \text{ rpm}}{0.105 \text{ rad/s}} = 0.0137 \frac{\text{V}}{\text{rad/s}}$$

$$\frac{\Omega_m(s)}{E_m(s)} \approx \frac{1/0.0137 \text{ rad/s/V}}{(1 + s/29.2)} = \frac{73 \text{ rad/s/V}}{(1 + s/29.2)}$$

$$G(s) = \frac{3.92 K_{AVP} \times 0.9 \times 73}{s(1 + s/29.2) \times 100} = \frac{2.57 K_{AVP}}{s(1 + s/29.2)}$$

$$\omega_{cp} = 2.57 K_{AVP} \approx 29.2 \text{ for 16 per cent overshoot}$$

$$K_{AVP} \approx \frac{29.2}{2.57} = 11.4$$

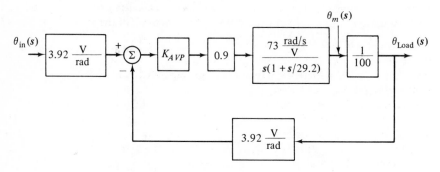

Figure E6-5a

As a practical matter it would be wise to have a gain of approximately 20 available, and to use a gain control at the input of the power amplifier to adjust the servo gain to give acceptable stability.

$$K_v \approx 29 \text{ s}^{-1}; \quad \text{for a 28-rpm load speed (maximum power velocity)}$$

$$\epsilon = \frac{28 \text{ rpm}}{29 \text{ s}^{-1}} \times \frac{6°/\text{s}}{\text{rpm}} = 5.8°$$

$$K_T = (N^2 J_m + J_2)\omega_m \omega_{cp} = 2J_L(\omega_m)^2$$
$$= 2 \times 33,000 \text{ g} \cdot \text{cm}^2 \times (29 \text{ rad/s})^2$$
$$= 66,000 \text{ g} \cdot \text{cm}^2 \times (29.2)^2 \text{s}^{-2} \times \frac{1}{70 \times 10^3} \frac{\text{in} \cdot \text{oz}}{\text{g} \cdot \text{cm}^2/\text{s}^2} = \frac{792 \text{ in} \cdot \text{oz}}{\text{rad}}$$

A steady torque of 50 in·oz at the load would have an error of

$$\epsilon_{K_T} = \frac{50 \text{ in} \cdot \text{oz}}{792 \text{ in} \cdot \text{oz/rad}} \times 57.3 \frac{\text{deg}}{\text{rad}} = 3.63°$$

Two-phase servomotors require that the reference and control phases be 90° out of phase because torque is proportional to the sine of the difference angle. An easy way to accomplish this is to shift the phase of the reference winding by 90° using the proper capacitor values C_1 and C_2* in the final diagram:

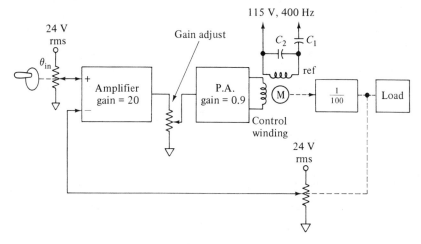

Figure E6-5b

6-11. summary

In this chapter a servo was developed by assuming a commercially available motor and an inertial load (a reasonable assumption). From this information the required gear ratio was calculated. The open-loop gain versus frequency response was also determined. From these frequency characteristics, a gain crossover frequency was set that assured adequate stability. From this gain crossover frequency, the amplifier gain magnitude was calculated. Based on this amplifier gain, an already established fact was confirmed: *The velocity constant K_v is equal to the asymptotic gain crossover frequency ω_{cp}.* Finally, an applied load torque was assumed; the resulting error was calculated and from this the servos' effective "stiffness" K_T was determined.

A pure inertial load was shown to be reasonable to assume because most loads behave as pure inertias without any appreciable damping. (If there is appreciable friction—normally Coulomb or static friction—the easiest approach to adequately accurate design information is to neglect these effects in calculating bandwidths and to consider them later as torque disturbances. Chapter 12 discusses torque disturbance error techniques.) The development

* John G. Truxal, *Control Engineer's Handbook* (New York: McGraw-Hill Book Company, Inc., 1958), Section 12.33.

of a general torque disturbance formula for steady torques was given and finally the concept of "direct design" was introduced.

problems

6-1. For a motor with $L_{arm} = 10 \times 10^{-3}$ H and $R_{arm} = 10\,\Omega$ and a power amplifier with an output resistance of $5\,\Omega$, find the electrical break frequency ω_e.

6-2. What gear ratio should be used for a motor with a maximum power velocity of 2000 rpm and a maximum required load velocity of 40 rpm?

6-3. A servomotor has a stall torque of 10 in·oz, a maximum velocity of 4000 rpm, a rotor inertia of 12 g·cm², a gear ratio of 50, and a load inertia of 10,000 g·cm². Find the motor break frequency ω_m.

6-4. A simple servomechanism based on Problems 6-1, 6-2, and 6-3 is to be constructed. Draw the block diagram given the following additional information:

Maximum motor voltage	20 V
Motor drive amplifier voltage gain	7.0
Transducer constant	0.03 V/deg
Maximum power amplifier output voltage	30 V

Determine the expression for $G(s)$ and calculate K_{AVP} based on a specification of no more than 16 per cent transient overshoot for a small step position command.

6-5. Calculate the value of the velocity error for the maximum input command velocity 40 rpm.

6-6. Determine the steady-state error for a load torque of 0.5 lb·ft.

6-7. Calculate the maximum torque that can be supplied to the load, the maximum load velocity (at zero torque) and the maximum load acceleration at stall.

6-8. Using a Clifton Precision Products 13-DM-☐-2 dc servomotor, load transducer, and drive amplifier as listed below, calculate (a) through (i) for a maximum transient overshoot of approximately 16 per cent.

(a) ω_e
(b) N (gear ratio) to supply required load velocity at maximum power velocity
(c) ω_m
(d) K_{AVP}
(e) velocity error
(f) torque errors
(g) maximum torque that can be supplied to the load
(h) maximum velocity that the load can be driven at (at zero load torque)
(i) maximum load acceleration at stall

Motor characteristics 13-DM-☐-2
L_{arm}: 4.6×10^{-3} H
R_{arm}: $16.5\,\Omega$

Maximum power velocity: 5000 rpm
Rotor inertia: 11.5 g·cm²
Maximum velocity: 10,000 rpm = 1050 rad/s
Maximum stall torque: 5 in·oz
Maximum unloaded voltage 28 V

Load characteristics
Inertia: 20,000 g·cm²
Maximum required torque: 150 in·oz
Maximum required speed: 100 rpm

Drive amplifier characteristics
Output resistance: 2 Ω
Maximum output voltage: 22 V
Maximum output current: 1.1 A
Voltage gain: 0.5

Transducer gain: 0.03 V/deg = 1.72 V/rad

6-9. Given a servo with ω_m = 20 rad/s, and the total inertia reflected to the load of 4 slug·ft², calculate:
(a) the stiffness error which could be expected for a 15-lb·ft steady load torque
(b) the velocity error which could be expected for a required load velocity of 10°/s
(c) the factor by which the inertia has to be changed to halve the torque error

6-10. For an Inland 1937–088 Torque Motor,

$$T_{max} = 45 \text{ oz·in}$$
$$J_{arm} = 0.0017 \text{ oz·in·s}^2$$
$$\Omega_{max} = 2100 \text{ rpm}$$

What load inertia coupled directly gives an ω_m of 10 rad/s for a 0-Ω drive amplifier? For this inertia, calculate:
(a) $\ddot{\theta}_{max}$
(b) K_v (reasonable value)
(c) the error due to 10 in·oz load torque (based on a reasonable estimate of ω_{cp})

6-11.
(a) Using a 13-DM-☐-2, find N for $\Omega_{L(max)}$ = 200 rpm (use maximum power velocity).
(b) For J_L = 10,000 g·cm², find ω_m.
(c) For $\omega_m = \omega_{cp}$, what is the steady-state error for $\Omega_{L(max)}$?
(d) At stall, what is the error due to 10-in·oz load torque?

6-12. Given a 13-DM-☐-2 motor, calculate:
(a) N (gear ratio) for a maximum load velocity of 10°/s for the motor operating at the maximum power point
(b) the total inertia reflected to the motor shaft if the load inertia is 400 slug·ft²
(c) ω_m (considering the load inertia)

6-13. Given a dc motor having the characteristics given in Fig. P6-13, calculate:

(a) K_{mTI}(oz·in/A)

$R_{arm} = 15.5\ \Omega$
$L_{arm} = 0$
$J_m = 1.6\ \text{g·cm}^2$ Figure P6-13

(b) $K_{mv\Omega}(\text{V/rad/s})$
(c) $\omega_m(\text{rad/s})$

6-14. Given a dc motor and load:

$R_{arm} = 15.5\ \Omega$
$L_{arm} = 0$
$J_m = 1.6\ \text{g·cm}^2$
$J_{load} = 8\ \text{g·cm}^2$
$E_{max} = 14\ \text{V}$
$\Omega_{max} = 16{,}500\ \text{rpm}$
$T_{max} = 1.0\ \text{in·oz}$

(a) Find ω_m.
(b) With 14 V applied to the motor, how long would it take to reach 8250 rpm?
(c) Repeat (a) and (b) for an added load inertia of 960 g·cm² geared down by 10:1 from the motor.

7

tachometer and back emf stabilization

For simple servos it has been shown that K_v is equal to ω_{cp} and ω_{cp} is limited to ω_m for stability reasons; as a result servo performance is severely limited when ω_m is low. The alternative is to compensate simple servos in some way to improve their characteristics. The two most direct methods of accomplishing this are through *tachometer stabilization* and *lead network compensation*. Tachometer stabilization is of fundamental importance and is considered here; lead network stabilization will be considered in Chapter 10.

7-1. tachometer stabilization

Figure 7-1 is the transfer-function block diagram for a dc motor and a tachometer; the input armature voltage is E_m, and the motor output angle is θ_m. Attached to the motor output shaft is a tachometer which has a gain of $sK_{GE\Omega}$. The output voltage of the tachometer is proportional to the input velocity to the tachometer as stated in Eq. (7-1). Equations (7-2) and (7-3) derive the gain of the tachometer as $sK_{GE\Omega}$.

$$e_G = K_{GE\Omega}\Omega_{IN} = K_{GE\Omega}\dot{\theta}_{IN} \tag{7-1}$$

$$E_G(s) = K_{GE\Omega}s\theta_{IN}(s) \tag{7-2}$$

$$\frac{E_G(s)}{\theta_{IN}(s)} = sK_{GE\Omega} \tag{7-3}$$

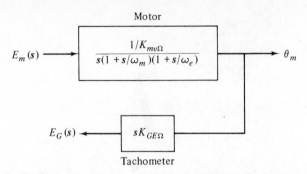

Figure 7-1.   Transfer function of dc motor and tachometer.

In Fig. 7-2 this tachometer and motor are enclosed in a loop; the voltage that comes from the tachometer generator is fed back to a summing point, the output of which is fed to a new amplifier K_{AVR}. Figure 7-2 is modified slightly using block-diagram algebra to obtain Fig. 7-3. The fact that this

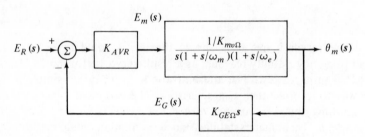

Figure 7-2.   Tachometer loop.

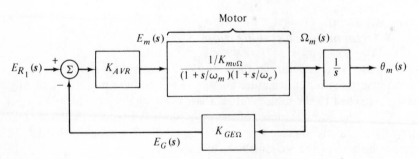

Figure 7-3.   Tachometer loop.

block-diagram manipulation is valid may be verified by checking the gain from $E_m(s)$ to $\theta_m(s)$ and from $E_m(s)$ to $E_G(s)$ for Figs. 7-2 and 7-3. The open-loop gain is expressed in Eq. (7-4); the constant terms are in the numerator and the dynamic terms are in the denominator.

$$G(s) = \frac{K_{AVR}K_{GE\Omega}/K_{mv\Omega}}{(1 + s/\omega_m)(1 + s/\omega_e)} \tag{7-4}$$

Figure 7-4 compares the loop gain plot of the tachometer loop with the

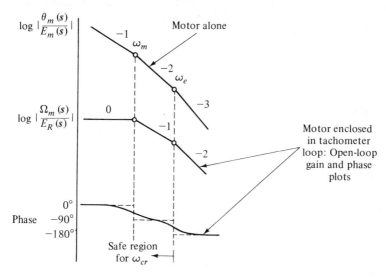

Figure 7-4.   Motor gain plot and open tachometer loop gain and phase plots.

loop gain of the motor by itself. The slopes of all regions of the tachometer loop gain plot are one less than for the motor loop. It is now clear that a safe region for the gain crossover frequency of this tachometer loop would be at some frequency less than ω_e, where the phase lag is certain to be less than $180°$. As a consequence, the gain crossover frequency of the rate loop ω_{cr} can approach ω_e; ω_{cr} can certainly be greater than ω_m but less than ω_e. As a result, tachometer stabilization greatly improves bandwidth; the fact that this improves position loop bandwidth above that obtainable in a simple servo will be shown subsequently.

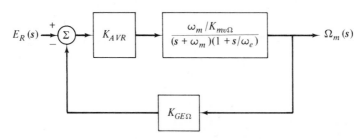

Figure 7-5.   Tachometer loop.

In Eq. (7-5) the magnitude of the loop gain at the gain crossover frequency ω_{cr} is, by definition, one. By equating the last part of Eq. (7-5) to unity and inverting, Eq. (7-6) is obtained.

$$|G(j\omega_{cr})| = 1 = \left| \frac{K_{AVR}K_{GE\Omega}/K_{mv\Omega}}{(1 + j\omega_{cr}/\omega_m)(1 + j\omega_{cr}/\omega_e)} \right| \approx \frac{K_{AVR}K_{GE\Omega}/K_{mv\Omega}}{\omega_{cr}/\omega_m}$$

$$= \frac{K_{AVR}K_{GE\Omega}\omega_m}{K_{mv\Omega}\omega_{cr}} \tag{7-5}$$

$$\omega_{cr} = \frac{K_{AVR}K_{GE\Omega}\omega_m}{K_{mv\Omega}} \tag{7-6}$$

This literal expression, which is determined as the acceptable value for ω_{cr}, is based on the very real stability requirement that ω_{cr} must be less than ω_e. Figure 7-6 is a block-diagram algebra simplification of Fig. 7-5; it may be

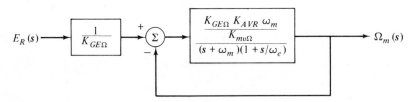

Figure 7-6.   Simplified tachometer loop.

seen that the gain constant of the forward loop block is equal to ω_{cr}. It is now possible to substitute this literal value of ω_{cr} for the gain constant; this is done in Fig. 7-7. Figure 7-7 is simpler than Fig. 7-6 but contains basically

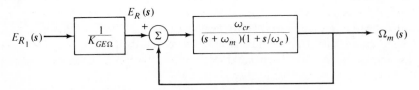

Figure 7-7.   Tachometer loop further simplified.

the same information. The parameter subject to adjustment in Fig. 7-6 was K_{AVR}, but in Fig. 7-7 it is ω_{cr}. This is a valuable step, because ω_{cr} is a basic constant of the system determined by stability considerations, whereas the value of K_{AVR} is not needed until the details of hardware design are finalized.

Now the closed-loop expression may be determined for the loop of Fig. 7-7; this is worked out in Eq. (7-7).

$$G'(s) = \frac{\Omega_m(s)}{E_r(s)} = \frac{\omega_{cr}/(s + \omega_m)(1 + s/\omega_e)}{1 + \omega_{cr}/(s + \omega_m)(1 + s/\omega_e)}$$

$$= \frac{\omega_{cr}}{(s + \omega_m)(1 + s/\omega_e) + \omega_{cr}} = \frac{\omega_{cr}\omega_e}{(s + \omega_m)(s + \omega_e) + \omega_{cr}\omega_e}$$

$$= \frac{\omega_{cr}\omega_e}{s^2 + \omega_m s + \omega_e s + \omega_{cr}\omega_e + \omega_m\omega_e}$$

$$\approx \frac{\omega_{cr}\omega_e}{s^2 + (\omega_{cr} + \omega_e)s + \omega_{cr}\omega_e} = \frac{\omega_{cr}\omega_e}{(s + \omega_{cr})(s + \omega_e)}$$

$$= \frac{1}{(1 + s/\omega_{cr})(1 + s/\omega_e)} \tag{7-7}$$

There is a simplification involved in this computation: the magnitudes of the two poles are said to be ω_{cr} and ω_e. This approximation is based on the development of Section 5-7. To be valid in this case, ω_{cr} must be kept appreciably below ω_e.

An accurate approximation of the closed-loop transfer function of the tachometer loop is given in Fig. 7-8. It can be seen that at low frequencies it

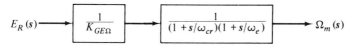

Figure 7-8.   Closed rate loop approximation.

has a constant gain of $1/K_{GE\Omega}$. The frequency terms in the second block represent the dynamics of the loop. Compared to the original dc motor, this loop bandwidth is ω_{cr}, which is much greater than ω_m: further, ω_m is no longer a system frequency limitation. The comparison of the open- and closed-loop Bode plots is given in Fig. 7-9; compared to the motor alone of Fig. 6-3,

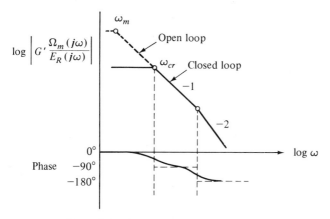

Figure 7-9.   Bode plot of closed rate loop.

the tachometer loop has removed the lowest-frequency pole and decreased the negative slope by one. The net result is to provide a velocity source with greatly improved bandwidth over that of a dc motor by itself. This is accomplished by applying greatly increased "synthetic" damping obtained by means of the tachometer. The tachometer voltage provides damping similar to that of back emf except that the effect is being increased by means of amplification (K_{AVR}). This is similar to increasing $K_{mv\Omega}$ in the motor (an increase of $K_{mv\Omega}$ increases ω_m).

Example 7-1. Determine the rate loop amplifier gain K_{AVR} for the rate loop shown in Fig. E7-1. Assume that $\omega_{cr} = \omega_e/10$. [$\Omega_{max} = 1$ rad/s; $T_{max} = 100$ lb·ft; $J_{total} = 2$ lb·ft·s².]

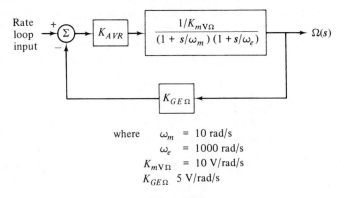

where ω_m = 10 rad/s
$\qquad\quad$ ω_e = 1000 rad/s
$\qquad\quad$ $K_{mV\Omega}$ = 10 V/rad/s
$\qquad\quad$ $K_{GE\Omega}$ 5 V/rad/s

Figure E7-1

solution

$$G_r(s) = \frac{K_{AVR}K_{GE\Omega}/K_{mv\Omega}}{(1 + s/\omega_m)(1 + s/\omega_e)} = \frac{0.5K_{AVR}}{(1 + s/10)(1 + s/1000)}$$

$$|G_r(j\omega_{cr})| = 1 = \left| \frac{0.5K_{AVR}}{(1 + j\omega_{cr}/10)(1 + j\omega_{cr}/1000)} \right|$$

For $\omega_{cr} = 100$ rad/s,

$$1 = \left| \frac{0.5K_{AVR}}{(1 + j10)(1 + j0.1)} \right| \approx \left| \frac{0.5K_{AVR}}{j10} \right|$$

Therefore

$$K_{AVR} = \frac{10}{0.5} = 20$$

Example 7-2. Using an Inland T-1352 torque motor (see specifications below) driven by a power amplifier with a voltage gain of 2 and a −3 dB break frequency of 20 Hz, draw the rate loop block diagram and label all block gains using a tachometer with a gain of 0.2 V/rad/s and (a) a load of 20×10^{-4} oz·in·s², (b) a load of 200×10^{-4} oz·in·s² (let $\omega_{cr} = 2\pi \times 20$ rad/s and neglect the tachometer inertia).

T-1352 torque motor characteristics

$T_{\max}$: 20 oz·in
$\Omega_{\max}$: 400 rad/s
R: 11.3 Ω
K_{mTI}: 8.7 oz·in/A
$K_{mv\Omega}$: 0.06 V/rad/s
L: 4 × 10⁻³ H
J_{motor}: 8.8 × 10⁻⁴ oz·in·s²

solution

(a) $J_{\text{total}} = (8.8 + 20) \times 10^{-4}\ \text{oz·in·s}^2 = 28.8 \times 10^{-4}\ \text{oz·in·s}^2$

$$\omega_e = \frac{R}{L} = \frac{11.3}{4 \times 10^{-3}} = 2820\ \text{rad/s}$$

$$\omega_m = \frac{K_{mTI}K_{mv\Omega}}{J_{\text{total}}R} = \frac{8.7\ \text{oz·in/A} \times 0.06\ \text{V/rad/s}}{28.8 \times 10^{-4}\ \text{oz·in·s}^2 \times 11.3\ \text{V/A}} = 16.05\ \text{rad/s}$$

$$\approx 16.1\ \text{rad/s}$$

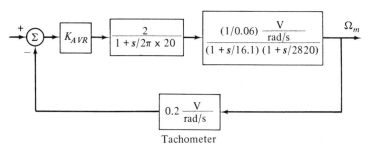

Figure E7-2a

$$G(s) = \frac{K_{AVR} \times 2(1/0.06)0.2}{(1 + s/126)(1 + s/16.1)(1 + s/2820)}$$

$$= \frac{6.67 K_{AVR}}{(1 + s/16.1)(1 + s/126)(1 + s/2820)}$$

$$= \frac{16.1 \times 6.67 K_{AVR}}{(s + 16.1)(1 + s/126)(1 + s/2820)} \approx \frac{16.1 \times 6.67 K_{AVR}}{s(1 + s/126)(1 + s/2820)}$$

$$\approx \frac{\omega_{cr}}{s(1 + s/126)}$$

$$\omega_{cr} = 16.1 \times 6.67 K_{AVR} = 126$$

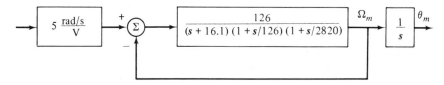

Figure E7-2b

and therefore

$$K_{AVR} = \frac{126}{16.1 \times 6.67} = 1.18$$

Approximate closed loop expression:

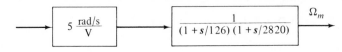

Figure E7-2c

(b) $J_{\text{total}} = (8.8 + 200) \times 10^{-4} \text{ oz·in·s}^2 = 208.8 \text{ oz·in·s}^2$

$$\omega_m = 16.05 \frac{28.8}{208.8} = 2.215 \approx 2.22 \text{ rad/s}$$

$$G(s) = \frac{K_{AVR}(2)(1/0.06)(0.2)}{(1 + s/126)(1 + s/2.22)(1 + s/2820)}$$

$$= \frac{6.67 K_{AVR}}{(1 + s/2.22)(1 + s/126)(1 + s/2820)}$$

$$= \frac{2.22 \times 6.67 K_{AVR}}{(s + 2.22)(1 + s/126)(1 + s/2820)} \approx \frac{2.22 \times 6.67 K_{AVR}}{s(1 + s/126)(1 + s/2820)}$$

$$= \frac{\omega_{cr}}{s(1 + s/126)}$$

$$\omega_{cr} = 2.22 \times 6.67 K_{AVR} = 126$$

and therefore

$$K_{AVR} = \frac{126}{2.22 \times 6.67} = 8.5$$

yielding the approximate closed-loop expression:

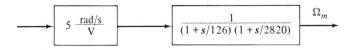

Figure E7-2d

Note in the solution to Example 7-2 that the approximate closed-loop transfer function in (b) is the same as in (a), and that the gain inside the loop has increased by the same ratio as the increase in inertia. This gain improvement results in improved stiffness at the cost of acceleration.

Example 7-3. Determine the rate loop transfer function and calculate K_{AVR} for a model T800-36 two-phase 400-Hz servomotor/tachometer (see specifications below) driving a load of 33,000 g·cm² through a gear reduction of 100: 1 and using a power amplifier with a gain of 0.9.

Motor characteristics

Phase 1: 115 V, 0.11 A
Phase 2 (control): 18 V (two windings in parallel)
$\qquad$ 0.7 A
Stall torque: 1.53 in·oz
Torque at P_{max}: 0.8 in·oz
Speed at P_{max}: 2600 rpm
Time constant: 0.0238
No-load speed: 4700 rpm

Generator (tachometer) characteristics

Excitation: 115 V, 0.073 A
Gain: 3.1 V/1000 rpm

General characteristics

Rotor inertia: 5.26 g·cm²

solution

$$\omega_m = \frac{T_{max}}{\Omega_{max} J_{motor}} \approx \frac{1}{\text{time constant}} \qquad \text{(for motor alone)}$$

$$\frac{T_m}{\Omega_{max} J_{motor}} = \frac{1.53 \text{ in·oz}}{4700 \text{ rpm} \times 5.26 \text{ g·cm}^2} \times \frac{1 \text{ rpm}}{0.105 \text{ rad/s}} \times \frac{70{,}000 \text{ rad/s}^2}{\text{in·oz/g·cm}^2}$$

$$= \frac{1.53 \times 70{,}000}{4700 \times 5.26 \times 0.105} \text{ rad/s} = 41.2 \text{ rad/s}$$

$$\omega_m \approx \frac{1}{\text{time constant}} = \frac{1}{0.0238} = 42 \text{ rad/s}$$

These agree quite well; to be conservative, assume that the lower value is correct (i.e., $\omega_m = 41.2 \text{ rad/s}$).

$$J_{total} = J_m + J_L$$

$$= 5.26 \text{ g·cm}^2 + \frac{33{,}000}{(100)^2} \text{ g·cm}^2$$

$$= (5.26 + 3.3) \text{ g·cm}^2 = 8.56 \text{ g·cm}^2$$

Therefore

$$\omega_m = 41.2 \times \frac{5.26}{8.56} = 25.4 \text{ rad/s}$$

Assuming a linear torque-speed curve:

$$\frac{\Omega_m(s)}{E_m(s)} = \frac{27.4 \text{ rad/s/V}}{(1 + s/25.4)}$$

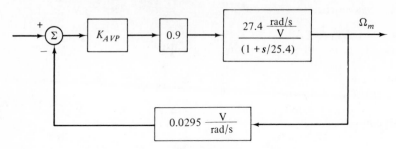

Figure E7-3a

$$\text{Tachometer gain} = \frac{3.1 \text{ V}}{1000 \text{ rpm}} \times \frac{\text{rpm}}{0.105 \text{ rad/s}} = 0.0295 \text{ V/rad/s}$$

$$G(s) = (K_{AVR}) \frac{0.9 \times 27.4}{1 + s/25.4} \times 0.0295 = \frac{0.737 K_{AVR}}{1 + s/25.4} = \frac{18.5 K_{AVR}}{s + 25.4}$$

This expression for $G(s)$ does not consider the bandwidth limitations of the amplifiers, those due to the 400-Hz carrier frequency, or those due to the R/L electrical break frequency of the motor control winding. Since modern solid-state servo amplifiers have very wide bandwidths, this effect may be neglected. The combined effect of the carrier lag and the electrical break frequency of the control winding may be lumped into a single break frequency. Unfortunately, this break frequency is (normally) not specified by ac servomotor manufacturers, and must be inferred from test data or estimated from typical system performance (Chapter 11 considers bandwidth limits). For a small instrument servo motor driven by a linear amplifier it is safe to consider this effect by assuming a rate loop bandwidth of one-tenth the carrier frequency:

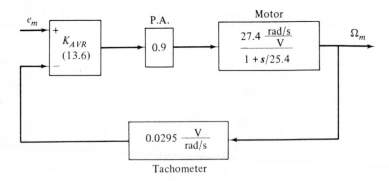

Figure E7-3b

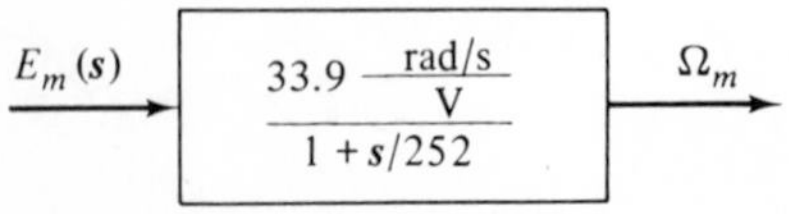

$$E_m(s) \quad \boxed{\frac{33.9 \dfrac{\text{rad/s}}{\text{V}}}{1 + s/252}} \quad \Omega_m$$

Figure E7-3c

$$G(s) = \frac{21.2 K_{AVR}}{s + 25.4} = \frac{\omega_{cr}}{s + 25.4}$$

$$\omega_{cr} = 2\pi \times 40 = 252 = 18.5 K_{AVR}$$

$$K_{AVR} = 13.6$$

$$\frac{\Omega_m(s)}{E_m(s)} \approx \frac{1/0.0295}{1 + s/\omega_{cr}} = \frac{33.9 \text{ rad/s/V}}{1 + s/252}$$

7-2. position loop around tachometer loop

In Fig. 7-10 a tachometer loop is enclosed in a position loop. Two poten-

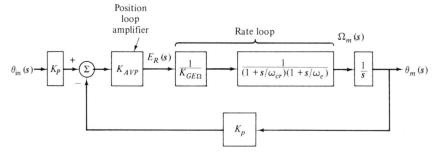

Figure 7-10. Position loop around closed rate loop.

tiometers, a position loop amplifier K_{AVP} and an integration from $\Omega_m(s)$ to $\theta_m(s)$, are added to the rate loop to complete the position loop. An expression for the gain crossover frequency ω_{cp} is given in Eq. (7-8); this is ω_{cp} because (if higher-frequency terms are neglected) the constant which appears over the integration term s of the loop gain expression is the gain crossover frequency.

$$\omega_{cp} = \frac{K_{AVP} K_p}{K_{GE\Omega}} \tag{7-8}$$

A simplified loop diagram is shown in Fig. 7-11; ω_{cp} is taken from Eq.

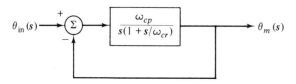

Figure 7-11. Simplified position loop.

(7-8) and substituted for the gain constants of Fig. 7-10. Equation (7-8) is also valuable for calculating the value of K_{AVP}. Figure 7-12 gives the Bode plot of this position loop, which has within it a tachometer loop. The position loop now has a -1 slope to ω_{cr} and then a -2 slope to ω_e; at higher

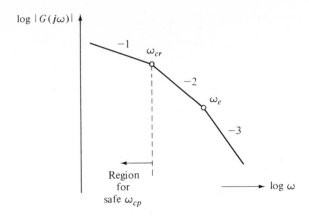

Figure 7-12. Bode plot of open position loop around closed rate loop.

frequencies it has a -3 slope. It is clear from Fig. 7-12 that the region for a safe position loop gain crossover frequency is at a frequency below ω_{cr}. Typically, the position loop gain crossover frequency should not be larger than one-third of the rate loop gain crossover frequency, because for higher values of ω_{cp} the transient performance becomes undesirably oscillatory. Sometimes ω_{cp} is lower than $\frac{1}{3}\omega_{cr}$ for greater stability or for noise-filtering reasons. Many tracking systems have narrow position loop bandwidths to cut down the tracking noise error. For instance, many early radar tracking systems had 1-Hz servo bandwidths in order to limit tracking errors due to receiver noise.

To demonstrate the improvement that a rate loop can provide, consider the servo design example of Chapter 6, where ω_{cp} and ω_m were 15.6 s^{-1}. Let us now assume that the power amplifier driving the motor has a cutoff frequency of 600 rad/s (above which the amplifier response falls off at a -1 slope). This lag would allow the rate loop to be closed at about that frequency; to be conservative, assume that ω_{cr} is 500 rad/s. If ω_{cp} is safely assumed to be $\frac{1}{4}\omega_{cr}$ or 125 rad/s, then K_v is now 125 s^{-1} (a great improvement over 15.6 s^{-1}). For a 1-rpm input, this K_v gives an error of 0.048° as calculated in Eq. (7-9).

$$1 \text{ rpm } K_v \text{ error} = 1 \text{ rpm} \times \frac{6 \text{ deg/s}}{\text{rpm}} \times \frac{1}{125 \text{ s}^{-1}} = 0.048° \qquad (7\text{-}9)$$

Example 7-4. Using potentiometer position transducers that have 350° active angles and are excited by the voltages indicated below, find the required position loop gains based on 120° phase lag at asymptotic gain crossover frequencies for the rate loops of Examples 7-1, 7-2, and 7-3.

Case (a): Example 7-1. Rate Loop: 3.5 V dc excitation for potentiometer.
Case (b): Example 7-2. Rate loop: 15 V dc potentiometer excitation.
Case (c): Example 7-3. Rate loop: 24 V rms potentiometer excitation.

solution

(a)
$$K_{trans} = \frac{3.5 \text{ V}}{350°} \times \frac{57.3°}{\text{rad}} = 0.573 \text{ V/rad}$$

$$G_p(s) = \frac{0.1146 \, K_{AVP}}{s(1 + s/100)}$$

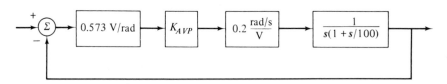

Figure E7-4a

For the above to have 120° lag, the $1 + j\omega_{cp}/100$ term must have 30° lag. Therefore

$$\tan 30° = \left| \frac{j\omega_{cp}}{100} \right| = 0.577 \quad \text{or} \quad \omega_{cp} = 57.7 \text{ rad/s}$$

(this neglects lag at 1000 rad/s). Therefore

$$0.1146 K_{AVP} = 57.7 \quad \text{or} \quad K_{AVP} = \frac{57.7}{0.1146} = 503.5$$

(b)
$$K_{trans} = \frac{15 \text{ V}}{350°} \times \frac{57.3°}{\text{rad}} = 2.45 \text{ V/rad}$$

$$G_p(s) = \frac{5 \times 2.45 K_{AVP}}{s(1 + s/126)(1 + s/2820)} = \frac{12.25 K_{AVP}}{s(1 + s/126)(1 + s/2870)}$$

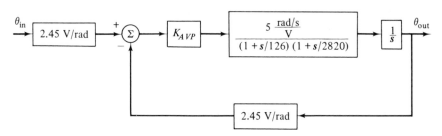

Figure E7-4b

Try $\omega_{cp} = 100$ rad/s to check phase lag.

$$G_p(j100) = \frac{12.25 K_{AVP}}{j100(1 + j100/126)(1 + j100/2820)}$$

$$= \frac{12.25 K_{AVP}/100}{(1 \angle +90°)(1 + j0.794)(1 + j0.0355)}$$

$$\approx \frac{12.25 K_{AVP}/100}{(1 \angle +90°)(1.28 \angle 38.4°)(1 \angle 2°)}$$

$$= \frac{12.25 K_{AVP}/100}{1.28 \angle 130.4°}$$

The phase lag due to the 126 rad/s lag must be reduced to 30°; tan 30° = 0.577 = $\omega_{cr}/126$. Therefore ω_{cr} = 0.577 × 126 = 72.7 rad/s; use the lower ω_{cp} = 70 rad/s to be conservative.

Therefore a gain crossover frequency of slightly greater than 70 rad/s will give 120° phase lag at the gain crossover frequency.

$$1 = \frac{12.25 K_{AVP}}{70} \quad \text{or} \quad K_{AVP} = \frac{70}{12.25} = 5.71$$

(c)
$$K_{\text{trans}} = \frac{24 \text{ V}}{350°} \times \frac{57.3°}{\text{rad}} = 3.93 \frac{\text{V}}{\text{rad}}$$

$$G_p(s) = \frac{33.9 \times 3.93 \times \frac{1}{100} K_{AVP}}{s(1 + s/252)} = \frac{1.33 K_{AVP}}{s(1 + s/252)}$$

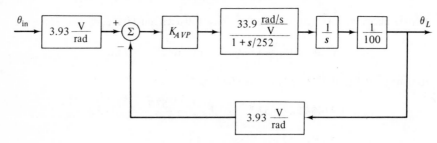

Figure E7-4c

Since approximately 30° lag due to the 252 rad/s lag term can be tolerated,

$$\tan 30° = 0.577 = \omega_{cp}/252$$

$$\omega_{cp} = 0.577 \times 252 = 145 \text{ rad/s};$$

$$1.33 K_{AVP} = \omega_{cp} = 145; \quad \text{then}$$

$$K_{AVP} = \frac{145}{1.33} = 109$$

7-3. block-diagram alternatives

In Fig. 7-13 the details of the position and rate loops are reconstructed so that the blocks contain actual gain terms; this figure is derived from Figs. 7-7 and 7-10, and Eq. (7-10). Figures 7-13 through 7-16 develop this from the simple form of Fig. 7-10 back to the point where the various gains in the loops can be identified.

$$K_{AVP} = \frac{K_{GE\Omega}\omega_{cp}}{K_p} \tag{7-10}$$

In Fig. 7-13, K_{AVP} is replaced by its equivalent [see Eqs. (7-8) and (7-10)]. In Fig. 7-14, the tachometer gain is included in the rate loop feedback line. In Fig. 7-15, the rate loop gain expression is shown as the motor transfer function preceded by an amplifier gain block. The expression in the gain block is determined by the fact that the forward rate loop gain must be the same as in Fig. 7-14. In Fig. 7-16, the motor is broken into its conceptual loop; this makes it possible to identify a point that is dimensionally torque.

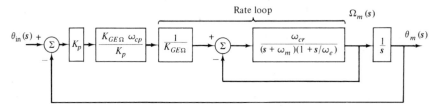

Figure 7-13.   Servo block diagram in alternative form.

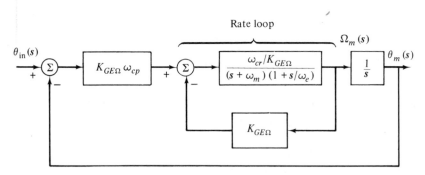

Figure 7-14.   Servo with rate loop in unreduced form.

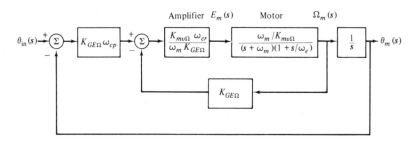

Figure 7-15.   Servo with rate loop hardware indicated.

7-4. *torque stiffness*

Equation (7-11) calculates the static error of the servo for a torque applied at the point indicated in Fig. 7-16.

$$\text{Static error} = \frac{T}{(K_{mTI}/R) \times (K_{mv\Omega}\omega_{cr}/\omega_m K_{GE\Omega}) \times (K_{GE\Omega}\omega_{cp})}$$

$$= \frac{T}{(K_{mTI}/R) \times (K_{mv\Omega}\omega_{cr}\omega_{cp}/\omega_m)} \tag{7-11}$$

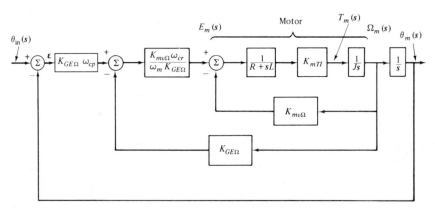

Figure 7-16.   Servo with motor in conceptual loop form.

The basis of this calculation is that the system is at rest and therefore the feedback signals due to motor velocity through $K_{mv\Omega}$ and $K_{GE\Omega}$ will be zero when the system comes to rest at its steady-state error. Further, the actual system error is the motion of the output due to the applied torque (assuming that θ_{in} is at some constant angle). Therefore the static error can be determined by finding the error necessary to support the applied disturbing torque; and this indicates how much the load has moved due to the torque disturbance. This static error is equal to the applied torque T divided by the gains between the torque point and the input summing point. Since the system comes to rest at some steady angle, the inductance causes a lag in the rise of motor current but will not affect the final steady-state position. Substituting Eq. (7-12), which defines ω_m, into Eq. (7-11) results in Eq. (7-13).

$$\omega_m = \frac{K_{mTI}K_{mv\Omega}}{RJ_{Tm}} \tag{7-12}$$

Therefore,

$$\text{Static error} = \frac{T}{(K_{mTI}/R) \times (K_{mv\Omega}\omega_{cr}\omega_{cp})(RJ_{Tm}/K_{mTI}K_{mv\Omega})} = \frac{T}{J_{Tm}\omega_{cr}\omega_{cp}}$$

(7-13)

This shows that the error to support a torque T is equal to the torque divided by the position and rate loop bandwidths and by the total inertia reflected to the motor (since torque is considered to be applied at the motor). This makes it possible to define a rate loop stabilized servo torque error constant K_T (stiffness), which is given in Eq. (7-14). This stiffness expression is similar to the stiffness expression for a simple motor servo (see Section 6-7), except that ω_m is replaced by ω_{cr}; the simple servo stiffness expression is given by Eq. (7-15). Since ω_{cr} is greater than ω_m and therefore the tachometer servo ω_{cp} is greater than ω_m, it is clear that the tachometer servo stiffness is much greater than that for the simple servo.

$$K_{T(\text{rate loop servo})} = J_{TM}\omega_{cr}\omega_{cp} \tag{7-14}$$

$$K_{T(\text{simple servo})} = J_{TM}\omega_m\omega_{cp} \approx J_{TM}(\omega_m)^2 \tag{7-15}$$

It is important to recognize that the preceding analysis was for a static case based on the assumption that there is no load motion. Since the system is reasonably assumed to be linear, the superposition theorem holds, and the effects of command velocity and load torque may be considered independently (as was previously noted). A further consideration is the dynamic character of the servo; settling transients after torque disturbances will behave stably as long as the servo position loop is stable.

Example 7-5. Find the torque stiffness K_T referred to the load and the velocity constant K_v for the servos of Examples 7-1, 7-2, 7-3, and 7-4. Find the errors for 10 per cent maximum torque and 10 per cent maximum speed.

solution

(a) From Examples 7-1 and 7-4, $\omega_{cr} = 100$ rad/s and $\omega_{cp} = 57.7$ rad/s.

$$K_T = J\omega_{cr}\omega_{cp} = 2\ \text{lb·ft·s}^2 \times 100\ \text{rad/s} \times 57.7\ \text{rad/s}$$
$$= 11{,}540\ \text{lb·ft/rad}$$

$$K_v = \omega_{cp} = 57.7\ \text{s}^{-1}$$

$$\epsilon_{K_T} = \frac{0.1 \times 100\ \text{lb·ft}}{11{,}540\ \text{lb·ft/rev}} \times 57.3\ \text{deg/rev} = 0.0497°$$

$$\epsilon_{K_v} = \frac{0.1 \times 1 \times 57.3\ \text{deg/s}}{57.7\ \text{s}^{-1}} = 0.0993°$$

(b) and (c) in Example 7-2 there are two values of J_{total}: 28.8×10^{-4} oz·in·s²
and 208.8 oz·in·s². In both cases

$$\omega_{cr} = 126 \text{ rad/s and } \omega_{cp} = 70 \text{ rad/s}$$

$$\Omega_{max} = 400 \text{ rad/s}$$

$$T_{max} = 20 \text{ in·oz}$$

$$K_T = J\omega_{cr}\omega_{cp}$$

(b) *dc servo with small load inertia*

$$K_T = 28.8 \times 10^{-4} \times 126 \times 70 \frac{\text{in·oz}}{\text{rad}} = 25.4 \frac{\text{in·oz}}{\text{rad}}$$

$$\epsilon_{KT} = \frac{0.1 \times 20 \text{ in·oz}}{25.4 \text{ in·oz/rad}} = 0.079 \text{ rad} = 4.51°$$

$$K_v = \omega_{cp} = 70 \text{ s}^{-1}$$

$$\epsilon_{K_v} = \frac{0.1 \times 400 \text{ rad/s}}{70 \text{ s}^{-1}} = 0.571 \text{ rad} = 32.8°$$

It should be noted that ω_{cr} and thus ω_{cp} are limited by the power amplifier
bandwidth of 20 Hz. In practice, an improvement in bandwidth and thus a greater
K_v could be expected. Chapter 11 will discuss these bandwidth limits.

(c) *dc servo with larger load inertia*

$$K_T = 208.8 \times 10^{-4} \times 126 \times 70 \frac{\text{in·oz}}{\text{rad}} = 184 \frac{\text{in·oz}}{\text{rad}}$$

$$\epsilon_{KT} = \frac{0.1 \times 20 \text{ in·oz}}{1842 \text{ in·oz/rad}} = 0.0109 \text{ rad} = 0.62°$$

(Note that the increased inertia results in a lower torque error.)

$$\epsilon_{K_v} = 32.8°$$

(Because ω_{cp} does not change, this error does not change due to increased inertia.)

(d) *ac servo*

$$K_T = \frac{8.56 \text{ g·cm}^2 \times 145 \text{ rad/s} \times 252 \text{ rad/s(oz·in/g·cm}^2)}{70,000 \text{ rad/s}^2}$$

$$= 4.47 \frac{\text{oz·in}}{\text{rad}} \quad \text{(at motor)}$$

$$\epsilon_{KT} = \frac{1.53}{10} \times \frac{1}{4.47} \times 57.3 = 1.96° \quad \text{at motor}$$

and

$$\frac{1.96°}{N} = \frac{1.96°}{100} = 0.0196° \quad \text{at load}$$

$$K_v = \omega_{cp} = 145 \text{ s}^{-1}$$

$$\epsilon_{K_v} = \frac{4700 \text{ rpm} \times 0.1}{145 \text{ s}^{-1}} \times \frac{6°/s}{\text{rpm}} = 19.45° \quad \text{at motor}$$

$$= 0.1945° \quad \text{at load}$$

7-5. *block-diagram algebra of disturbances*

With the help of Fig. 7-17, disturbances may also be examined from a

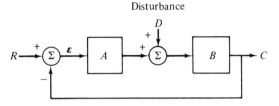

Figure 7-17.   General block diagram for analyzing disturbances.

different point of view. Looking at this figure, it may be seen that there are two gains in the forward loop, A and B, respectively. A disturbance D is applied to this loop at a point between blocks A and B. It may be assumed that the reference input variable R is zero. It is desired to find out what error results from this disturbance. Two methods are used to find this error. The first is the most straightforward: The system as shown in Fig. 7-18 is solved by

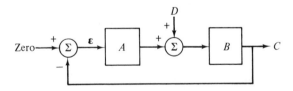

Figure 7-18.   Disturbance block diagram with zero input.

conventional block-diagram algebra (see Section 2-5). Since the reference input is zero, Fig. 7-19 may be drawn. This loop is solved in Eq. (7-16) and the error expression is given in Eq. (7-17).

$$\frac{C}{D} = \frac{B}{1 + AB} \tag{7-16}$$

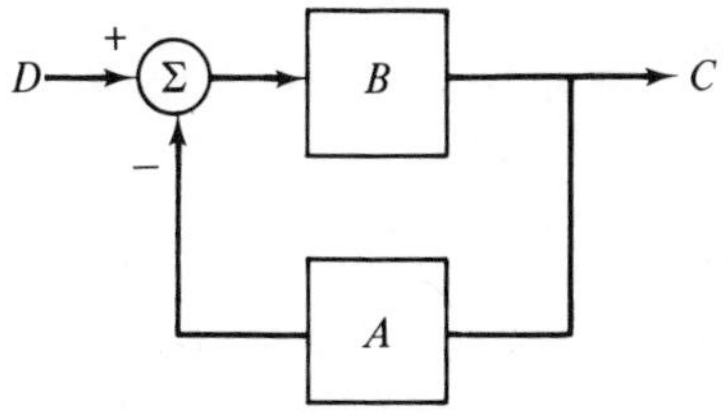

Figure 7-19.   Disturbance block diagram
equivalent.

$$\epsilon = -C = \frac{-BD}{1 + AB} \tag{7-17}$$

The same result can also be reached using a second possible method. Let us now consider that the D input of Fig. 7-17 is equivalent to D/A input at the summing point output of Fig. 7-17; this is shown in Fig. 7-20. This is the same as a disturbance input of D/A applied to the normal reference input;

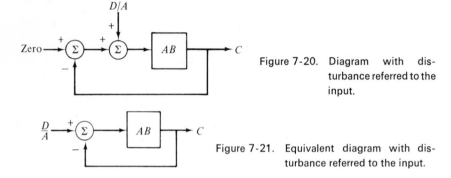

Figure 7-20. Diagram with disturbance referred to the input.

Figure 7-21. Equivalent diagram with disturbance referred to the input.

this result is shown in Fig. 7-21. The resulting output, C, is calculated in Eq. (7-18). Since the error is equal to minus the output due to the disturbance, the error can be represented as given in Eq. (7-19), which is the same as Eq. (7-17).

$$C = \frac{D}{A} \times \frac{AB}{1 + AB} = \frac{DB}{1 + AB} \tag{7-18}$$

$$\epsilon = -C = \frac{-DB}{1 + AB} \tag{7-19}$$

This second technique is very convenient for working out effects of disturbances in closed-loop systems; the reason is that the $AB/(1 + AB)$ part of Eq. (7-18) is the closed-loop gain transfer function, a characteristic which must be reasonably well defined in the early steps of design. The gain A, a portion of the forward loop gain, is known from the servo design. Therefore it is a very simple matter to take a disturbance D, divide it through by whatever forward loop gain precedes it, and then multiply the result by the closed-loop gain. The value of this approach is made more apparent in the examination of error budgets in Chapter 12.

7-6. back emf stabilization

Back emf stabilization is similar to tachometer stabilization, except that the motor itself is used to sense its own speed, and it is not as precise a velocity-measuring device as a tachometer. Therefore back emf-stabilized rate loops may not behave as well as tachometer-stabilized rate loops. A further effect of importance in the analysis to follow is that the motor brush voltage drop is neglected and, as a result, some starting and cogging errors are also neglected (these types of errors are discussed in Chapter 12).

Figure 7-22 shows a part of the system to be considered. Of great impor-

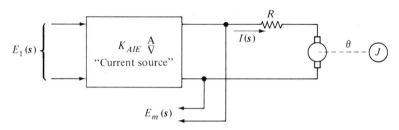

Figure 7-22.   dc motor driven by a "current source" amplifier.

tance in this diagram is the first block, which is a "current source" type of amplifier. This means that the output current is proportional to the input voltage and that the output current is unaffected by the voltage of the load. This type of characteristic may be obtained by feeding back the voltage from a current-sensing resistor for comparison against an input command voltage. A simpler type of unipolar current source may be made by connecting to the collector circuit of a silicon transistor; this exhibits a high impedance, which is the essential characteristic of a current source. A high impedance is characteristic of a current source because if the load impedance is very small compared to the internal impedance of the source, the current coming from the drive is unaffected by the load voltage drop.

Equations (7-20) and (7-21) describe the simple drive system of Fig. 7-22.

$$T(s) = E_1(s)K_{AIE}K_{mTI} = J\theta(s)s^2 \tag{7-20}$$

$$E_M(s) = I(s)R + \theta(s)sK_{mv\Omega} = E_1(s)K_{AIE}R + \theta(s)sK_{mv\Omega} \tag{7-21}$$

An inversion of Eq. (7-20) is given in Eq. (7-22). Another inversion is given in Eq. (7-23), and the overall gain is given in Eq. (7-24).

$$\theta(s) = \frac{E_1(s)K_{AIE}K_{mTI}}{Js^2} \tag{7-22}$$

$$E_1(s) = \frac{J\theta(s)s^2}{K_{AIE}K_{mTI}} \tag{7-23}$$

Equation (7-25) is a restatement of Eq. (7-21) using Eq. (7-23) for the input voltage.

$$\frac{\theta(s)}{E_1(s)} = \frac{K_{AIE}K_{mTI}}{Js^2} \tag{7-24}$$

$$E_m(s) = \frac{J\theta(s)s^2}{K_{AIE}K_{mTI}}K_{AIE}R + \theta(s)sK_{mv\Omega} = \frac{J\theta(s)s^2R}{K_{mTI}} + \theta(s)sK_{mv\Omega}$$

$$= \theta(s)sK_{mv\Omega}\left(1 + \frac{JRs}{K_{mTI}K_{mv\Omega}}\right) = \Omega(s)K_{mv\Omega}(1 + s/\omega_m)$$

$$= sK_{mv\Omega}(1 + s/\omega_m)\theta(s) \tag{7-25}$$

It should be noted that the final expression for the motor voltage of Eq. (7-25) is stated in terms of the back emf constant of the motor and the motor break frequency. This expression is used in Fig. 7-23, the transfer-function

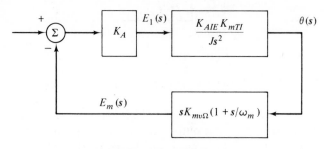

Figure 7-23.   Back emf rate loop.

diagram of the simple back emf rate loop. The open-loop gain expression for this system is given in Eq. (7-26), and the Bode plot is given in Fig. 7-24.

$$G(s) = \frac{K_A K_{AIE}K_{mTI}sK_{mv\Omega}(1 + s/\omega_m)}{Js^2} = \frac{K_A K_{AIE}K_{mTI}K_{mv\Omega}(1 + s/\omega_m)}{Js} \tag{7-26}$$

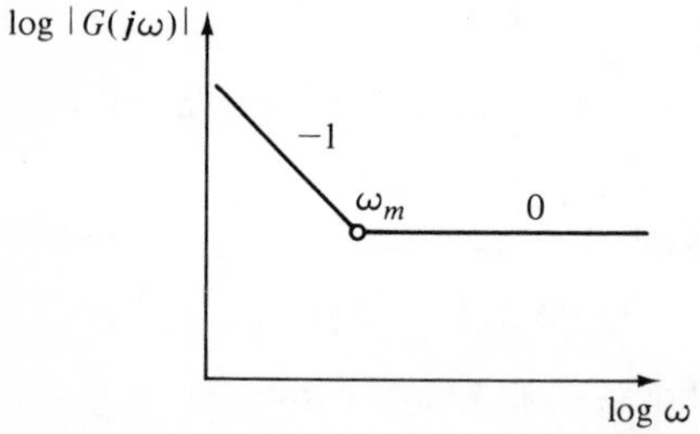

Figure 7-24.   Bode plot of back emf rate loop.

It should be noted that the -1 slope continues until the motor break frequency, above which the gain remains constant (up to ω_e or other high-frequency limitation). Higher open-loop gain at low frequencies may be obtained if the gain continues on a -1 slope above ω_m. Therefore a lag is introduced in Fig. 7-25 to compensate for the lead at the motor break frequency. The resulting loop gain expression is given in Eq. (7-27), and the expression for the rate loop gain crossover frequency is given in Eq. (7-28).

$$G(s) = \frac{K_A K_{AIE}K_{mTI}}{Js^2} \times sK_{mv\Omega} = \frac{K_A K_{AIE}K_{mTI}K_{mv\Omega}}{Js} \tag{7-27}$$

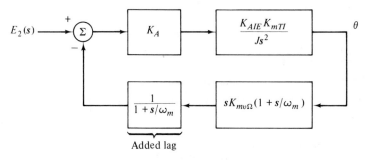

Figure 7-25.   Compensated back emf rate loop.

$$\omega_{rb} = \frac{K_A K_{AIE} K_{mTI} K_{mv\Omega}}{J} \tag{7-28}$$

The overall gain for the closed-loop system is given in Eqs. (7-29) and (7-30).

$$\frac{\theta(s)}{E_2(s)} = \frac{1}{sK_{mv\Omega}} \times \frac{1}{1 + s/\omega_{rb}} \tag{7-29}$$

$$\frac{\dot{\theta}(s)}{E_2(s)} = \frac{1/K_{mv\Omega}}{1 + s/\omega_{rb}} \tag{7-30}$$

Figure 7-26 is the loop diagram for the rate loop with the torque disturbance input shown at the equivalent torque point. Equation (7-31) is an

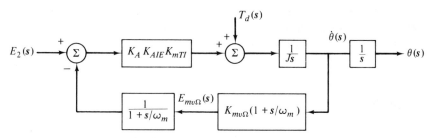

Figure 7-26.   Compensated back emf loop showing torque disturbance input.

expression for the rate loop gain crossover frequency, and Fig. 7-27 shows the overall loop diagram in standard form.

$$\omega_{rb} = \frac{K_A K_{AIE} K_{mTI} K_{mv\Omega}}{J} \tag{7-31}$$

$$K_A K_{AIE} K_{mTI} K_{mv\Omega} = J\omega_{rb} \tag{7-32}$$

The error-to-torque gain of the rate loop for Fig. 7-27 is expressed in Eq. (7-32). Figure 7-28 shows the overall rate loop in bandwidth form. This diagram can be used in much the same way as a rate loop would be used,

Figure 7-27. Reduced stabilized back emf loop with torque disturbance.

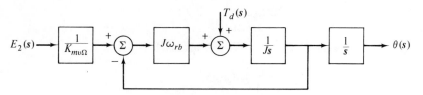

Figure 7-28. Simplest form of stabilized back emf loop with torque disturbance.

the only difference being that the dc gain for the back emf loop is $1/K_{mv\Omega}$, and for the rate loop using a tachometer it is $1/K_{GE\Omega}$.

7-7. summary

Tachometer loop behavior including improvements in ω_{cp}, K_v, and torque stiffness K_T were examined. The block-diagram algebra of disturbances was introduced, and back emf stabilization as a means of improving simple motor servo performance was presented.

problems

7-1. Calculate the value of K_{AVR} for a rate loop with the following characteristics:

$$\omega_m = 20 \text{ rad/s}$$
$$\omega_{cr} = 200 \text{ rad/s}$$
$$\omega_e = 2000 \text{ rad/s}$$
$$K_{mv\Omega} = 1.0 \text{ V/rad/s}$$
$$K_{GE\Omega} = 4.0 \text{ V/rad/s}$$

7-2. For the rate loop of Problem 7-1, calculate K_{AVP} for $\omega_{cp} = 50 \text{ rad/s}$ and a position transducer gain of 10 V/rev. Also calculate K_T and K_v for J_{total} of 0.1 lb·ft·s^2. What errors would there be for $\Omega_{\text{in}} = 40 \text{ deg/s}$ at $T_{\text{load}} = 20 \text{ lb·ft}$?

7-3. Using an Inland T-1352 torque motor, a power amplifier with a voltage gain of 0.9, and a -3 dB break frequency of 50 Hz, a second Inland T-1352 motor as a

tachometer, and a load of 0.02 oz·in·s², calculate:
(a) a reasonable value for ω_{cr} (assume $120°$ phase lag at ω_{cr})
(b) K_{AVR}
(c) the equivalent block diagram of the closed rate loop (external characteristics)
(d) a reasonable value for ω_{cp} (assume $\omega_{cr}/4$)
(e) the position loop diagram assuming a transducer with $K_{trans} = 0.1$ V/deg
(f) K_T error for a steady load torque of 5 in·oz
(g) K_v error for a 20 deg/s steady input signal

7-4. (a) Calculate the maximum acceleration at stall for Problem 7-3, assuming 1 A maximum current. If the total inertia is doubled, calculate (b) maximum acceleration, and (c) K_T error.

7-5. For a total inertia of 3 slug·ft² and a rate loop bandwidth of 10 Hz, what errors could be expected for (a) a steady load velocity of 20 rpm, (b) a steady load torque of 4 lb·ft? (Let $\omega_{cp} = \omega_{cr}/4$ to be on the conservative side.)

7-6. Make an approximate comparison of the torque stiffness K_T and velocity constant K_v of a simple servo and a servo with a tachometer loop using a power amplifier with a bandwidth of 40 Hz and $\omega_m = 10$ rad/s.

8

stability

The stability of servos may be examined in a number of different ways. This chapter develops the concept of relative stability analytically. System transient response from the location of poles in the s plane is developed. Relative stability from a frequency-response (gain versus frequency) standpoint is developed, concluding with the Nichols chart.

8-1. poles and zeros

Figure 8-1 shows the basic servo block diagram for a fully fed-back system. Equation (8-1) gives an assumed expression for $G(s)$. The Laplace variable is a complex variable consisting of a real part sigma (σ) and an imaginary part $j\omega$ as given in Eq. (8-2).

$$G(s) = \frac{k(s + b)}{s(s + a)} \tag{8-1}$$

$$s = \underset{\text{Real}}{\sigma} + \underset{\text{Imaginary}}{j\omega} \tag{8-2}$$

Two dimensions are required to specify s (real and imaginary), and a third dimension, therefore, is needed to plot the magnitude of $G(s)$. Examination of Fig. 8-2 suggests how a three-dimensional plot may be made of the expression of Eq. (8-1). Equation (8-1) indicates that when $s = 0$, the denominator goes to zero and therefore the gain goes to infinity; this is shown in Fig. 8-2 as a "pole" at the origin. It is called a pole because the gain goes up vertically above the s plane very much as a pole rises above the ground. In this plot of Fig. 8-2 there are two poles, one at the origin and the other at

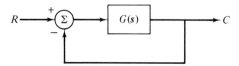

Figure 8-1. The standard diagram.

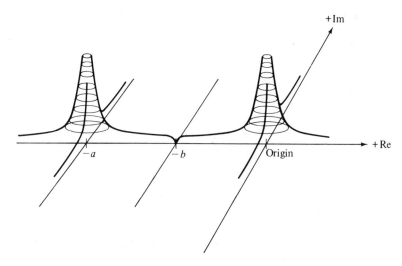

Figure 8-2. The Three-dimensional plot of a complex function
$k(s + b)/s(s + a)$.

$s = -a$. This latter pole is present because the gain expression also goes to infinity at $s = -a$. In the three-dimensional representation of Fig. 8-2 there are two points at which the magnitude of $G(s)$ goes to infinity; these are at zero and $-a$. The numerator of Eq. (8-1) has a "zero" at $-b$; it is called a "zero" because the gain magnitude goes to zero when $s = -b$. The three-dimensional plot shown in Fig. 8-2 shows the magnitude of the gain function of Eq. (8-1) as the value of s varies over the complex plane. When s is *real* and *negative*, the two poles and one zero may be plotted.

As s is allowed to take on values along the imaginary axis, there is a different effect. For s equal to $j\omega$ (along the imaginary axis), the expression becomes $G(j\omega)$, and the frequency response is determined. It can be seen that when the frequency is zero ($j\omega = 0$), the gain function goes to infinity. Another example is shown in Fig. 8-3; in this figure there are conjugate poles at $-c + j\omega_1$, and at $-c - j\omega_1$.

$$G(s) = \frac{s + b}{s(s + a)(s + c + j\omega_1)(s + c - j\omega_1)}$$

$$= \frac{s + b}{s(s + a)[(s + c)^2 + (\omega_1)^2]} \tag{8-3}$$

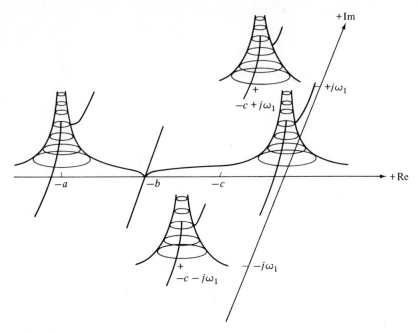

Figure 8-3.   Three-dimensional gain plot showing real and complex
poles.

In this case, as the frequency variable moves along the positive imaginary axis and approaches $s = +j\omega_1$, the gain becomes quite high in this region of resonance.

In summary, when s equals a denominator root, the gain goes to infinity and the system has a pole. When s equals a numerator root, the gain magnitude goes to zero and the system has a zero. When s moves along the imaginary axis near a complex pole, the gain in the region of resonance is determined.

Figure 8-4 is a simplified representation of Fig. 8-3. This representation, instead of being a three-dimensional drawing, is reduced to two dimensions by indicating pole locations on the s plane as crosses and zero locations as small circles. The magnitude plot can be pictured as coming up out of the paper; crosses indicate high magnitudes and circles indicate the magnitude dropping to zero at the surface of the paper.

There is a direct correspondence between pole position and transient performance. For instance, a pole at $-a$ corresponds to an e^{-at} response. If there is a pole at $+a$ (to the right of the imaginary axis), this will give an e^{+at} term; this is an unstable response, since it implies a continually increasing output. Figure 8-5 shows the complex s plane; stable poles are to the left of the imaginary axis and unstable poles are to the right of the imaginary

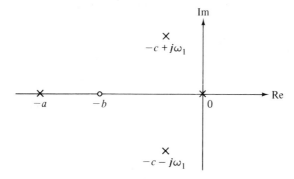

Figure 8-4.   Two-dimensional representation of three-dimensional plot.

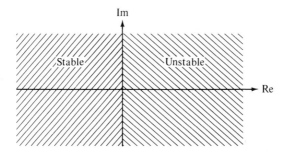

Figure 8-5.   Complex s plane showing regions for stable and unstable poles (denominator roots).

axis. Since design is the main concern of this book, and since systems have to be stable to be useful, this book deals primarily with the left half-plane.

8-2. s-plane quadratic response

Consider Fig. 8-6; this represents an integration (a pole at the origin) and a pole in the left half-plane at $-\alpha$. The closed-loop gain is expressed in

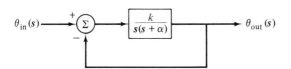

Figure 8-6.   Standard diagram of integration and lag term in loop.

Eq. (8-4). Equation (8-5) defines the output function in terms of the input and the closed-loop gain.

$$G'(s) = \frac{G(s)}{1 + G(s)} = \frac{k/s(s + \alpha)}{1 + (k/s(s + \alpha))} = \frac{k}{s^2 + \alpha s + k} \qquad (8\text{-}4)$$

$$\theta_{\text{out}}(s) = \theta_{\text{in}}(s)G'(s) \qquad (8\text{-}5)$$

If an input step function is assumed, the output function is given in Eq. (8-6). This output function has three roots; one root is at zero because of the input step function.

$$\theta_{\text{out}}(s) = \frac{k}{s(s^2 + \alpha s + k)} \qquad (8\text{-}6)$$

The closed-loop system has two conjugate poles at $(-\alpha + \sqrt{\alpha^2 - 4k})/2$ and $(-\alpha - \sqrt{\alpha^2 - 4k})/2$ (these are also called roots).

The closed-loop gain of Eq. 8-4 is in the form of a quadratic and lends itself to a generalized interpretation. Equation (8-7) considers what is commonly called "Case 1"; this is for α^2 greater than $4k$.

$$Case\ 1 \qquad \alpha^2 > 4k \qquad (8\text{-}7)$$

For this case, the term under the square-root sign is a positive number and therefore there are two distinct (different) real roots at $-p_1$ and $-p_2$. Equation (8-8) defines this output function in terms of the known poles.

$$\theta_{\text{out}}(s) = \frac{k_1}{s} + \frac{k_2}{s + p_1} + \frac{k_3}{s + p_2} \qquad (8\text{-}8)$$

The k_1 term is for the input step function, the k_2 term is for the pole at $-p_1$, and the k_3 term is for the pole at $-p_2$. The resulting time function is given in Eq. (8-9).

$$\theta_{\text{out}}(t) = k_1 + k_2 e^{-p_1 t} + k_2 e^{-p_2 t} \qquad (8\text{-}9)$$

Figure 8-7 shows the two system poles on the s plane; the pole at the origin

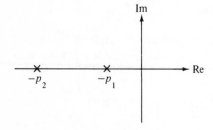

Figure 8-7.   Case 1 : Two real roots.

is not shown because it is due to the applied step function input and is not due to the system itself.

Figure 8-8 and Eqs. (8-10) through (8-12) consider "Case 2."

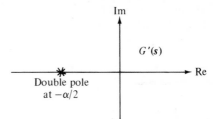

Figure 8-8.   Case 2: Two repeated real
              roots.

Case 2 $\alpha^2 = 4k$ (8-10)

$$\theta_{\text{out}}(s) = \frac{k_4}{s} + \frac{k_5}{(s + \alpha/2)^2} + \frac{k_6}{s + \alpha/2}$$ (8-11)

$$\theta_{\text{out}}(t) = k_4 + k_5 te^{-(\alpha/2)t} + k_6 e^{-(\alpha/2)t}$$ (8-12)

For this case α^2 is equal to $4k$, and the root part of the expression becomes zero; therefore there are two identical real roots, both at $-\alpha/2$. These poles are shown in Fig. 8-8; the resulting output function is given in Eq. (8-12). It will be noted that because there is a repeated root (double pole), one transient term is multiplied by t.

For "Case 3," Fig. 8-9 and Eqs. (8-13) through (8-15) show the pole positions and define the response.

Case 3 $\alpha^2 < 4k$ (8-13)

$$\theta_{\text{out}}(s) = \frac{k_7}{s} + \frac{k_8}{s + \alpha - j\omega} + \frac{k_9}{s + \alpha + j\omega}$$ (8-14)

$$\theta_{\text{out}}(t) = k_7 + k_{10} e^{-\alpha t} \sin(\omega t + \phi)$$ (8-15)

For Case 3, α^2 is less than $4k$ and the quantity under the square-root sign then becomes negative. As a result, the poles have imaginary as well as real parts, and by definition are complex. The root locations are at $-\alpha \pm j\omega$ and are shown on Fig. 8-9. The exponentially decaying sinusoidal output function is given in Eq. (8-15).

These three cases are the three basic cases for a closed-loop quadratic

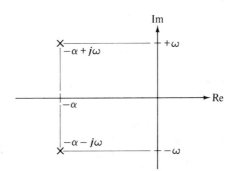

Figure 8-9.   Case 3: Two complex
              conjugate roots.

system; the closed loop quadratic results from two open-loop poles. In the third case, where there are two complex roots, one root is the complex conjugate of the other.

8-3. a closed-loop example

Figure 8-10 is an example of a system with assumed real open-loop poles at the origin and at -8 rad/s ($\frac{1}{8}$ s time constant); this gain is expressed in

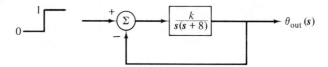

Figure 8-10.   Standard diagram with step-function input.

Eq. (8-16). By varying the gain term k, the closed-loop poles will vary in position.

$$G(s) = \frac{k}{s(s + 8)} \qquad (8\text{-}16)$$

These positions will be plotted to give an indication of system behavior. Equations (8-17) and (8-18) define the basic system in parametric form; the roots are defined as poles at locations given in Eq. (8-18).

$$G'(s) = \frac{k}{s^2 + 8s + k} \qquad (8\text{-}17)$$

$$\text{Poles at} \qquad s = \frac{-8}{2} \pm \sqrt{\frac{8^2}{4} - \frac{4k}{4}} = -4 \pm \sqrt{16 - k} \qquad (8\text{-}18)$$

For the gain constant $k = 7$, a Case 1 system results. The closed-loop poles are located at -1 and at -7, and the response is given in Eq. (8-21).

$$G(s) = \frac{7}{s(s + 8)} \qquad (8\text{-}19)$$

$$G'(s) = \frac{7}{s^2 + 8s + 7} \qquad (8\text{-}20)$$

$$\theta_{out}(s) = \frac{7}{s(s + 1)(s + 7)}$$

$$= \frac{A}{s} + \frac{B}{s + 1} + \frac{C}{s + 7} \longrightarrow 1 - \frac{7}{6}e^{-t} + \frac{1}{6}e^{-7t} \qquad (8\text{-}21)$$

The remaining parts of this example are discussed by means of Eqs. (8-22) through (8-39) and show that as the gain is increased from 7 to 64, the resulting closed-loop poles are at different values as indicated in Eqs. (8-23), (8-27), (8-31), and (8-39).

$$s = -4 \pm \sqrt{16 - 15} = -4 \pm 1 = -5, -3 \tag{8-22}$$

$$\theta_{\text{out}}(s) = \frac{15}{s(s + 3)(s + 5)} = \frac{1}{s} - \frac{\frac{5}{2}}{s + 3} + \frac{\frac{3}{2}}{s + 5} \tag{8-23}$$

$$\theta_{\text{out}}(t) = 1 - \tfrac{5}{2}e^{-3t} + \tfrac{3}{2}e^{-5t} \tag{8-24}$$

$$G(s) = \frac{16}{s(s + 8)} \tag{8-25}$$

$$G'(s) = \frac{16}{s^2 + 8s + 16} = \frac{16}{(s + 4)^2} \tag{8-26}$$

$$\theta_{\text{out}}(s) = \frac{16}{s(s + 4)^2} = \frac{1}{s} - \frac{4}{(s + 4)^2} - \frac{1}{s + 4} \longrightarrow 1 - 4te^{-4t} - e^{-4t} \tag{8-27}$$

$$G(s) = \frac{17}{s(s + 8)} \tag{8-28}$$

$$G'(s) = \frac{17}{s^2 + 8s + 17} \tag{8-29}$$

$$s = -4 \pm \sqrt{16 - 7} = -4 \pm j1 \tag{8-30}$$

$$\theta_{\text{out}}(s) = \frac{17}{s(s^2 + 8s + 17)}$$

$$= \frac{17}{s(s + 4 + j1)(s + 4 - j1)} \longrightarrow 1 + \sqrt{17}e^{-4t}\sin(t - 166°) \tag{8-31}$$

$$G(s) = \frac{64}{s(s + 8)} = \frac{8}{s(1 + s/8)} \tag{8-32}$$

$$G'(s) = \frac{64}{s^2 + 8s + 64} \tag{8-33}$$

$$\theta_{\text{out}}(s) = \frac{64}{s(s^2 + 8s + 64)} \tag{8-34}$$

$$\frac{1}{s[(s + \alpha)^2 + \beta^2]} \longrightarrow \frac{1}{\beta_0^2} + \frac{1}{\beta_0\beta}e^{-\alpha t}\sin(\beta t - \psi) \tag{8-35}$$

$$\psi \triangleq \tan^{-1}\frac{\beta}{-\alpha} \tag{8-36}$$

$$\beta_0^2 \triangleq \alpha^2 + \beta^2 \tag{8-37}$$

$$\theta_{\text{out}}(t) = 64\left[\frac{1}{64} + \frac{1}{8 \times 4\sqrt{3}}e^{-4t}\sin(4\sqrt{3}\,t - 120°)\right] \tag{8-38}$$

$$\theta_{\text{out}}(t) = 1 + 1.16e^{-4t}\sin(6.9t - 120°) \tag{8-39}$$

Figure 8-11 shows the locations of these closed-loop poles for the various open-loop poles; as the gain k increases, the closed-loop poles move away from the open-loop poles. Initially, as the gain increases, the two poles move toward each other along the real axis. These poles come together at -4;

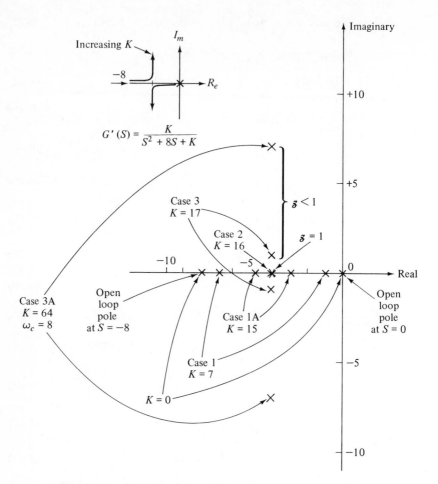

Figure 8-11. Location of closed-loop poles as a function of gain.

this is Case 2, given by Eq. (8-26), in which there are two identical roots, for a gain of 16. For gains increasing beyond 16, the poles keep the same real value of -4 but take on equal and opposite imaginary components. It should be noted that in Case 3, for $k = 64$, ω_{cp}, the gain crossover frequency, is equal to the value of the original open-loop pole at 8 rad/s; this is the frequency at which the open-loop gain would have a phase lag of 135°; it can be seen by Eq. (8-39) that the resulting response is somewhat oscillatory and will have a maximum possible step-function response overshoot of 16 per cent.

The preceding is a qualitative discussion of stability considerations as viewed from the *s* plane. Figure 8-11 shows the motion of the poles of the

closed-loop system as a function of the open-loop gain. This diagram introduces the concept of *root-locus analysis*. In root-locus analysis the motions
of the poles are examined as a function of gain and open-loop pole locations.
It is possible using this technique to sythesize particular desired pole-zero
configurations to result in specific closed-loop system responses. This is a
valuable analytical tool and is useful for complex dynamic systems. For
the approach to practical servosystem design as discussed in this book, the
root-locus technique is unnecessary and will therefore receive no further
attention.

8-4. the standard quadratic

Equation (8-40) gives the homogeneous quadratic second-order differential equation in Laplace form; this is simplified to give Eqs. (8-41) and
(8-42).

$$Js^2\theta(s) + Bs\theta(s) + k\theta(s) = 0 \tag{8-40}$$

$$\left(s^2 + \frac{B}{J}s + \frac{k}{J}\right)\theta(s) = 0 \tag{8-41}$$

$$[s^2 + 2\zeta\omega_n s + (\omega_n)^2]\theta(s) = 0 \tag{8-42}$$

$$(\omega_n)^2 = \frac{k}{J} \tag{8-43}$$

$$\omega_n = \sqrt{\frac{k}{J}} \tag{8-44}$$

$$2\zeta\omega_n = \frac{B}{J} \tag{8-45}$$

$$\begin{aligned}p_{1,2} &= -\zeta\omega_n \pm \omega_n\sqrt{\zeta^2 - 1} \\ &= -\zeta\omega_n \pm j\omega_n\sqrt{1 - \zeta^2}\end{aligned} \tag{8-46}$$

Equations (8-43) and (8-44) define the natural frequency ω_n. The second term
of Eq. (8-42) is a damping term, where ζ (zeta) is the damping ratio. The poles
(roots) of Eq. (8-42) are given in Eq. (8-46). For this general quadratic form,
as in the previous development, there are three cases: (1) when $\zeta > 1$, the
roots are real and distinct; (2) when $\zeta = 1$, the roots are real and identical;
(3), when $\zeta < 1$, the roots are complex conjugates. Referring back to Fig.
8-11, Case 1 is for the roots along the real axis; Case 2 is for $k = 16$ and the
two real poles are equal; in Case 3, the poles have moved away from the real
axis in the positive and negative imaginary directions. These three cases are
for ζ greater than one, equal to one, and less than one, respectively.

Figure 8-12 shows the magnitude of the peak transient overshoot resulting from a step function applied to a system with quadratic response.

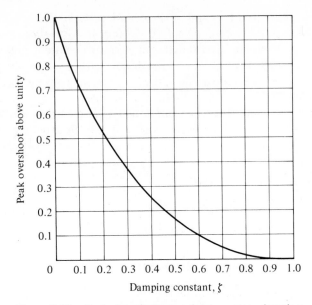

Figure 8-12. Peak transient overshoot versus damping constant ζ for a system with quadradic response.

Example 8-1. For $G(s) = k/s(s + 12)$, for a fully fed-back system, find $G'(s)$, ω_n, and ζ (or real pole locations instead of ω_n and ζ) for (a) $k = 10$, (b) $k = 36$, and (c) $k = 100$.

solution

(a) $G'(s) = \dfrac{k/s(s + 12)}{1 + k/s(s + 12)} = \dfrac{k}{s^2 + 12s + k}$

For $k = 10$,

$$G'(s) = \frac{10}{s^2 + 12s + 10}$$

yielding poles at

$$\frac{-12 \pm \sqrt{144 - 40}}{2} = -6 \pm \sqrt{26} = -6 \pm 5.1$$
$$= -0.9 \text{ s}^{-1}, -11.1 \text{ s}^{-1} \quad \text{(real poles)}$$

(b) $G'(s) = \dfrac{36}{s^2 + 12s + 36}$

Poles are at

$$\frac{-12 \pm \sqrt{144 - 144}}{2} = -6, -6$$

(critically damped case, both real poles, $\zeta = 1$).

(c) $G'(s) = \dfrac{100}{s^2 + 12s + 100}$

Poles are at

$$\frac{-12 \pm \sqrt{144 - 400}}{2} = \frac{-12 \pm \sqrt{-256}}{2} = -6 \pm j8$$

$$\omega_n = \sqrt{36 + 64} = 10 \text{ rad/s}$$

$$\zeta = \tfrac{1}{2} \times \tfrac{12}{10} = 0.6$$

Example 8-2. A motor with a time constant of 0.002 s is loaded with an inertia of twice J_m, its maximum speed is 6000 rpm for an input voltage of 20 V, using a 350° potentiometer excited by 2 V dc. What voltage gain is needed to give critically damped response (Case 2)?

solution

$$\omega_{m(\text{unloaded})} = \frac{1}{0.002} = 500 \text{ rad/s}$$

$$\omega_{m(\text{loaded})} = \frac{500}{3} = 167 \text{ rad/s}$$

$$K_{mv\Omega} = \frac{20 \text{ V}}{6000 \text{ rpm}} \times \frac{1 \text{ rpm}}{0.105 \text{ rad/s}} = 0.0318 \frac{\text{V}}{\text{rad/s}}$$

$$K_{\text{trans}} = \frac{2 \text{ V}}{350°} \times \frac{57.3°}{\text{rad}} = 0.327 \frac{\text{V}}{\text{rad}}$$

$$G(s) = \frac{0.327 \text{ (V/rad)} \times K_{AVP} \times 1/0.0318 \text{ rad/s/V}}{s(1 + s/167)} = \frac{10.3 K_{AVP}}{s(1 + s/167)}$$

$$= \frac{10.3 K_{AVP} \times 167}{s(s + 167)} = \frac{1720 K_{AVP}}{s(s + 167)} = \frac{k}{s(s + 167)}$$

$$G'(s) = \frac{k/s(s + 167)}{1 + (k/s(s + 167))} = \frac{k}{s^2 + 167s + k}$$

Poles are at

$$\frac{-167 \pm \sqrt{(167)^2 - 4k}}{2}; \quad \text{for critical damping:}$$

$$4k = (167)^2 = 27,890 \quad \text{or} \quad k = 6970 = 1720 K_{AVP}$$

then

$$K_{AVP} = \frac{6970}{1720} = 4.05 \text{ V/V}$$

8-5. geometric properties of standard quadratic poles

In Fig. 8-13 a pole pair is shown for Case 3. The real component of the distance of both of these poles from the origin is $-\zeta\omega_n$, and the imaginary parts are $\pm\omega_n\sqrt{1 - \zeta^2}$ [see Eq. (8-46)]. In Eq. (8-47), the distance of either of these poles from the origin is calculated by taking the square root of the sum of the squares of the real and imaginary parts; the magnitude of this distance is equal to the natural frequency, ω_n:

$$r = \sqrt{(-\zeta\omega_n)^2 + (\omega_n\sqrt{1 - \zeta^2})^2} = \sqrt{\zeta^2(\omega_n)^2 + (\omega_n)^2(1 - \zeta^2)} = \omega_n \tag{8-47}$$

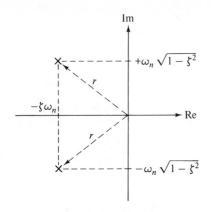

Figure 8-13.   Real and imaginary components of a complex
pole pair.

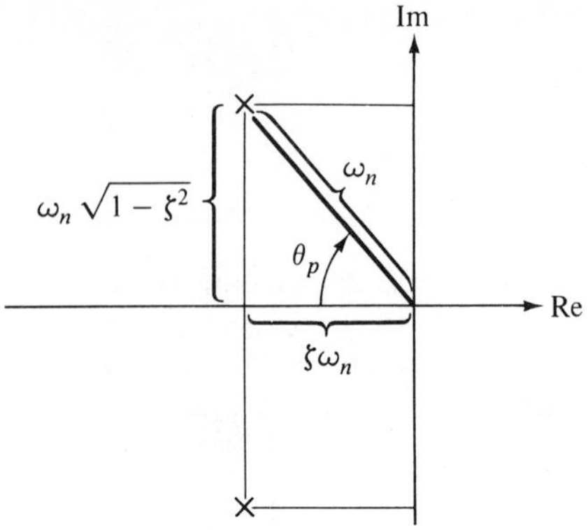

Figure 8-14.   Geometric properties of complex conjugate poles.

Figure 8-14 is an s-plane diagram of two complex conjugate poles. The angle of either of these poles from the negative real axis is θ_p: Eq. (8-48) shows that the cosine of θ_p is ζ, the damping constant.

$$\cos \theta_p = \frac{\zeta \omega_n}{\omega_n} = \zeta \tag{8-48}$$

Therefore the radial distance of a complex pole from the origin is its natural frequency. The cosine of the angle of the pole from the negative real axis is the damping constant, and the resonant frequency is $\omega_n \sqrt{1 - \zeta^2}$, the vertical distance from the real axis.

Recalling that the frequency response of a function of s is plotted as s increases along the imaginary axis, the minimum distance exists between the sample variable $j\omega$ and a complex pole when $j\omega = j\omega_n \sqrt{1 - \zeta^2}$. Since this distance between $s(=j\omega)$ and the complex pole appears as a denominator factor in the gain expression, the gain assumes a maximum value at $s = j\omega_n \sqrt{1 - \zeta^2}$; this is sometimes called the *damped natural frequency*. Consider an example for an open-loop break frequency of ω_{cp} and a gain crossover frequency of ω_{cp} as given in Eq. (8-49). Equation (8-50) gives the closed-loop equivalent for this case; the natural frequency is ω_{cp} and ζ is 0.5.

$$G(s) = \frac{\omega_{cp}}{s(1 + s/\omega_{cp})} = \frac{(\omega_{cp})^2}{s(s + \omega_{cp})} \tag{8-49}$$

$$G'(s) = \frac{(\omega_{cp})^2/s(s + \omega_{cp})}{1 + (\omega_{cp})^2/s(s + \omega_{cp})} = \frac{(\omega_{cp})^2}{s^2 + s\omega_{cp} + (\omega_{cp})^2} \tag{8-50}$$

In this case, the closed loop has 1 dB of peaking (approximately 12 per cent) in the frequency response; this is quite well behaved (it will be recalled that the transient response due to a step function will have a 16 per cent overshoot).

Example 8-3. If the gain in Example 8-2 is changed to 14, calculate (a) ζ and ω_n, and (b) the angle of the poles from the negative real axis.

solution

(a) $G'(s) = \dfrac{k_1}{s^2 + 167s + k_1}$

$$k_1 = 6970 \times \dfrac{14}{4.05} = 24{,}100 = (\omega_n)^2$$

$$\omega_n = \sqrt{24{,}100} = 155 \text{ rad/s}$$

$$2\zeta\omega_n = 167 = 2 \times 155 \times \zeta$$

(b) $\zeta = \dfrac{167}{310} = 0.54$

$$\cos\theta = 0.54 = 57.4°$$

8-6. *transient response from pole location*

Figure 8-15 shows a group of poles s_1 through s_6; s_1 and s_2 are conjugate poles. The approximate step-function response of a system with these

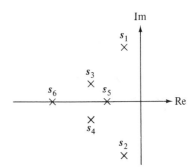

Figure 8-15. Assumed pole locations.

two poles is shown in the upper part of Fig. 8-16. The two poles, s_3 and s_4, which are a conjugate pair, are characterized by the second time function in Fig. 8-16; it can be seen that the decay rate for these poles is faster than for s_1 and s_2, although the frequency is lower. The decay time decreases as the distance of the poles to the left of the imaginary axis increases; also, the resonant frequency increases as the position of the poles moves farther away from the real axis. The real negative pole s_5 is characterized by a simple exponential decay. A pole which is farther to the left than s_5 is s_6, and it therefore has a more rapid simple exponential decay. This diagram shows that it is possible from pole positions to visualize directly the system response: The farther poles are to the left of the origin, the faster (smaller) the time constant (or the shorter the decay time); the higher the complex poles are above the origin, the greater their resonant frequency.

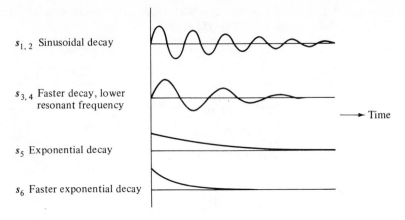

$s_{1,2}$ Sinusoidal decay

$s_{3,4}$ Faster decay, lower resonant frequency

s_5 Exponential decay

s_6 Faster exponential decay

→ Time

Figure 8-16.   Step-function responses for assumed pole locations.

8-7. phasor gain

Figure 8-17 shows a single phasor point of a general polar plot of $G(j\omega)$, the gain function. The gain can be characterized as a magnitude $G(j\omega)$ (the

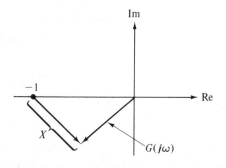

Figure 8-17.   Vector representation (polar plot) of open-loop gain and one-plus-gain.

length of a phasor) and the angle of that phasor from the real axis (equivalent to the phase angle associated with the complex gain term). A second phasor X is also shown in this figure; it can be seen from Eqs. (8-51) and (8-52) that X is equal to the expression $1 + G(j\omega)$.

$$G(j\omega) - X = -1 \qquad (8\text{-}51)$$

$$X = 1 + G(j\omega) \qquad (8\text{-}52)$$

The fact that the phasor from the -1 point to the end of the $G(j\omega)$ phasor is $1 + G(j\omega)$ allows a relatively simple means of visualizing the closed-loop gain of a system from a graphical construction. Figure 8-18 demonstrates this fact and shows that for the gain function G (the curve) the closed-loop gain (which is $G/(1 + G)$) becomes large only as $1 + G$ becomes small (at the left hump of G curve). If this curve of G humps farther to the

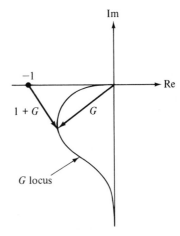

Figure 8-18.   Locus of gain vector *G* and one-
          plus-gain vector 1 + *G*.

left to approach more closely the −1 point, the closed-loop gain becomes extremely large. If the *G* locus curve actually passes through the −1 point, the gain goes to infinity, thus providing a totally unstable system (an oscillator). Therefore, in servo design it is important that this locus of *G* be such that the ratio of $G/(1 + G)$ never exceeds one by very much. One can see that for $|G| \gg 1$, and the *G* locus close to the negative imaginary axis, the closed-loop gain is close to unity (*G* and 1 + *G* are essentially the same magnitude). It is only in the region where the *G* curve approaches the origin that the closed-loop gain is potentially troublesome; it is only in this region that the ratio of *G* to 1 + *G* can possibly be greater than unity.

Equation (8-53) defines a relatively simple open-loop transfer function for a servo; its polar plot is shown in Fig. 8-19.

$$G(s) = \frac{k}{s(1 + s/\omega_x)} \tag{8-53}$$

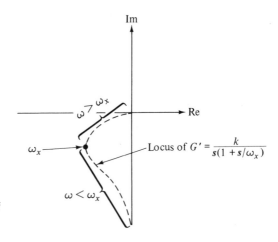

Figure 8-19.   Polar   plot   of
          $k/s(1 + s/\omega_x)$.

It may be seen that at ω_x (the break frequency of the lag term) the phase angle of $G(s)$ is $-135°$. This is important because it gives a means of visualizing the shape of the G locus from the terms of the open-loop gain. By examining Eq. (8-53) it may be seen that when the magnitude of s is appreciably less than ω_x, the system looks essentially like an integrator; in this region the open-loop expression has a phase shift of approximately $-90°$. Figure 8-20

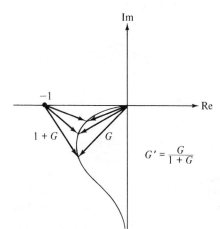

Figure 8-20. Open-loop polar plot that has well-behaved closed-loop transient response.

shows a reasonably stable gain plot; the closed-loop gain never becomes appreciably greater than unity because the curve does not come very close to the -1 point. Figure 8-21 shows the open-loop gain polar plot for a system that has a fairly unstable closed-loop characteristic because the phasor $1 + G$ becomes small compared to G, thus providing a closed-loop gain greater than unity.

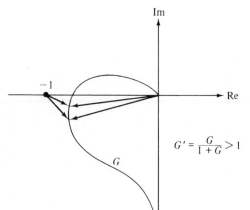

Figure 8-21. Open-loop polar plot that has oscillatory closed-loop transient response.

8-8. M circles

Figure 8-22 shows a plot of (so-called) *M circles*. These circles are defined mathematically in Eq. (8-54). *M* circles represent the loci of constant closed-

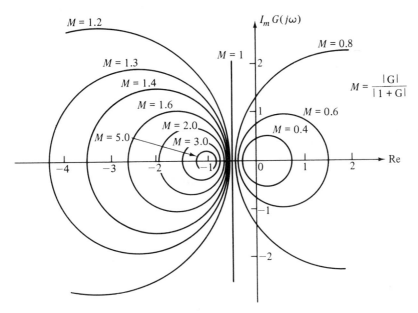

Figure 8-22.   *M* circles.

loop gain *G'*, and simplify the process of obtaining closed-loop gain information from open-loop polar plot data.

$$M = \frac{|G|}{|1 + G|} \tag{8-54}$$

The *M* circle labeled $M = 2$, for instance, indicates that for any open-loop gain phasor from the origin touching that *M* circle, the closed-loop gain has a magnitude of 2. Polar paper may be obtained with printed *M* circles, making it possible to do fairly rapid sketching of closed-loop gain magnitude from open-loop gain and phase. The radius of the *M* circles is defined in Eq. (8-55); the center locations of these *M* circles are defined in Eq. (8-56).

$$M \text{ circle radius} = \left| \frac{M}{M^2 - 1} \right| \tag{8-55}$$

$$\text{Center of } M \text{ circle} = \left(\frac{-M^2}{M^2 - 1} ; 0 \right) \tag{8-56}$$

There are more convenient methods of obtaining closed-loop gain from open-loop data (e.g., Nichols charts, which will be discussed in Section 8-10); *M* circles were useful prior to (and serve as an introduction to) the more valuable Nichols charts. A performance term that is still frequently used is M_p, which represents the maximum closed-loop gain of a given function. M_p occurs at the frequency of highest closed-loop gain; when the peaking is not exactly on a particular circle, interpolation between circles is required. For quadratic systems the value of M_p is defined in Eq. (8-57) in terms of the damping factor ζ.

$$M_p = \frac{1}{2\zeta\sqrt{1 - \zeta^2}} \qquad \text{for } 0 \leq \zeta \leq 0.707 \qquad (8\text{-}57)$$

Example 8-4. For a quadratic system, what peaking in frequency response (M_p) can be expected for $\zeta_1 = 0.05$, $\zeta_2 = 0.02$, and $\zeta_3 = 0.5$?

solution

$$M_p = \frac{1}{2\zeta\sqrt{1 - \zeta^2}}$$

$$M_{p_1} = \frac{1}{2 \times 0.05\sqrt{1 - 25 \times 10^{-4}}} = \frac{10}{\sqrt{0.9975}} = 10.013$$

$$M_{p_2} = \frac{1}{2 \times 0.2\sqrt{1 - 0.04}} = \frac{2.5}{\sqrt{0.96}} = \frac{2.5}{0.9798} = 2.551$$

$$M_{p_3} = \frac{1}{2 \times 0.5\sqrt{1 - 0.25}} = \frac{1}{\sqrt{0.75}} = \frac{1}{0.86603} = 1.155$$

8-9. gain and phase margin

Figure 8-23 shows a polar plot of a particular function; two characteristics of this polar plot are shown: gain margin and phase margin. *Gain*

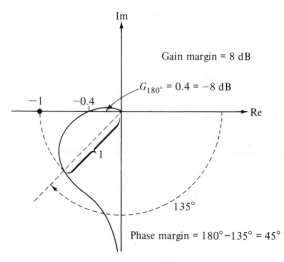

Gain margin = 8 dB

$G_{180°} = 0.4 = -8$ dB

-1 -0.4 Re

Im

1

135°

Phase margin = $180° - 135° = 45°$

Figure 8-23. Polar plot demonstrating gain margin and phase margin.

Margin is defined as the amount of additional gain required at the frequency of 180° phase lag to cause the gain plot to pass through the −1 point and thus produce oscillation. In the case of the diagram shown, the gain is 0.4 when the phase is −180°; therefore the gain margin is the reciprocal of 0.4, which is $2\frac{1}{2}$ or 8 dB. *Phase Margin* is defined as the amount of additional phase lag required at the frequency of unity gain to cause the gain plot to pass through the −1 point and thus produce oscillation. The plot of Fig. 8-23 has a phase margin of 45°. In essence, gain margin and phase margin represent how much more destabilization of either gain or phase is required to make the plot go directly through the −1 oscillation point.

Figure 8-24, in conjunction with Fig. 8-25, shows how a closed-loop

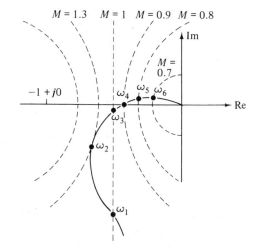

Figure 8-24. Obtaining closed-loop frequency response using *M* circles.

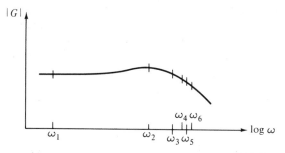

Figure 8-25. Closed-loop frequency-response plot obtained from *M* circles.

gain plot can be made from open-loop data using *M* circles. As may be seen from Fig. 8-24, a number of different points, labeled ω_1, ω_2, ω_3, ω_4, ω_5, and ω_6, are plotted; each of these points have particular equivalent *M* circle points. Figure 8-25 plots the magnitudes of these five points as a function of frequency.

8-10. Nichols charts

Figure 8-26 shows a Nichols chart. The ordinate of this chart is the logarithm of open-loop gain $\log |G|$; and the abscissa is open-loop phase shift.

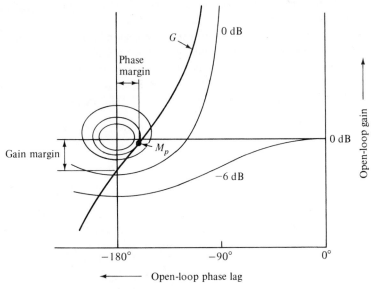

Figure 8-26.   Nichols chart.

For any given open-loop gain and phase point, there is a unique closed-loop gain and phase point; the two are related by the basic relation $G' = G/(1 + G)$. It is therefore possible to plot information similar to M circles on a chart that has logarithmic coordinates (decibels). The loci of M circles on this Nichols chart are no longer circular, since the coordinates are logarithmic. Closed-loop phase curves are orthogonal to these gain curves. Nichols charts are very valuable as practical tools in determining the performance of servos or of general closed-loop systems. They become very handy graphical reference tables to give the closed-loop gain and phase based on the open-loop gain and phase.

$$G(s) = \frac{\omega_{cp}}{s(1 + s/82)} \tag{8-58}$$

Equation (8-58) is an example of an open-loop gain plot which has a simple lag in the denominator at 82 rad/s. The gain crossover frequency of the loop, ω_{cp}, is chosen to be 82 rad/s. Table 8-1 also gives the various components of the gain expression for eight different frequencies. These points are plotted on the Nichols chart of Fig. 8-27. The closed-loop data is determined from the Nichols chart and is given in the last column of Table 8-1. It can be seen from Fig. 8-27 that the maximum peaking point M_p is approximately 1.3 dB at about 58 rad/s. (shown on Fig. 8-27 by $\otimes$).

Table 8-1. open-loop gain tabulation for nichols chart

ω (rad/s)	$82/j\omega$ (dB/deg)	$\dfrac{1}{1 + j\omega/82}$ (dB/deg)	$\dfrac{82}{j\omega(1 + j\omega/82)}$ (dB/deg)	$G'(j\omega)$ (dB/deg)
8.2	$+20\angle-90°$	$-0.1\angle-6$	$+19.9\angle-96$	$+0.05\angle-6$
16.4	$+14\angle-90°$	$-0.2\angle-11$	$+13.8\angle-101$	$+0.15\angle-12$
41.0	$+6\angle-90°$	$-1.0\angle-26$	$+5.0\angle-116$	$+1.0\angle-35$
65.6	$+2\angle-90°$	$-2\angle-39$	$0\angle-129$	$+1.2\angle-65$
82.0	$0\angle-90°$	$-3\angle-45$	$-3\angle-135$	$0\angle-90$
98.4	$-1.5\angle-90°$	$-4\angle-50$	$-5.5\angle-140$	$-2\angle-110$
114.8	$-3\angle-90°$	$-4.8\angle-55$	$-7.8\angle-145$	$-4.5\angle-125$
147.6	$-5\angle-90°$	$-6.3\angle-61$	$-11.3\angle-150$	$-9.2\angle-140$

A frequently used criterion for peaking is that the magnitude of the transient overshoot should be 30 per cent or less (for a quadratic, this is equivalent to 2.2 dB peaking of the frequency response). To obtain this amount of peaking for the example, the open-loop gain has to be increased by 2.5 dB, which means that the open-loop curve is moved upwards by 2.5 dB. One might wonder why it is desirable to make the system more unstable by increasing the open-loop gain; the reason is that higher open-loop gain means reduced system errors and more rapid response. The price for these improvements, however, is reduced stability; the stability degradation is limited to a 30 per cent transient overshoot in this case. Therefore it is desirable to increase the open-loop gain to the point where the stability is as specified; then one has the best performance for the specified stability. In the example just given, the increase of 2.5 dB of open-loop gain is equivalent to a factor of 35 per cent; therefore the new gain crossover frequency will be 35 per cent greater than 82 rad/s and becomes 110 rad/s (approximately 17.5 Hz).

Example 8-5. Using a Nichols chart, find the following points:

(a) $G'(-j10)$
(b) $G'(10\angle-120°)$
(c) $G'(10\angle-180°)$
(d) $G'(-j1.2)$
(e) $G'(1.2\angle-120°)$
(f) $G'(1.2\angle-165°)$

solution   The gain factor 10 is equivalent to $+20$ dB. For (a) the phase angle is $-90°$, so the point $+20$ dB $\angle-90°$ can be determined on the accompanying Nichols chart (Fig. E8-5). The closed-loop gain and phase for (a) can be read from the figure as -0.1 dB $\angle-6°$. Parts (b) and (c) have the same open-loop gain as (a) but have greater phase lags; therefore they are plotted to the left of point (a). The gain factor 1.2 is equivalent to $20\log_{10} 1.2$ dB $= 20 \times 0.08$ dB $= 1.6$ dB; using this quantity, the open-loop gains for parts (d), (e), and (f) are determined by plotting the points at the proper phase lags. The resulting closed-loop gain and phase values are listed below.

(a) $G'(-j10) = -0.1$ dB $\angle-6°$
(b) $G'(10\angle-120°) = +0.4$ dB$\angle-5°$

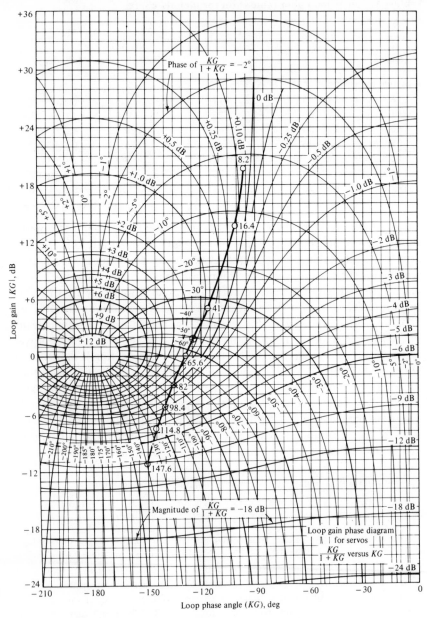

Figure 8-27. Using a Nichols chart to obtain closed-loop frequency response from open-loop data.

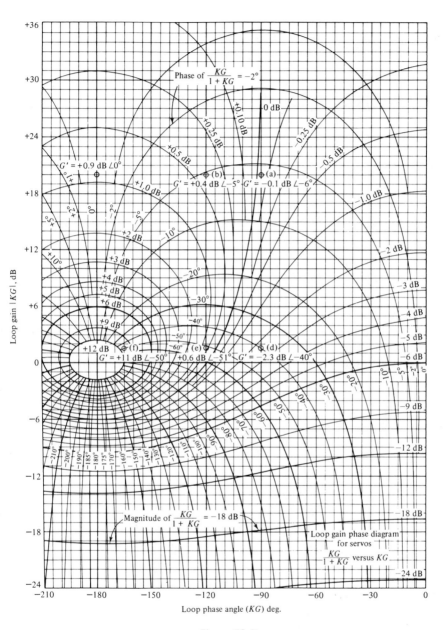

Figure E8-5

(c) $G'(10\angle -180°) = +0.9\ dB \angle 0°$
(d) $G'(-j1.2) = -2.3\ dB \angle -40°$
(e) $G'(1.2\angle -120°) = +0.6\ dB \angle -51°$
(f) $G'(1.2\angle -165°) = +11\ dB \angle -50°$

8-11. Nichols chart example

The system parameters for this example are given in Table 8-2. The rate

Table 8-2.   servo data for Nichols chart example

1937–050   torque motor

$$J_L = 0.01\ oz \cdot in \cdot s^2$$
$$R_A = 0$$
$$\omega_e = 5000\ rad/s$$
$$\omega_m = 7\ rad/s$$
$$\omega_{PA} = 400\ rad/s$$

loop bandwidth is assumed to be equal to the power amplifier break frequency, ω_{PA}. The position loop bandwidth is conservatively estimated to be at one-fourth the rate loop bandwidth. Equations (8-59) and (8-60) give the expression for the open-loop gain of the rate loop.

$$G_r(s) = \frac{\omega_{cr}}{(s + \omega_m)(1 + s/\omega_{PA})(1 + s/\omega_e)} \tag{8-59}$$

$$= \frac{400}{(s + 7)(1 + s/400)(1 + s/5000)} \tag{8-60}$$

$$G_r(j\omega) = \frac{400}{(j\omega + 7)(1 + j\omega/400)(1 + j\omega/5000)}$$

$$= \frac{400/7}{(1 + j\omega/7)(1 + j\omega/400)(1 + j\omega/5000)} \tag{8-61}$$

Equation (8-61) presents the same open rate loop gain as a function of $j\omega$, in a slightly modified form to simplify Nichols chart plotting. The gains of the various terms are given in Table 8-3 for frequencies from 20 to 1000 rad/s. The combined open-loop complex gain at those frequencies is given in the far right column of Table 8-3 in decibels and in degrees.

Table 8-4 gives the closed-loop gains for the same frequencies based on the Nichols Chart plot shown in Fig. 8-28. If the open-loop gain is decreased by 2 dB, the closed rate loop will then have a maximum peaking of $+0.5$ dB (the gain curve becomes tangent to the $+0.5$-dB curve). The new closed rate loop gain is given in the right-hand column of Table 8-4. The new rate loop

Table 8-3. open rate loop data for Nichols chart example

ω rad/s	$20 \log_{10} \dfrac{400}{7}$ dB	$\dfrac{\omega}{7}$	$\dfrac{1}{1 + j\omega/7}$ dB/deg	$\dfrac{\omega}{5000}$	$\dfrac{1}{1 + j\omega/5000}$ dB/deg	$\dfrac{\omega}{400}$	$\dfrac{1}{1 + j\omega/400}$ dB/deg	$G_r(j\omega)$ dB/deg
20	+35	1.86	$-6\angle-63$	0.004	$0\angle 0$	0.05	$0\angle-3$	$+29\angle-66$
50	+35	7.15	$-17\angle-82$	0.01	$0\angle-1$	0.125	$0\angle-7$	$+18\angle-90$
100	+35	14.3	$-23\angle-86$	0.02	$0\angle-1$	0.25	$0\angle-14$	$+12\angle-101$
200	+35	28.6	$-29\angle-88$	0.04	$0\angle-2$	0.5	$-1\angle-26$	$+5\angle-116$
300	+35	42.9	$-33\angle-89$	0.06	$0\angle-4$	0.75	$-2\angle-37$	$0\angle-130$
400	+35	57.1	$-35\angle-90$	0.08	$0\angle-5$	1.0	$-3\angle-45$	$-3\angle-140$
500	+35	71.5	$-37\angle-90$	0.1	$0\angle-7$	1.25	$-4\angle-52$	$-6\angle-149$
1000	+35	143	$-43\angle-90$	0.2	$0\angle-12$	2.5	$-9\angle-68$	$-17\angle-170$

Table 8-4. closed rate loop data for Nichols chart example

ω rad/s	$G_r(j\omega)$ dB/deg	$G'_r(j\omega)$ dB/deg	decreased $\lvert G_r \rvert$ dB	G'_r dB/deg
20	+29∠-66	-0.2∠-2	+27	-0.2∠-2
50	+18∠-90	-0.1∠-7	+16	-0.1∠-9
100	+12∠-101	+0.1∠-15	+10	+0.1∠-19
200	+5∠-116	+0.9∠-35	+3	+0.5∠-43
300	0∠-130	+1.4∠-65	-2	0∠-80
400	-3∠-140	+0.9∠-95	-5	-1.6∠-108
500	-6∠-149	-2∠-124	-8	-4.5∠-132
1000	-17∠-170	-15∠-170	-19	-18∠-170

bandwidth is 310 rad/s, which is a 22 per cent decrease below the previously assumed 400 rad/s.

Equation (8-62) defines the open position loop gain in terms of the closed rate loop gain and the position loop bandwidth ω_{cp}. It can be seen that the closed-loop points listed in Table 8-4 can be used for the bracketed part of Eq. (8-62).

$$G_p(j\omega) = [G'_r(j\omega)]\frac{\omega_{cp}}{j\omega} \qquad (8\text{-}62)$$

The open position loop points are listed in the fourth column of Table 8-5.

Table 8-5. open and closed position loop data for Nichols chart example

B rad/s	$G'_r(j\omega)$ dB/deg	$\dfrac{100}{j\omega}$ dB/deg	G_p dB/deg	G'_p dB/deg	increased $\lvert G_p \rvert$ dB	G'_p dB/deg
20	-0.2∠-2	+14∠-90	+13.8∠-92	-0.1∠-12	+17.3	0∠-8
50	-0.1∠-9	+6∠-90	+5.9∠-99	-0.5∠-30	+9.4	0∠-20
100	+0.1∠-19	0∠-90	+0.1∠-109	-1.2∠-52	+3.6	0∠-39
200	+0.5∠-43	-6∠-90	-5.5∠-133	-3∠-102	-2.0	+0.5∠-80
300	0∠-80	-10∠-90	-10∠-170	-6.5∠-164	-6.5	-1.0∠-160
400	-1.6∠-108	-12∠-90	-13.6∠-198	-11.5∠-203	-10.1	-7.0<∠205
500	-4.5∠-132	-14∠-90				
1000	-18∠-170	-20∠-90				

Figure 8-29 shows the locus of this open position loop plot on a Nichols chart; it can be seen from this locus that the position loop gain may be increased by 3.5 dB (a factor of 1.5) in order to reach a 1-dB closed position loop peaking (at 250 rad/s). This then results in the position loop bandwidth being increased from 100 to 150 rad/s to give a maximum peaking of 1 dB.

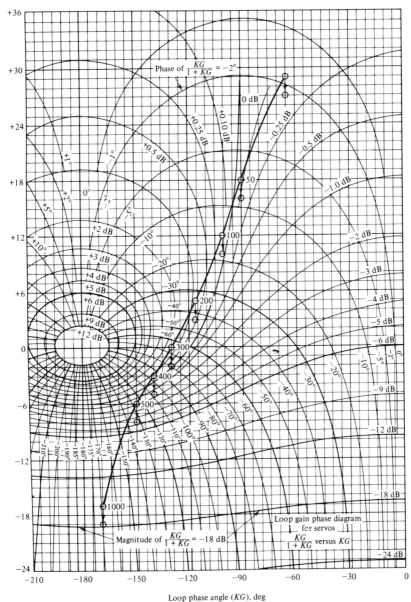

Figure 8-28.   Using a Nichols chart to obtain closed rate loop frequency response from open rate loop data.

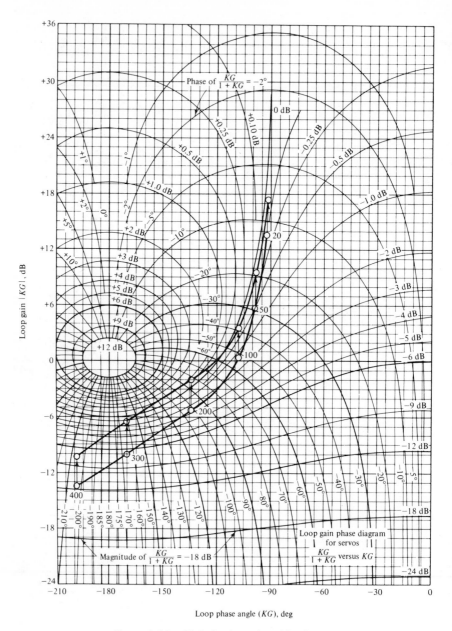

Figure 8-29. Nichols chart of position loop.

For this position loop bandwidth the velocity constant is 150 (s^{-1}) [see Eq. (8-63)]. For this velocity constant, an input rate of 15°/s results in an error of 0.1° (see Eq. 8-64).

$$k_v = \omega_{cp} = 150 \text{ s}^{-1} \tag{8-63}$$

$$\text{Rate error} = \frac{15°/s}{150 \text{ s}^{-1}} = 0.1° \tag{8-64}$$

For an assumed steady torque of 10 oz·in, the torque error determined in Eq. (8-65) is 1.23°.

$$\text{Torque error} = \frac{T}{J\omega_{cp}\omega_{cr}} = \frac{10 \text{ oz·in}}{0.01 \text{ oz·in·s} \times 310 \text{ s}^{-1} \times 150 \text{ s}^{-1}}$$

$$= \frac{10}{465} \text{ rad} = \frac{573}{465} \text{ deg} = 1.23° \tag{8-65}$$

8-12. summary

The characteristics of poles and zeros were examined, including the correspondence between pole location and transient response. The general quadratic response was examined analytically, viewed as a model of a closed-loop system with varying gain and considered from a geometric point of view; although actual servos have responses more complex than quadratics, the quadratic model is valuable to assist the visualization of servo performance. Phasor gain was introduced to develop M circles. The Nichols chart, which simplifies quantitative evaluation of closed-loop frequency response (gain versus frequency) from open-loop data, was described. Finally, an example was given using Nichols charts to determine final values of rate and position loop gains.

problems

8-1. Given $G(s) = k/s(s + 40)$ for a fully fed-back system. Find the pole locations for (a) $k = 100$, (b) $k = 400$, and (c) $k = 1000$. (d) Find ζ and ω_n for any complex poles of (a), (b), or (c). (e) Find the angle from the negative real axis of the poles for each case. (f) Find M_p for each case.

8-2. For a fully fed-back system with $G'(s) = 0.2K_{AVP}/s(1 + s/25)$, what should K_{AVP} be for no transient overshoot (critical damping, Case 2)?

8-3. For Problem 8-2, given $K_{AVP} = 80$, find (a) ω_n, (b) ζ, (c) the angle of the poles from the negative real axis, and (d) M_p.

8-4. Using a Nichols chart, find the closed-loop gains for the following open-loop gains:

(a) $5\angle-90°$ (b) $5\angle-135°$ (c) $5\angle-165°$ (d) $5\angle-180°$

(e) $1.1\angle-90°$ (f) $1.1\angle-135°$ (g) $1.1\angle-165°$

8-5. If a closed-loop system has a closed-loop gain of $1.05\angle-4°$ at a particular frequency, estimate how much the phase lag will change if the open-loop gain is reduced by a factor of 3? (Use a Nichols chart).

8-6. A servo has the following open-loop characteristic:

$$G(s) = \frac{37}{s(1 + s/40)(1 + s/300)}$$

Find (a) the closed-loop response at 5, 20, 30, 40, and 80 rad/s, and (b) M_p for the system.

9

integral network compensation

The addition of an *integral network* inside the position loop of a stable servo improves the velocity constant K_v and the torque stiffness K_T. It is possible to add an integral network to a simple servo (a motor in a position loop having no stabilizing network), but normally other methods of improvement are used first. For instance, either tachometer stabilization or lead network compensation improve the bandwidth ω_{c_p} as well as the torque stiffness K_T and the velocity constant K_v. If further improvements are required, then the tachometer-stabilized system is further improved by an integral network.

Figure 9-1 shows a tachometer-stabilized servo. The inner loop is the tachometer loop and the outer loop is the position loop. For frequencies above ω_m, this system may be accurately approximated by the simplified diagram of Fig. 9-2. In this case the rate loop appears as a low-pass filter having a simple break at the rate loop crossover frequency ω_{cr}. This approximation is justified by Eq. (9-1).

$$G_r'(s) = \frac{G_r(s)}{1 + G_r(s)} = \frac{\omega_{cr}/(s + \omega_m)}{1 + \omega_{cr}/(s + \omega_m)} = \frac{\omega_{cr}}{s + \omega_m + \omega_{cr}}$$

$$\approx \frac{\omega_{cr}}{s + \omega_{cr}} = \frac{1}{1 + s/\omega_{cr}} \tag{9-1}$$

$$\frac{\omega_{cr}/s}{1 + \omega_{cr}/s} = \frac{\omega_{cr}}{s + \omega_{cr}} = \frac{1}{1 + s/\omega_{cr}} \tag{9-2}$$

Equation (9-2) points out that if the rate loop is considered as a pure inte-

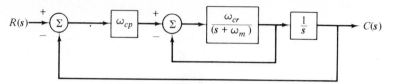

Figure 9-1. Tachometer-stabilized servo in standard form.

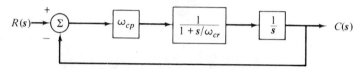

Figure 9-2. Simplified diagram of tachometer-stabilized servo.

grator with a crossover frequency of ω_{cr}, the closed rate loop gain is the same as that approximated by Eq. (9-1). This provides another way of looking at a rate loop, that is, as a pure integration with a gain crossover frequency of ω_{cr}.

Figure 9-3 shows the open position loop gain for the assumed rate loop;

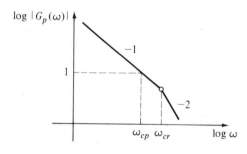

Figure 9-3. Bode gain plot of tachometer-stabilized open position loop.

the rate loop causes a break frequency at ω_{cr} inside the position loop. The closed position loop is stable for a position loop gain crossover frequency ω_{cp} less than ω_{cr}. Equation (9-3) shows that for frequencies appreciably below the gain crossover frequency the open-loop gain is large, and therefore the closed-loop gain is essentially unity.

$$\frac{G_p(j\omega)}{1 + G_p(j\omega)}\bigg|_{|G_p(j\omega)| \gg 1} \approx \frac{G_p(j\omega)}{G_p(j\omega)} = 1 \qquad (9\text{-}3)$$

In general, if the magnitude of the open-loop gain is large, the closed-loop gain is close to unity regardless of the open-loop phase, and the system must be stable at these frequencies. Therefore, for frequencies appreciably less than ω_{cp} it is possible to increase the open-loop gain and still have a stable system, as long as the gain in the region of the original ω_{cp} is not increased significantly. It is this fact that makes the addition of an integral network possible. An integral network increases the gain of the position loop for frequencies appreciably below the gain crossover frequency; this provides reduced low-frequency errors because of the greater loop gain at these frequencies.

9-1. integral networks

Equation (9-4) gives the gain transfer function of an integral network, and Fig. 9-4 shows the Bode plot of this network.

$$G_{int}(s) = \frac{s + \omega_i}{s + \omega_i/\alpha} \tag{9-4}$$

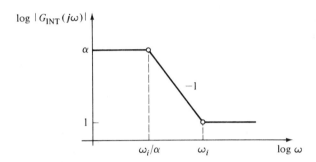

Figure 9-4. Bode gain plot of integral network.

An example of a *passive* integral network is given in Fig. 9-5 (this requires an external gain of α (alpha) to give the characteristic of Fig. 9-4). Figure 9-6 shows an *active* operational amplifier (see Appendix A) integral network. The passive network of Fig. 9-5 has the problem that its attenuation gets very large for large α. Therefore practical applications of Fig. 9-5 are limited to designs with α of the order of 10 or less. For Fig. 9-6, α may become essentially infinite (by letting R_2 approach infinity) without any attenuation.

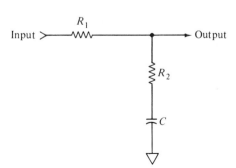

Figure 9-5. Passive integral network suitable for low α.

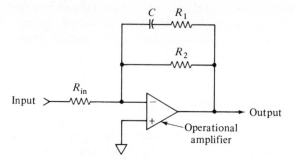

Figure 9-6.   Operational amplifier implementation of an
integral network.

Example 9-1. Design (a) a passive integral network with an input resistor of
10 kΩ, $\alpha = 10$, and $\omega_i = 40$ rad/s; (b) an active integral network with a dc gain
of approximately 1. (Use an operational amplifier with an input resistor of 10 kΩ,
$\alpha = 100$, and $\omega_i = 40$ rad/s.)

solution

(a) $R_{in} = 10$ kΩ, $\alpha = 10$, $\omega_i = 40$ rad/s.
$G_i(j0) = 1$, $G_i(j\infty) = R_2/(R_{in} + R_2)$, so

$$\alpha = \frac{R_{in} + R_2}{R_2} = 1 + \frac{R_{in}}{R_2}$$

$$\frac{R_{in}}{R_2} = 9 \quad \text{and} \quad R_2 = \frac{10 \text{ k}\Omega}{9} = 1.1 \text{ k}\Omega$$

$$\omega_i = \frac{1}{R_2 C} = \frac{1}{(1.1 \times 10^3)C}$$

$$C = \frac{1}{1.1 \times 10^3 \times 40} = 22.7 \ \mu\text{F}$$

(b) $R_{in} = 10$ kΩ, $\alpha = 100$, $\omega_i = 40$ rad/s.

$$\omega_i = \frac{1}{R_1 C}$$

$$\alpha = \frac{R_1 + R_2}{R_1}$$

$$\text{dc gain} = \frac{R_2 \| R_1}{R_{in}}$$

$$R_2 \| R_1 = 10 \text{ k}\Omega = \frac{R_1 R_2}{R_1 + R_2} \approx R_1$$

Let $R_1 = 10$ kΩ. Then

$$40 = 1/10^4 C$$

$$C = 2.5 \ \mu\text{F}$$

$$\alpha = \frac{R_1 + R_2}{R_1} = 1 + \frac{R_2}{R_1}$$

$$\frac{R_2}{R_1} = \alpha - 1 = 99$$

$$R_2 = 99 \times 10\ \text{k}\Omega = 990\ \text{k}\Omega = 0.99\ \text{M}\Omega \approx 1\ \text{M}\Omega$$

9-2. position loop

The open position loop gain expression of a system using an integral network in the position loop is given in Eq. (9-5); its Bode plot is shown in Fig. 9-7.

$$G_p(s) = \frac{\omega_{cp}(s + \omega_i)}{s(s + \omega_i/\alpha)(1 + s/\omega_{cr})} \tag{9-5}$$

$$\omega_{cr} > \omega_{cp} > \omega_i > \frac{\omega_i}{\alpha} \tag{9-6}$$

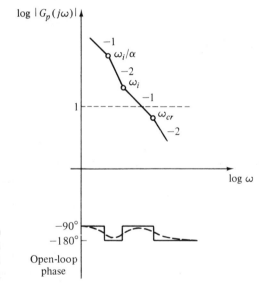

Figure 9-7. Open-loop Bode gain plot of an integral network compensated servo in standard form.

Equation (9-6) notes the relationship between the various frequencies in Eq. (9-5). In considering those relationships, the plot of Fig. 9-7 may be sketched by inspection. Based on Eq. (9-6), the open-loop gain at the gain crossover frequency is determined in Eq. (9-7) to be the expected value of unity.

$$|G_p(j\omega_{cp})| = \left| \frac{\omega_{cp}(j\omega_{cp} + \omega_i)}{j\omega_{cp}(j\omega_{cp} + \omega_i/\alpha)(1 + j\omega_{cp}/\omega_{cr})} \right|$$

$$\approx \left| \frac{\omega_{cp}(j\omega_{cp})}{j\omega_{cp}(j\omega_{cp})(1)} \right| = \left| \frac{1}{j} \right| = 1 \tag{9-7}$$

The result is that the integral network does not disturb the gain in the region of the gain crossover frequency but has increased the lower frequency gain, thus improving system stiffness and system velocity constant.

The gain constant of Eq. (9-5) is the gain crossover frequency ω_{cp}, because poles and zeros above ω_{cp} are expressed as $1 + s/\omega_x$ (the only one is $1 + s/\omega_{cr}$), and poles and zeros below ω_{cp} are expressed as $(s + \omega_i)$ and $(s + \omega_i/\alpha)$. Equation (9-5) gives the gain crossover frequency as the gain constant because in the region of the gain crossover frequency the gains due to the terms with poles *above* the gain crossover frequency approach unity. Similarly, those gains due to terms for poles and zeros *below* ω_{cp} take on the value of s (thus the integral network pole and zero cancel each other for $s \approx j\omega_{cp}$).

Example 9-2. For $\omega_{cr} = 100$ rad/s and $\omega_{cp} = 20$ rad/s, calculate (a) reasonable values for ω_i and α if a K_v of 100 is desired, (b) ω_i/α.

solution: Let $\omega_i = \omega_{cp}/4 = 5$ rad/s.

$$K_v = \alpha\omega_{cp} = 20\,\alpha = 100$$

Therefore,

$$\alpha = 5$$

$$\frac{\omega_i}{\alpha} = 1 \text{ rad/s}$$

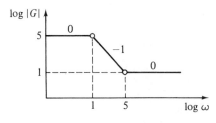

Figure E9-2

9-3. integral network servo performance

Figure 9-8 shows a servo with an integral network. It will be noted that $\Omega_{command}$ must be considered dimensionally as angular rate because it is coming into a loop whose output is dimensionally angular rate; therefore the command from the output of the integral network is a velocity command (to the rate loop). Since the inner tachometer loop of Fig. 9-8 has been reduced to standard form, the inverse of the tachometer gain has been incorporated into the ω_{cp} block, and therefore the input to the rate loop is dimensionally angular rate rather than voltage. For an assumed ramp input as shown in Fig. 9-9, the system behaves according to Eq. (9-8) (after transients have settled).

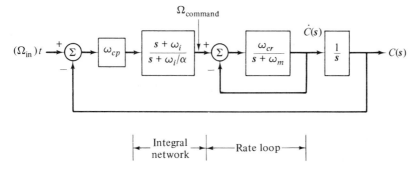

Figure 9-8. Tachometer-stabilized integral network compensated servo in standard form.

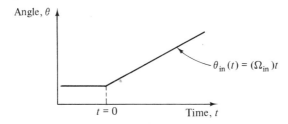

Figure 9-9. Time plot of ramp function starting at $T = 0$.

$$(\Omega_{in})t - C(t) = \epsilon \qquad C(t) = (\Omega_{in})t - \epsilon \qquad \dot{C}(t) = \Omega_{in} \qquad (9\text{-}8)$$

Therefore the derivatives of the input and the output are equal and the servo output velocity is the same as the ramp velocity in Fig. 9-9. Clearly, this is necessary to prevent servo runaway: If the input and output velocities are not equal, the error either gains or diminishes in value, either case being an impossible situation. In the steady state, therefore, the error settles to a constant value and the output velocity equals the input velocity. As a result, Eq. (9-9) expresses the fact that the input velocity is equal to the $\Omega_{command}$ velocity.

$$\Omega_{command} = \Omega_{in} \qquad (9\text{-}9)$$

$$\Omega_{command}(s) = \epsilon(s)\omega_{cp}\frac{s + \omega_i}{s + \omega_i/\alpha} \qquad (9\text{-}10)$$

$$\left.\frac{s + \omega_i}{s + \omega_i/\alpha}\right|_{s=0} = \alpha \qquad (9\text{-}11)$$

$$\Omega_{command}(s)|_{s=0} = (\epsilon(s)\omega_{cp}|_{s=0})\alpha \qquad (9\text{-}12)$$

Equation (9-10) expresses the relationship between this command velocity and the error in the system. Equation (9-11) gives the dc gain of the integral network portion of Eq. (9-10) as α.

$$(\Omega_{\text{command}})_{\text{dc}} = \epsilon_{\text{dc}}\omega_{cp}\alpha \qquad (9\text{-}13)$$

$$\epsilon_{\text{dc}} = \frac{\Omega_{\text{command}}}{\omega_{cp}\alpha} \qquad (9\text{-}14)$$

$$K_v = \alpha\omega_{cp} \qquad (9\text{-}15)$$

Equations (9-12) and (9-13) show that the command velocity is equal to the error times the bandwidth times α; Eqs. (9-14) and (9-15) show that the system K_v is $\alpha\omega_{cp}$. It has been shown that the steady-state command velocity must equal the input ramp velocity, and that the system error may be determined knowing the magnitude of the command velocity and the system K_v (the product of the integral network dc gain and the position loop bandwidth: $\alpha\omega_{cp}$).

Example 9-3. Use the Inland T-1352 torque motor rate loops of Example 7-1 and a 350° potentiometer excited by 15 V dc.
(a) Calculate K_{AVP} for $\omega_{cp} = 40$ rad/s.
(b) Specify the K_{AVP} amplifier using an operational amplifier with an input resistance of 10 kΩ (see Appendix A); find K_v and K_T.
(c) Design a separate operational amplifier integral network with an input resistance of approximately 10 kΩ, an α of 50, and $\omega_i = 10$ rad/s; find K_v and K_T.

solution

(a) $K_{\text{trans}} = \dfrac{15\text{ V}}{350°} \times \dfrac{57.3°}{\text{rad}} = 2.46\dfrac{\text{V}}{\text{rad}}$

$\omega_{cp} = 40$ rad/s

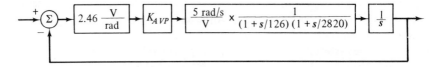

Figure E9-3a

$$G_p(s) = \frac{2.46K_{AVP} \times 5}{s(1 + s/126)(1 + s/2820)} = \frac{12.3K_{AVP}}{s(1 + s/126)(1 + s/2820)}$$

$$= \frac{\omega_{cp}}{s(1 + s/126)(1 + s/2820)}$$

$12.3K_{AVP} = 40$

$K_{AVP} = 3.25$

(b) Figure E9-3b gives an operational amplifier implementation of the K_{AVP} amplifier for a gain of 3.25.

Actually, 33 kΩ resistors (commercial values) may be specified; in practice, 47-kΩ resistors may be used in both cases with a potentiometer gain control at the output, as shown in Fig. E9-3c.

It is possible that the position loop may have positive feedback connected as shown; this may be remedied by exchanging the two inputs. Another possible prob-

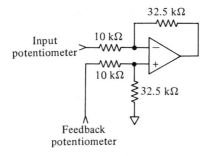

Figure E9-3b

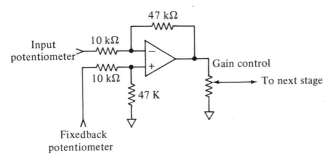

Figure E9-3c

lem is that errors due to potentiometer loading may be unacceptable; for instance, if the transducer potentiometers have resistances of 1 kΩ, as much as approximately 1.5 percent error can exist between the actual potentiometer voltage and the theoretically correct voltage for the shaft angle. A practical solution to this loading problem is to use buffer amplifiers as shown in Fig. E9-3d.

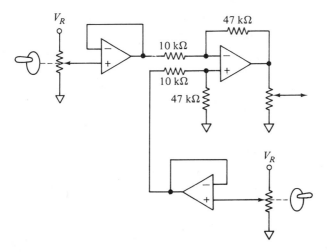

Figure E9-3d

K_v for the above is $\omega_{cp} = 40 \text{ s}^{-1}$. $K_T = J_{total}\omega_{cp}\omega_{cr}$; there are two values of J_{total}: 28.8 oz·in·s^2 and 208.8 oz·in·s^2.

$$K_{T_1} = 28.8 \times 10^{-4} \text{ oz·in·s}^2 \times 126 \times 40 \text{ s}^{-2} = 14.5 \text{ oz·in/rad}$$

$$K_{T_2} = K_{T_1} \times \frac{208.8}{28.8} = 110 \frac{\text{oz·in}}{\text{rad}}$$

(c) $R_{in} = 10 \text{ k}\Omega$, $\alpha = 50$, $\omega_i = 10 \text{ rad/s}$.

$$\omega_i = \frac{1}{R_1 C}$$

$$\alpha = \frac{R_1 + R_2}{R_1}$$

$$C = \frac{1}{\omega_1 R_1} = \frac{1}{10 \times 10^4} = 10 \ \mu\text{F}$$

High-frequency gain $\approx G(j\omega_{cp}) = \dfrac{R_1 \| R_2}{R_{in}} = \dfrac{R_1 R_2/(R_1 + R_2)}{R_{in}} = 1$

$$\alpha = \frac{R_1 + R_2}{R_1} = 50$$

Therefore,

$$\frac{0.02 R_2}{R_{in}} = 1 \quad \text{or} \quad R_2 = 50 \ R_{in} = 500 \text{ k}\Omega$$

$$\alpha = 1 + \frac{R_2}{R_1} = 50$$

Therefore,

$$\frac{R_2}{R_1} = 49$$

$$R_1 = \frac{500 \text{ k}\Omega}{49} = 10.2 \text{ k}\Omega \approx 10 \text{ k}\Omega$$

$K_v = \alpha\omega_{cp} = 50 \times 40 = 2000 \text{ s}^{-1}$

$$K_{T_1} = \alpha J \omega_{cp}\omega_{cr} = 14.5 \times 50$$

$$= 725 \frac{\text{in·oz}}{\text{rad}}$$

$$K_{T_2} = 110 \times 50 = 5500 \frac{\text{in·oz}}{\text{rad}}$$

9-4. K_v form

Many authors have expressed the open-loop transfer function in so-called "K_v form," which is shown in Eq. (9-16).

$$G_p(s) = \frac{K_v(\tau_1 s + 1)\cdots}{s(\tau_2 s + 1)(\tau_3 s + 1)\cdots} \tag{9-16}$$

In this form the constant in the numerator is the K_v of the servo and the various poles and zeros are all expressed in $\tau s + 1$ form. Equation (9-17) is the same as Eq. 9-5; this may be expressed in K_v form by converting the various poles and zeros to time-constant form by multiplying and dividing by the appropriate factors.

$$G_p(s) = \frac{\omega_{cp}(s + \omega_i)}{s(s + \omega_i/\alpha)(1 + s/\omega_{cr})} \tag{9-17}$$

This is shown in Eq. (9-18); it can be seen that the constant in the numerator is the K_v of the system.

$$G_p(s) = \frac{\omega_{cp}\omega_i(\tau_i s + 1)}{s(\tau_{i\alpha}s + 1)\omega_i/\alpha(\tau_r s + 1)} = \frac{\alpha\omega_{cp}(\tau_i s + 1)}{s(\tau_{i\alpha}s + 1)(\tau_r s + 1)}$$

$$= \frac{K_v(\tau_i s + 1)}{s(\tau_{i\alpha}s + 1)(\tau_r s + 1)} \tag{9-18}$$

This particular K_v form is not recommended as the most valuable for the servo design approach discussed in this book, but it is important to realize that this form *is* a valid expression of gain and does give K_v directly.

The development of Eqs. (9-19) through (9-24) derives K_v using the final value theorem.

To prove:

$$K_v = \alpha\omega_{cp}. \tag{9-19}$$

$$G_p(s) = \frac{\omega_{cp}(s + \omega_i)}{s(s + \omega_i/\alpha)(1 + s/\omega_{cr})} \tag{9-20}$$

$$\theta_{in}(s) = \frac{\Omega_{in}}{s^2} \tag{9-21}$$

$$\epsilon(s) = \frac{\theta_{in}(s)}{1 + G_p(s)} = \frac{\Omega_{in}/s^2}{1 + \omega_{cp}(s + \omega_i)/[s(s + \omega_i/\alpha)(1 + s/\omega_{cr})]}$$

$$= \frac{\Omega_{in}s(s + \omega_i/\alpha)(1 + s/\omega_{cr})}{s^2[s(s + \omega_i/\alpha)(1 + s/\omega_{cr}) + \omega_{cp}(s + \omega_i)]} \tag{9-22}$$

$$\epsilon(t) = \lim_{t\to\infty} s\epsilon(s) = \lim_{s\to 0} \frac{\Omega_{in}s^2(s + \omega_i/\alpha)(1 + s/\omega_{cr})}{s^2[s(s + \omega_i/\alpha)(1 + s/\omega_{cr}) + \omega_{cp}(s + \omega_i)]}$$

$$= \frac{\Omega_{in}}{\alpha\omega_{cp}} \tag{9-23}$$

Therefore

$$K_v = \alpha\omega_{cp} \tag{9-24}$$

9-5. *integral network servo torque stiffness*

The torque error gain for this integral network compensated tachometer-stabilized servo is developed using Fig. 9-10 and is given in Eq. (9-25).

$$\frac{\epsilon_{T_1}(s)}{T_L(s)} = \frac{1}{J\omega_{cr}[(s + \omega_i)/(s + \omega_i/\alpha)]\omega_{cp}} G'_p(s) = \frac{(s + \omega_i/\alpha)G'_p(s)}{J\omega_{cr}\omega_{cp}(s + \omega_i)}$$

$$\approx \frac{(s + \omega_i/\alpha)}{J\omega_{cr}\omega_{cp}(s + \omega_i)(1 + s/\omega_{cp})} \tag{9-25}$$

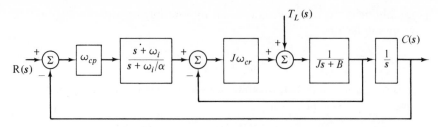

Figure 9-10. Tachometer-stabilized integral network compensated servo with external torque disturbance.

The technique used to determine the error is to apply a load torque $T_L(s)$ at the proper point in the system and divide through by the gain prior to this point to get the equivalent system input. Then, multiply by the closed-loop gain $G'_p(s)$ to get the resulting output motion due to the applied torque (the validity of this technique is proved in Chapter 12; a simpler version of the method was given in Section 7-5). The resulting error gain expression is given in Eq. (9-25) (this is the reciprocal of $K_T(s)$, the torque stiffness expression). The Bode plot of this error gain expression is shown in Fig. 9-11. The value

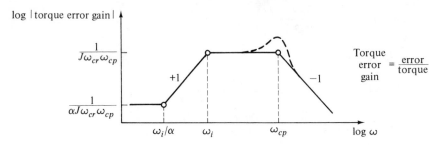

Figure 9-11. Bode torque error gain.

at zero frequency is determined by substituting zero for s. The lowest break frequency is ω_i/α; at that frequency the gain starts to increase along a $+1$ slope and continues to increase until ω_i is reached. From this frequency to ω_{cp} the gain remains flat; at ω_{cp} the gain starts to decline at a -1 slope. It may be seen from this Bode plot that the stiffness at the origin (zero frequency) is improved by α due to the addition of the integral network. The shape of this error gain plot indicates that errors will be maximum for torques with frequency components in the region between ω_i and ω_{cp}, with possible peaking near ω_{cp} for slightly unstable systems.

9-6. integral network gain expressions

Equation (9-26) defines the transfer function of an integral network; Fig. 9-12 is the Bode plot of this network.

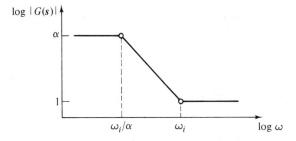

Figure 9-12.   Bode gain plot of integral network

$$G_T(s) = \frac{s + \omega_i}{s + \omega_i/\alpha} \qquad (9\text{-}26)$$

Figure 9-13 shows an operational amplifier implementation of this integral network. The operational amplifier circuit performance may be visualized by realizing in general, that, the overall gain $(E_{\text{out}}/E_{\text{in}})$ is as defined in Eq. (9-27); Appendix A develops this relationship.

$$\frac{E_{\text{out}}}{E_{\text{in}}} = -\frac{Z_{\text{FB}}}{R_{\text{in}}} \qquad (9\text{-}27)$$

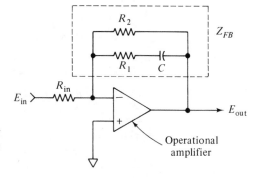

Figure 9-13.   Operational amplifier implementation of an integral network.

At very low frequencies the impedance of C approaches infinity, and therefore R_2 is the predominant feedback impedance. At very high frequencies (because C has a very low impedance), R_1 becomes the predominant feedback impedance. If R_2 is appreciably larger than R_1, then the gain at low frequencies is appreciably higher than the high-frequency gain. The expression for the feedback impedance is given in Eq. (9-28) and further developed in Eqs. (9-29) through (9-34).

$$Z_{\text{FB}} = R_2 \,\|\, \left(R_1 + \frac{1}{sC}\right) = \frac{R_2(R_1 + 1/sC)}{R_2 + R_1 + 1/sC} = \frac{R_2(1 + R_1 sC)}{1 + (R_1 + R_2)sC}$$

$$= \frac{R_2(1 + R_1 sC)}{1 + [(R_1 + R_2/R_1]R_1 sC} \qquad (9\text{-}28)$$

$$R_1 C = \frac{1}{\omega_i} \qquad (9\text{-}29)$$

$$Z_{FB} = \frac{R_2(1 + s/\omega_i)}{1 + [(R_1 + R_2)/R_1]s/\omega_i} \tag{9-30}$$

$$\frac{R_1 + R_2}{R_1} = \alpha \tag{9-31}$$

$$Z_{FB} = \frac{R_2(1 + s/\omega_i)}{1 + \alpha s/\omega_i} = \frac{R_2(1 + s/\omega_i)}{1 + s/(\omega_i/\alpha)} \tag{9-32}$$

$$= \frac{R_2(1 + s/\omega_i)}{1 + s/(\omega_i/\alpha)} = \frac{(R_2/\omega_i)(s + \omega_i)}{(\alpha/\omega_i)(s + \omega_i/\alpha)} = \frac{R_2(s + \omega_i)}{\alpha(s + \omega_i/\alpha)} \tag{9-33}$$

$$\frac{R_2}{\alpha} = \frac{R_2}{(R_1 + R_2)/R_1} = \frac{R_1 R_2}{R_1 + R_2} = R_1 \| R_2 \tag{9-34}$$

For stability considerations, it was seen that the gain of the integral network must be close to unity in the region of ω_{cp}; therefore the input resistance R_{in} must be $R_1 R_2/(R_1 + R_2)$. Equations (9-35) through (9-40) develop relationships leading to the component formulas of Table 9-1.

$$R_{in} = \frac{R_1 R_2}{R_1 + R_2} = \frac{R_2}{\alpha} \tag{9-35}$$

$$\frac{R_1 + R_2}{R_1} = \alpha \tag{9-36}$$

$$R_1 + R_2 = R_1\alpha \tag{9-37}$$

$$R_2 = R_1(\alpha - 1) \tag{9-38}$$

$$C = \frac{1}{\omega_i R_1} \tag{9-39}$$

$$R_{in} = \frac{R_2}{\alpha} = \frac{R_1(\alpha - 1)}{\alpha} = R_1\left(1 - \frac{1}{\alpha}\right) \tag{9-40}$$

Table 9-1. integral network component formulas

$$C_1 = \frac{1}{\omega_i R_1}$$
$$R_2 = (\alpha - 1)R_1$$
$$R_{in} = \left(1 - \frac{1}{\alpha}\right)R_1$$

9-7. integral network servo design example

Table 9-2 shows assumed break frequencies and other parameters required for the design of an integral network. This is used to investigate the effect of the integral network on closed-loop stability of the Nichols chart servo example of Chap. 8. Table 9-3 lists the various constants associated with that servo, and Eq. (9-41) gives the open rate loop transfer function.

Table 9-2. parameters and component values for integral network design example

$$\omega_i \;=\; 30 \text{ rad/s}$$
$$\alpha \;=\; 20$$
$$R_1 \;=\; 100 \text{ k}\Omega$$
$$C_1 \;=\; \frac{1}{\omega_i R_1} = \frac{1}{30 \times 10^5} = 0.33 \;\mu\text{F}$$
$$R_2 \;=\; (\alpha - 1)R_1 = 19 \times 100 \text{ k}\Omega = 1.9 \text{ M}\Omega$$
$$R_{\text{in}} \;=\; \left(1 - \frac{1}{\alpha}\right)R_1 = (1 - 0.05)\,100 \text{ k}\Omega = 95 \text{ k}\Omega$$

Table 9-3. servo basic data

$$J_L \;=\; 0.01 \text{ oz} \cdot \text{in} \cdot \text{s}^2$$
$$R_A \;=\; 0 \;\Omega$$
$$\omega_{pa} = 400 \text{ rad/s}$$
$$\omega_e \;=\; 5000 \text{ rad/s}$$
$$\omega_{cr} = 310 \text{ rad/s}$$
$$\omega_{cp} = 150 \text{ rad/s}$$
$$\omega_m \;=\; 7 \text{ rad/s}$$

$$
\begin{aligned}
G_r(j\omega) &= \frac{310}{(j\omega + 7)(1 + j\omega/400)(1 + j\omega/5000)} \\
&= \frac{310/7}{(1 + j\omega/7)(1 + j\omega/400)(1 + j\omega/5000)}
\end{aligned}
\tag{9-41}
$$

$$
\begin{aligned}
G_p(s) &= \frac{150(s + \omega_i)}{s(s + \omega_i/\alpha)}G_r'(s) = \frac{150(s + 30)}{s(s + 1.5)}G_r'(s) \\
&= \frac{150 \times 30(1 + s/30)}{s \times 1.5(1 + s/1.5)}G_r'(s) = \frac{(1 + s/30)G_r'(s)}{(s/3000)(1 + s/1.5)}
\end{aligned}
\tag{9-42}
$$

Table 9-4 lists the closed-loop gains for a rate loop bandwidth of 310 rad/s

Table 9-4. closed rate loop data for servo design example

ω	$G_r'(j\omega)$ for $\omega_{cr} = 310$ rad/s (dB/deg)
20	$-0.2 \angle -2$
50	$-0.1 \angle -9$
100	$+0.1 \angle -19$
200	$+0.5 \angle -43$
300	$0 \angle -80$
400	$-1.6 \angle -108$
500	$-4.5 \angle -132$
1000	$-18 \angle -170$

Table 9-5. Integral network compensated position loop data (dB/deg)

ω	$G_r{}'(j\omega)$	$\dfrac{3000}{(j\omega)}$	$\dfrac{1}{1+j\omega/1.5}$	$1+j\omega/30$	$G_p(j\omega)$	$G_p{}'(j\omega)$
20	$-0.2\angle-2$	$+43.5\angle-90$	$-22.5\angle-81$	$+1.6\angle+34$	$+22.4\angle-139$	$+0.5\angle-3$
50	$-0.1\angle-9$	$+35.5\angle-90$	$-30\angle-88$	$+6\angle+60$	$+11.4\angle-127$	$+1.2\angle-15$
100	$+0.1\angle-19$	$+29.5\angle-90$	$-36.5\angle-90$	$+10.8\angle+74$	$+3.9\angle-125$	$+1.8\angle-41$
200	$+0.5\angle-43$	$+23.5\angle-90$	$-42.5\angle-90$	$+16.6\angle+81$	$-1.9\angle-142$	$+2.4\angle-89$
300	$0\angle-80$	$+20\angle-90$	$-46\angle-90$	$+20\angle+84$	$-6.0\angle-176$	$0\angle-170$
400	$-1.6\angle-108$	$+17.5\angle-90$	$-48.5\angle-90$	$+22\angle+86$	$-10.6\angle-202$	$-8\angle-209$
500	$-4.5\angle-132$	$+15.5\angle-90$	$-50.5\angle-90$	$+24.5\angle+86$	$-15.0\angle-226$	
1000	$-18\angle-170$	$+9.5\angle-90$	$-56.5\angle-90$	$+30\angle+88$	$-35.0\angle-262$	

for eight different frequencies. Equation (9-42) defines the open position loop response function for the system including the integral network.

Table 9-5 gives the integral network and the overall position loop response data; it also gives the closed position loop response determined from the Nichols chart of Fig. 9-14. Notice that the position loop which previously

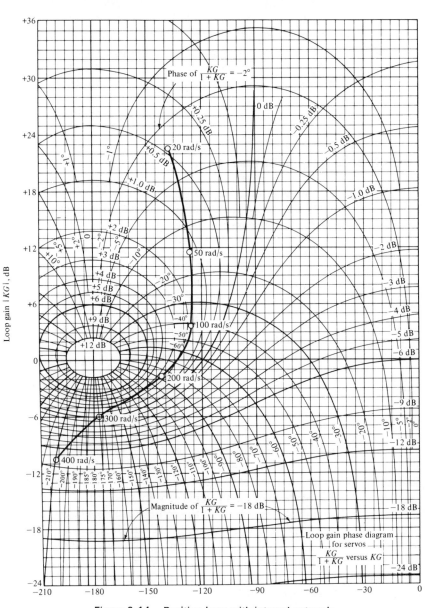

Figure 9-14.   Position loop with integral network.

had a maximum peaking of 1 dB now has a maximum peaking of 3 dB at approximately 250 rad/s; the only difference is that an integral network has been added. Therefore the integral network produces some destabilizing effect on the closed-loop system even though the upper break frequency of the integral network is well below the position loop gain crossover frequency (30 and 150 rad/s, respectively). Examination of the Nichols chart of Fig. 9-14 indicates that it is no longer possible to assure an M_p of 1 dB; 1 dB peaking in the region of 250 rad/s may be assured, but lower frequencies in the region of 100 rad/s and less have greater closed-loop gains. Lowering the gain 1 dB to give an ω_{cp} of 135 rad/s yields an M_p of 1.5 dB. Equation (9-43) gives the new velocity constant of this system, which is now 2700 (formerly 150).

$$K_v = \alpha \omega_{cp} = 20 \times 135 = 2700 \ (\text{s}^{-1}) \tag{9-43}$$

9-8. specifying hardware

Figure 9-15 represents the rate loop gain expression in literal form; from this Eq. (9-44) may be written to define the rate loop gain crossover frequency ω_{cr} in terms of the constants.

$$\omega_{cr} = \frac{K_{AVR}K_{GE\Omega}\omega_m}{K_{mv\Omega}} \tag{9-44}$$

$$K_{AVR} = \frac{\omega_{cr}K_{mv\Omega}}{K_{GE\Omega}\omega_m} = \frac{310(\text{s}^{-1}) \times 40 \ \text{V}/(290 \ \text{rad/s})}{0.14 \ \text{V/rad/s} \times 7 \ \text{rad/s}} = 43.6\frac{\text{V}}{\text{V}} \tag{9-45}$$

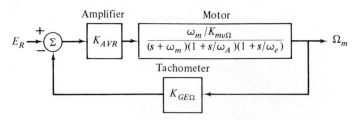

Figure 9-15.   Rate loop transfer-function block diagram.

Equation (9-45) is an inversion of Eq. (9-44) and gives the rate loop amplifier gain, K_{AVR}. Now the rate loop parameters are fully specified.

Figure 9-16 is the block diagram of the complete servo; the angle transducers both have gains of 1 V/deg. Reducing the rate loop to its equivalent form allows drawing the simplified position loop transfer-function block diagram as Fig. 9-17; the position loop gain expression is given in Eq. (9-46). Equation (9-47) defines the gain in the region of ω_{cp}, and Eq. (9-48) inverts this to obtain an expression for ω_{cp}.

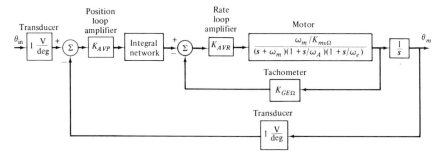

Figure 9-16. Tachometer (rate)-stabilized integral network compensated servo.

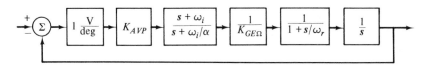

Figure 9-17. Reduced diagram of tachometer-stabilized integral network compensated servo.

$$G_p(s) = 1\frac{V}{deg}K_{AVP}\left(\frac{s + \omega_i}{s + \omega_i/\alpha}\right)\frac{1}{K_{GE\Omega}}\left(\frac{1}{1 + s/\omega_{cr}}\right)\left(\frac{1}{s}\right) \qquad (9\text{-}46)$$

$$|G(j\omega_{cp})| = \left|1\frac{V}{deg}K_{AVP}\left(\frac{1}{K_{GE\Omega}}\right)\left(\frac{1}{j\omega_{cp}}\right)\right| \approx 1 \qquad (9\text{-}47)$$

Therefore

$$\omega_{cp} \approx \frac{K_{AVP}}{K_{GE\Omega}}\left(1\frac{V}{deg}\right) \qquad (9\text{-}48)$$

or

$$K_{AVP} = \frac{\omega_{cp}K_{GE\Omega}}{1\ V/deg} = \frac{\omega_{cp}K_{GE\Omega}}{57.3\ V/rad}$$

$$= \frac{135\ rad/s \times 0.14\ V/rad/s}{57.3\ V/rad} = 0.33\frac{V}{V}. \qquad (9\text{-}49)$$

Finally, the position loop amplifier gain is given in Eq. (9-49). The complete servo is now specified.

Figure 9-18 shows the implementation of the complete servo. The first amplifier has the required gain of 0.33 (this amplifier may be eliminated by increasing the input resistor to the next stage by 3). The integral network is specified in Table 9-2. The rate loop voltage amplifier K_{AVR} has the required gain of 491 from both the position loop integral network and the tachometer to the power amplifier. The unity voltage gain power amplifier supplies the required electrical power to drive the torque motor because operational amplifiers can normally supply only a fraction of a watt of output power.

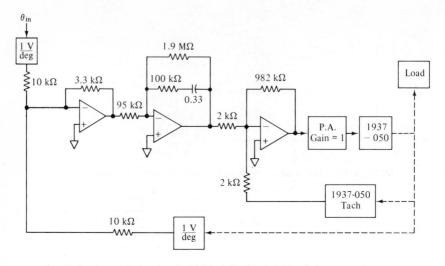

Figure 9-18.   The final servo.

9.9 summary

The basic relationships for an integral network compensated tachometer-stabilized servo were developed. It is possible to use integral networks in position loops because, at frequencies appreciably below the gain crossover frequency, increases in open-loop gain have only a small effect on system stability. The parameter equations for an operational amplifier implementation of an integral network were developed. An earlier servo design example was modified to include a position loop integral network; it was found that the addition of the integral network had a slight destabilizing effect on the position loop. The detailed implementation of the servo was developed using operational amplifiers.

problems

9-1. Using 8.1-kΩ input resistors, design (a) a passive integral network with $\alpha = 15$ and $\omega_i = 20$ rad/s, and (b) an operational amplifier integral network with $\alpha = 60$, $\omega_i = 20$ rad/s, and a high-frequency gain of approximately 0.5.

9-2. For a servo using a rate loop with

$$G'_r(s) = \frac{1}{(1 + s/80)(1 + s/800)}$$

a tachometer coupled to the motor with $K_{GE\Omega}$ of 2.5 V/rad/s, and a gear ratio of 20:1, design:

(a) an operational amplifier position loop amplifier for $\omega_{cp} = 20$ rad/s using trans-ducers with $K_{trans} = 5.7$ V/rad and input R's of 5.1 kΩ;

(b) an operational amplifier integral network with $\alpha = 40$, $\omega_i = 5$ rad/s, an input R of 5.1 kΩ, and a gain in the region of ω_{cp} of unity.

9-3.

(a) Using a Nichols chart, adjust ω_{cp} of Problem 9-2 to give 0.25 dB closed-loop peaking without the integral network, and determine the new amplifier compo-nent values. (b) Observe the effect of adding the integral network, and estimate a good value for ω_{cp} if the M_p is to stay safely below 1.5 dB.

9-4. Determine how much phase lag and gain change an integral network with $\alpha = 40$ causes at $4\omega_i$.

10

lead network and viscous coupled inertial damped servos

Figure 10-1 is the Bode plot of a dc motor which has an electromechanical break frequency at ω_m and an electrical break frequency at ω_e. $\omega_{c p_1}$ shows the gain crossover frequency which may be obtained with no compensation; at this frequency the open-loop phase lag is approximately 135°. If a lead network is added in series with this motor, the dashed Bode plot results; it may be seen that the gain crossover frequency is increased to $\omega_{c p_2}$, at which frequency there is also a phase lag of 135° (shown dashed in the phase curve). Therefore it is possible to increase the bandwidth of the servo above that obtainable with no compensation by "leading" the phase back to 135° at a frequency appreciably higher than the motor break frequency.

10-1. lead network characteristics

Figure 10-2 shows a lead network usable for compensation of a dc servo. Examination of the schematic indicates that at low frequencies the network has an attenuation due to the voltage dividing effect between R_1 and R_2; at high frequencies there is an increase in gain due to C, up to a maximum value of unity. Figure 10-3 shows the basic characteristics of this network on a Bode plot. Equation (10-1) is a direct solution for the gain of

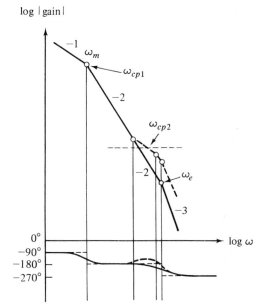

Figure 10-1. Bode plot of servo
motor and of servo
motor and lead net-
work (dashed).

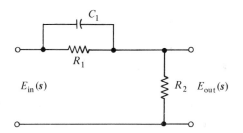

Figure 10-2. Circuit diagram of
lead network.

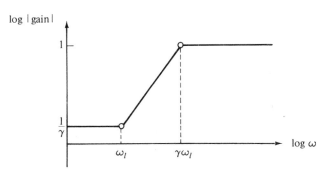

Figure 10-3. Bode plot of lead network.

the network. After substitution of simplifying constants ω_l and k, Eq. (10-2) results.

$$\frac{E_{out}(s)}{E_{in}(s)} = \frac{R_2}{(R_1 \parallel 1/sC_1) + R_2} = \frac{R_2}{[R_1/sC_1/(R_1 + 1/sC_1)] + R_2}$$

$$= \frac{R_2(R_1 + 1/sC_1)}{(R_1/sC_1) + R_2(R_1 + 1/sC_1)} = \frac{R_2(1 + R_1sC_1)}{R_1 + R_2(1 + R_1sC_1)} \quad (10\text{-}1)$$

$$\frac{E_{out}(s)}{E_{in}(s)} = \frac{R_2(1 + R_1sC_1)}{R_1 + R_2(1 + R_1sC_1)} = \frac{R_2(1 + s/\omega_l)}{R_1 + R_2(1 + s/\omega_l)}$$

$$= \frac{R_2(1 + s/\omega_l)}{R_2[(R_1/R_2) + 1 + s/\omega_l]} = \frac{1 + s/\omega_l}{k + 1 + s/\omega_l}$$

$$= \frac{1 + s/\omega_l}{s/\omega_l + (1 + k)} = \frac{s + \omega_l}{s + (1 + k)\omega_l} \quad (10\text{-}2)$$

$$\text{for } R_1C_1 = \frac{1}{\omega_l} \text{ and } k = \frac{R_1}{R_2}$$

Let $1 + k = \gamma$. Then $\quad\quad\quad\quad\quad\quad\quad\quad\quad\quad\quad\quad\quad\quad\quad\quad$ (10-3)

$$\frac{E_{out}(s)}{E_{in}(s)} = \frac{s + \omega_l}{s + \gamma\omega_l} = \frac{s + \omega_l}{\gamma\omega_l(1 + s/\gamma\omega_l)} \quad (10\text{-}4)$$

A further substitution is made using γ as defined in Eq. (10-3) to give the final expression of Eq. (10-4). By examination of the first part of Eq. (10-4) it can be seen that at very low frequencies, where s is essentially zero, the network has a gain of $1/\gamma$; this is shown in Fig. 10-3. Therefore, at low frequencies this network gives an attenuation, and at high frequencies the network has a gain of unity. To provide the system modification to give $\omega_{c_{p_2}}$ as shown in Fig. 10-1, a dc gain of γ would have to be added.

Example 10-1. Calculate values of R_1 and C_1 for a lead network with the following characteristics:

$$\omega_l = 20 \text{ rad/s}$$
$$\gamma = 10$$
$$R_2 = 10 \text{ k}\Omega$$

solution

$$\gamma = 1 + k = 1 + \frac{R_1}{R_2}$$

$$\frac{R_1}{R_2} = \gamma - 1 = 9$$

$$R_1 = 9R_2 = 90 \text{ k}\Omega$$

$$R_1C_1 = \frac{1}{\omega_l} \quad \text{or} \quad C_1 = \frac{1}{R_1\omega_l}$$

$$C_1 = \frac{1}{90 \times 10^3 \times 20} = 0.556 \text{ }\mu\text{F}$$

10-2. lead network servo position loop

Figure 10-4 shows a dc servo using a lead network. Equation (10-5) states the open-loop gain of this system. Equation (10-6) states that the gain at ω_{cp} is essentially unity.

$$G_p(s) = \frac{K_{\text{trans}}K_{AVP}K_A K_{mTE}(s + \omega_l)}{(s + \gamma\omega_l)(J_m s + B_m)sN}$$

$$= \frac{K_{\text{trans}}K_{AVP}K_A K_{mTE}(s + \omega_l)}{J_m(s + \omega_m)(s + \gamma\omega_l)sN} \tag{10-5}$$

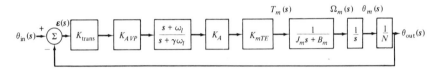

Figure 10-4. Block diagram of lead network servo.

For $\omega_l < \omega_{cp} < \gamma\omega_l$, $\omega_{cp} > \omega_m$:

$$1 \approx |G_p(j\omega_{cp})| = \left| \frac{K_{\text{trans}}K_{AVP}K_A K_{mTE}(j\omega_{cp} + \omega_l)}{J_m(j\omega_{cp} + \omega_m)(j\omega_{cp} + \gamma\omega_l)j\omega_{cp}N} \right|$$

$$\approx \frac{K_{\text{trans}}K_{AVP}K_A K_{mTE}\omega_{cp}}{J_m\omega_{cp}\gamma\omega_l\omega_{cp}N}$$

$$= \frac{K_{\text{trans}}K_{AVP}K_A K_{mTE}}{J_m\omega_{cp}\gamma\omega_l N} \tag{10-6}$$

$$\omega_{cp} \approx \frac{K_{\text{trans}}K_{AVP}K_A K_{mTE}}{J_m\gamma\omega_l N} \tag{10-7}$$

Inversion of Eq. (10-6) provides Eq. (10-7), which allows determination of the gain crossover frequency in terms of the constants of the servo. In Eq. (10-7), note that all the constants are known with the exception of K_{AVP}, which is the position loop dc gain. Equation (10-8) is a somewhat simpler version of the gain expression.

$$G_p(s) = \frac{K_{\text{trans}}K_{AVP}K_A K_{mTE}(s + \omega_l)}{J_m Ns(s + \omega_m)(s + \gamma\omega_l)} \tag{10-8}$$

$$G_p(s) = \frac{\gamma\omega_l\omega_{cp}(s + \omega_l)}{s(s + \omega_m)(s + \gamma\omega_l)} = \frac{\omega_{cp}(s + \omega_l)}{s(s + \omega_m)(1 + s/\gamma\omega_l)} \tag{10-9}$$

Equation (10-9) gives the open-loop gain in terms of ω_{cp}. It is noted that in the "ω_{cp}" form all poles and zeros below ω_{cp} are in $s + \omega_x$ form and those above ω_{cp} are in $1 + s/\omega_x$ form.

Figure 10-5 shows the Bode plot of the open-loop gain of this lead net-

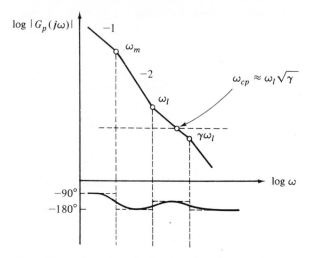

Figure 10-5. Open-loop bode plot of lead network servo.

work servo. Note that the gain crossover frequency ω_{cp} is set at the geometric mean between ω_l and $\gamma\omega_l$. Analysis of this Bode plot indicates that the system is conditionally stable (i.e., either an increase in gain or a decrease in gain causes the system to become unstable). Therefore care must be exercised in those cases where the loop gain may vary. An example of a case where the gain may vary appreciably is in an automatic tracking system that depends on radio frequency (RF) equipment for the angular error signal. If this RF equipment has a reduction in gain due to changes in antenna or feed characteristics, then the servo system may go unstable.

10-3. lead network servo torque stiffness

The solution for the torque error gain of this lead network servo results directly from Eq. (10-10) and is given in Eq. (10-11).

$$
\frac{T_m(s)}{\epsilon(s)} = K_{\text{trans}}K_{AVP}K_A K_{mTE}\frac{(s + \omega_l)}{(s + \gamma\omega_l)}
$$

$$
= J_m\gamma\omega_l N\omega_{cp}\frac{(s + \omega_l)}{(s + \gamma\omega_l)} \tag{10-10}
$$

$$
\frac{\theta_{\text{out}}(s)}{T_m(s)} = \frac{s + \gamma\omega_l}{J\gamma\omega_l N\omega_{cp}(s + \omega_l)}G'_p(s)
$$

$$\approx \frac{1 + s/\gamma\omega_l}{JN\omega_{cp}(s + \omega_l)(1 + s/\omega_{cp})} \tag{10-11}$$

$$\frac{\theta_{\text{out}}(j0)}{T_m(j0)} = \frac{\gamma\omega_l}{J\gamma\omega_l N\omega_{cp}\omega_l} = \frac{1}{JN\omega_{cp}\omega_l} \tag{10-12}$$

$$\text{Error at load} = \frac{1}{J_m N^2\omega_{cp}\omega_l} = \frac{1}{J_{\text{at load}}\omega_{cp}\omega_l} \tag{10-13}$$

If Eq. (10-11) is solved for low frequencies by allowing s to approach zero, then Eq. (10-12) results, which gives the torque error gain at dc. Equation (10-13) expresses this error reflected to the load.

Figure 10-6 shows the Bode plot of the output error due to a torque dis-

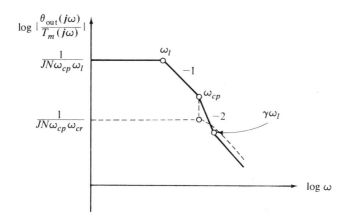

Figure 10-6.   Bode plot of torque error gain of lead network servo and tachometer servo (dashed).

turbance. It can be seen that the stiffness at zero frequency or dc is its worst value; therefore the error is maximum at dc and then falls off, starting at the lead network frequency ω_l. For comparison, the Bode plot of a tachometer-stabilized servo is shown, dashed, in Fig. 10-6. It may be seen that the tachometer servo has a lower error at dc (i.e., a greater stiffness at dc) than does the lead network servo, because ω_{cr} can be greater than ω_l (ω_{cr} is comparable to $\gamma\omega_l$). A comparison of the stiffness of these two servo types is given in Eqs. (10-14) and (10-15).

$$K_{T(\text{lead network})} = J\omega_{cp}\omega_l \qquad (\omega_l < \omega_{cp}) \tag{10-14}$$

$$K_{T(\text{tach loop})} = J\omega_{cp}\omega_{cr} \qquad (\omega_{cr} > \omega_{cp}) \tag{10-15}$$

10-4. lead network servo velocity constant

The velocity constant (K_v) of a lead network servo may be calculated in Eq. (10-16) using the final value theorem. The denominator of Eq. (10-16), P, is solved in Eq. (10-17).

$$K_v = \lim_{s \to 0} \frac{1}{(s\{(1/s^2)1/[1 + G(s)]\})} = \frac{1}{P} \tag{10-16}$$

$$P = \lim_{s \to 0} \left[\frac{1}{s} \times \frac{1}{1 + G(s)} \right]$$

$$= \lim_{s \to 0} \frac{1}{s\{1 + \omega_{cp}(s + \omega_l)/[s(s + \omega_m)(1 + s/\gamma\omega_l)]\}}$$

$$= \lim_{s \to 0} \frac{s(s + \omega_m)(1 + s/\gamma\omega_l)}{s[s(s + \omega_m)(1 + s/\gamma\omega_l) + \omega_{cp}(s + \omega_l)]}$$

$$= \lim_{s \to 0} \frac{(s + \omega_m)(1 + s/\gamma\omega_l)}{s(s + \omega_m)(1 + s/\gamma\omega_l) + \omega_{cp}(s + \omega_l)}$$

$$= \frac{\omega_m}{\omega_{cp}\omega_l} \tag{10-17}$$

$$K_v = \frac{1}{P} = \omega_{cp}\left(\frac{\omega_l}{\omega_m}\right) \tag{10-18}$$

From this, K_v is expressed in Eq. (10-18). Note that the velocity constant is the gain crossover frequency times the ratio of the lead network lead frequency to the motor break frequency. Recall that in a simple servo the velocity constant is just the gain crossover frequency; in the case of a lead network there is an improvement in K_v over a simple servo by the ratio of the lead network lead frequency to the motor break frequency times the ratio of the improved ω_{cp} to the simple servo ω_{cp}.

10-5. lead network servo design example

In Chapter 6, a simple servo was designed using a motor with an ω_m of 15.6 rad/s and a power amplifier with an upper break frequency of 600 rad/s. Using the same motor in a lead network servo, it is reasonable to assume the lag frequency of the lead network ($\gamma\omega_l$) to be 500 rad/s. For an assumed γ of 10, $\omega_l = 50$ rad/s. The Bode plot for this system is shown in Fig. 10-7.

Figure 10-8 shows the lead network and its parameter calculations. The resulting values of the network components are given for the above case.

Figure 10-9 gives the block-diagram representation for this lead network system, and Eq. (10-19) expresses the open-loop gain of this system. Equation (10-20) is the expression for the gain crossover frequency, and Eq. (10-21) states the value of the position loop voltage gain K_{AVP}.

$$G_p(s) = \frac{K_{trans}K_{AVP}K_AK_{mTE}}{NJ_m} \times \frac{(s + \omega_l)}{s(s + \omega_m)(s + \gamma\omega_l)}$$

$$= \frac{K_{trans}K_{AVP}K_AK_{mTE}}{NJ_m\gamma\omega_l} \times \frac{s + \omega_l}{s(s + \omega_m)(1 + s/\gamma\omega_l)} \tag{10-19}$$

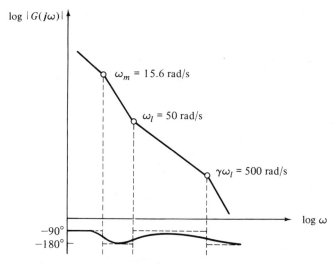

Figure 10-7.   Bode plot of lead network servo (open loop).

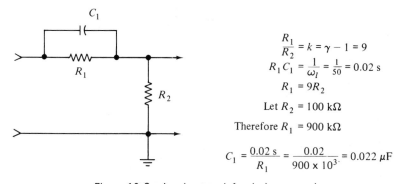

Figure 10-8.   Lead network for design example.

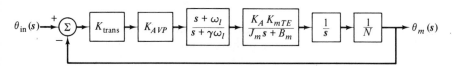

Figure 10-9.   Block diagram of lead network servo.

$$\omega_{cp} = \frac{K_{trans}K_{AVP}K_A K_{mTE}}{NJ_m\gamma\omega_l} \tag{10-20}$$

$$K_{AVP} = \frac{NJ_m\gamma\omega_l\omega_{cp}}{K_{trans}K_A K_{mTE}} \tag{10-21}$$

Figure 10-10 shows the characteristic break frequencies of this system

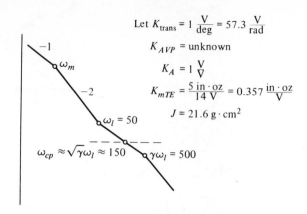

$$\text{Let } K_{\text{trans}} = 1 \frac{V}{\text{deg}} = 57.3 \frac{V}{\text{rad}}$$

$$K_{AVP} = \text{unknown}$$

$$K_A = 1 \frac{V}{V}$$

$$K_{mTE} = \frac{5 \text{ in} \cdot \text{oz}}{14 \text{ V}} = 0.357 \frac{\text{in} \cdot \text{oz}}{V}$$

$$J = 21.6 \text{ g} \cdot \text{cm}^2$$

Figure 10-10.   Bode plot of lead network servo design example.

and the basic system parameters. The position loop voltage gain K_{AVP} is calculated in Eq. (10-22) as 114. Figure 10-11 is the final system diagram.

$$
\begin{aligned}
K_{AVP} &= \frac{NJ_m\gamma\omega_l\omega_{cp}}{K_{\text{trans}}K_AK_{mTE}} = \frac{100 \times 21.5 \times 500 \times 150 (\text{g}\cdot\text{cm}^2)(\text{rad/s})(\text{rad/s})}{57.3 \times 1 \times 0.357 (\text{V/rad})(\text{V/V})(\text{in}\cdot\text{oz/V})} \\
&\quad \times \frac{(\text{in}\cdot\text{oz/g}\cdot\text{cm}^2)}{(70{,}000 \text{ rad}\cdot\text{s}^2)} \\
&= \frac{162 \times 10^6}{20.4 \times 70{,}000} = 114 \frac{V}{V}
\end{aligned}
\tag{10-22}
$$

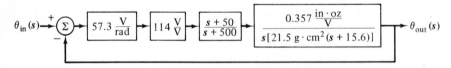

Figure 10-11.   Block diagram of lead network servo design example.

Equation (10-23) is the open-loop gain expression for the system. Equation (10-24) gives the open-loop gain at the gain crossover frequency.

$$
\begin{aligned}
G(s) &= \frac{57.3 \text{ V/rad}}{100} \times \frac{114(s + 50)}{(s + 500)} \times \frac{0.357 \text{ in}\cdot\text{oz/V}}{s[21.6 \text{ g}\cdot\text{cm}^2(s + 15.6)]} \\
&\quad \times \frac{70{,}000 \text{ rad/s}^2}{\text{in}\cdot\text{oz/g}\cdot\text{cm}^2} \\
&= \frac{57.3 \times 114 \times 0.357 \times 70{,}000}{21.6 \times 100} \times \frac{s + 50}{s(s + 500)(s + 15.6)} \\
&= \frac{75{,}000(s + 50)}{s(s + 500)(s + 15.6)} = \frac{150(s + 50)}{s(s + 15.6)(1 + s/500)}
\end{aligned}
\tag{10-23}
$$

$$G(j150) = \frac{150(j150 + 50)}{(j150)(j150 + 15.6)(1 + j150/500)}$$

$$= \frac{150(1 + 50/j150)}{(j150 + 15.6)(1 + j150/500)} = \frac{150(1 - j\frac{1}{3})}{(15.6 + j150)(1 + j0.3)}$$

$$= \frac{(1 - j\frac{1}{3})}{(j + 15.6/150)(1 + j0.3)} = \frac{1 - j\frac{1}{3}}{j(1 - j0.104)(1 + j0.3)}$$

$$= \frac{1.05\angle -18.4°}{j(1\angle -6°)(1.045\angle +16.7°)} = 1.01\angle -119.1° \qquad (10\text{-}24)$$

Equation (10-24) indicates that the gain is essentially unity, with a phase lag of approximately 119° (leaving a safe 61° phase margin). Equation (10-25) expresses the velocity constant, which is determined as 481 s^{-1}.

$$K_v = \omega_{cp} \times \frac{\omega_l}{\omega_m} = 150 \times \frac{50}{15.6} = 481 \text{ s}^{-1} \qquad (10\text{-}25)$$

$$K_v \text{ Error} = \frac{10°/\text{s}}{480 \text{ s}^{-1}} = 0.208° \approx 0.02° \qquad (10\text{-}26)$$

The velocity constant error is expressed in Eq. (10-26) as 0.02° for a 10°/s input.

Bridged-T networks act as lead networks for ac servo systems (suppressed carrier systems), and make it possible to improve the performance without demodulation. These networks, unfortunately, are sensitive to carrier frequency variations and also reduce the signal-to-noise ratio; for these reasons the viscous coupled inertial damped (VCID) type of servo (Section 10-6) is an easier and more dependable way to improve the performance of small ac servos; for larger servos, tachometer stabilization and the use of integral networks with appropriate demodulation and remodulation is usually recommended.

10-6. introduction to viscous coupled inertial damped servos

The advantages of *viscous coupled inertial damped* (VCID) *servos*, sometimes called *acceleration damped servos*, are that the complete compensation is accomplished by means of a mechanical component attached to the motor; no electrical circuitry is required other than the motor drive and loop gain amplifiers. Before investigating the characteristics of VCID servos, it is desirable to review the performance of a simple servomotor.

10-7. servomotors and simple servos

Figure 10-12 shows the conceptual loop of a dc motor. The solution of this loop in Eq. (10-27) gives the correct known characteristic of the dc servo motor.

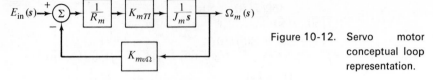

Figure 10-12. Servo motor conceptual loop representation.

$$\frac{\Omega_m(s)}{E_{in}(s)} = \frac{K_{mTI}/R_m J_m s}{1 + K_{mTI}K_{mv\Omega}/R_m J_m s} = \frac{K_{mTI}}{R_m J_m s + K_{mTI}K_{mv\Omega}}$$

$$= \frac{K_{mTI}/R_m}{J_m(s + K_{mTI}K_{mv\Omega}/R_m J_m)} = \frac{K_{mTE}}{J_m(s + \omega_m)}$$

$$= \frac{K_{mTE}}{J_m s + B_m} \tag{10-27}$$

Note that in the denominator of the final part of Eq. (10-27) there are two terms, one involving inertia and the second involving viscous damping. Analysis of Fig. 10-13 provides the transfer function of Eq. (10-30); similar

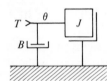

Figure 10-13. Inertia with viscous damping.

to Eq. (10-27), it also has an inertia and a damping term in the denominator.

$$B_m = J_m \omega_m \qquad \left(\omega_m = \frac{B_m}{J_m}\right) \tag{10-28}$$

$$T = B\dot{\theta} + J\ddot{\theta} \longrightarrow Bs\theta(s) + Js^2\theta(s)$$
$$= B\Omega(s) + Js\Omega(s) = (Js + B)\Omega(s) \tag{10-29}$$

$$\frac{\Omega(s)}{T(s)} = \frac{1}{Js + B} \tag{10-30}$$

Examination of Fig. 10-13 indicates, for a constant torque input, that the inertia and damper accelerate until the viscous damping force is exactly equal to the applied torque. Thus there is a certain maximum speed associated with any given torque applied to this simple mechanical system. The same is true in a dc motor in that for a given voltage applied to the motor, a certain maximum torque results. Consequently, there is a certain maximum unloaded speed associated with that particular torque and thus with that particular voltage. The characteristic of a motor of this type is shown in Eq. (10-31),

$$T(t) = K_{mTE}[e_m(t) - K_{mv\Omega}\Omega_m(t)] \tag{10-31}$$

and demonstrated graphically in Fig. 10-14 (see also Fig. 5-1). It is therefore possible to represent a simple motor as shown in Fig. 10-15, similar to its equivalent shown in Fig. 10-13. The transfer function of Eq. (10-32), there-

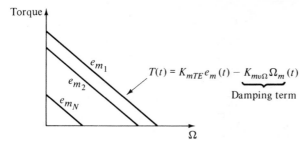

Figure 10-14.   dc motor torque-speed characteristic.

Figure 10-15.   Alternate representation of servo motor.

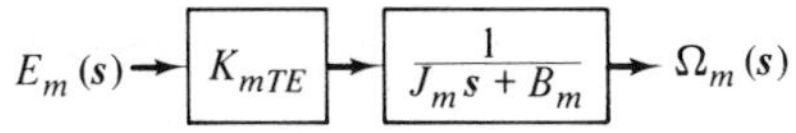

$$E_m(s) \rightarrow \boxed{K_{mTE}} \rightarrow \boxed{\frac{1}{J_m s + B_m}} \rightarrow \Omega_m(s)$$

fore, is a proper representation of the motor characteristic. Figure 10-16 shows this model of a motor in a simple servo loop.

$$\frac{\Omega_m(s)}{E_m(s)} = \frac{K_{mTE}}{J_m s + B_m} = \frac{K_{mTE}}{J_m(s + \omega_m)} \qquad (10\text{-}32)$$

$$G_p(s) = \frac{K_{trans}K_A K_{mTE}}{J_m s(s + \omega_m)} \qquad (10\text{-}33)$$

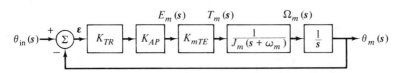

Figure 10-16.   Block diagram of "simple" servo.

Equation (10-33) is the open-loop gain of this simple servo system. Equation (10-34) is a statement of the loop gain at the gain crossover frequency. Inversion of Eq. (10-34) allows the solution for ω_{cp} as given in Eq. (10-35).

$$\text{for } \omega_{cp} < \omega_m \qquad 1 = \frac{K_{trans}K_A K_{mTE}}{J_m \omega_{cp} \omega_m} \qquad (10\text{-}34)$$

or

$$\omega_{cp} = \frac{K_{trans}K_A K_{mTE}}{J_m \omega_m} \qquad (10\text{-}35)$$

but

$$\omega_m = \frac{B_m}{J_m} \qquad (10\text{-}36)$$

Therefore

$$\omega_{cp} = \frac{K_{trans}K_A K_{mTE}}{B_m} \qquad (10\text{-}37)$$

By substituting Eq. (10-36), the expression for the motor break frequency, it is possible to represent the gain crossover frequency ω_{cp} as given in Eq. (10-37). Solving this equation for the three constant gain terms shown in Fig. 10-16 results in Eq. (10-38); substituting this equivalent into the diagram of Fig. 10-16 gives the new diagram of Fig. 10-17, which is the simplified

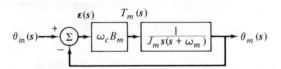

Figure 10-17.   Alternative block diagram of "simple" servo.

representation of this loop in terms of the gain crossover frequency and the motor break frequency.

$$K_{\text{trans}}\, K_A\, K_{mTE} = \omega_{cp} B_m \tag{10-38}$$

Equation (10-39) solves for an equivalent motor form; substituting this result gives Fig. 10-18.

$$\frac{1}{J_m s(s + \omega_m)} = \frac{1}{J_m \omega_m s(1 + s/\omega_m)} = \frac{1}{B_m s(1 + s/\omega_m)} \tag{10-39}$$

$$T_m(s) = \theta_{\text{in}}(s)\omega_{cp} B_m \tag{10-40}$$

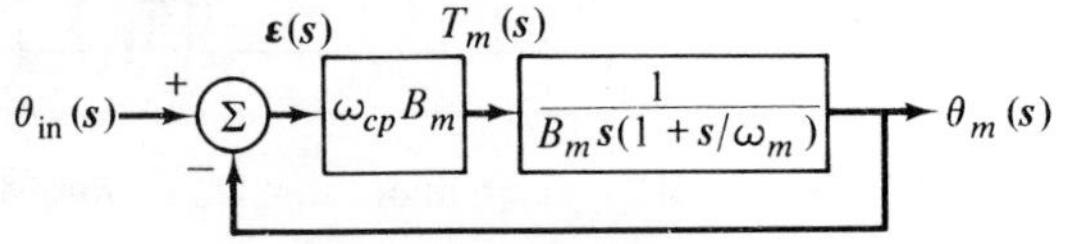

$$\theta_{\text{in}}(s) \xrightarrow{\;+\;} \boxed{\Sigma} \xrightarrow{\;\varepsilon(s)\;} \boxed{\omega_{cp} B_m} \xrightarrow{T_m(s)} \boxed{\frac{1}{B_m s(1 + s/\omega_m)}} \longrightarrow \theta_m(s)$$

Figure 10-18.   Modified alternative block diagram of "simple" servo.

But

$$B_m = J_m \omega_m \tag{10-41}$$

or

$$T_m(s) = \theta_{\text{in}}(s)\omega_{cp} J_m \omega_m \tag{10-42}$$

and

$$\theta_{\text{in}}(s) = \frac{T_m(s)}{J_m \omega_{cp} \omega_m} \tag{10-43}$$

$$\theta_m(s) = \theta_{\text{in}}(s)G_p'(s) = \frac{T_{\text{dist}}(s)}{J_m \omega_{cp}\omega_m(1 + s/\omega_{cp})} \tag{10-44}$$

Equations (10-40) through (10-43) lead to the torque error expression of Eq. (10-44). The torque error gain is shown in the Bode plot of Fig. 10-19.

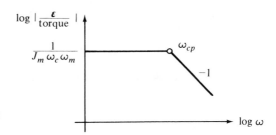

Figure 10-19.   Torque error gain
             of simple servo.

10-8. viscous coupled inertial dampers

Figure 10-20 shows how a viscous coupled inertial damper (VCID) is
added to a simple servo. In effect, a mechanical damping device is coupled to
the motor load shaft. Normally, dampers are built as part of the motor
assembly and the damper itself is coupled directly to the motor shaft. Figure
10-21 shows the mechanical schematic of a motor/damper system. The system

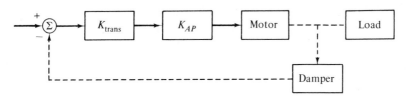

Figure 10-20.   VCID compensated servo.

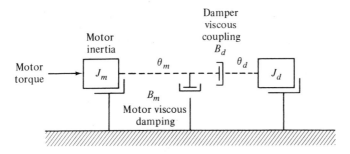

Figure 10-21.   Equivalent block diagram of motor and VCID.

shown consists of the motor inertia J_m and its associated damping B_m (as
just discussed) viscously coupled to the damper inertia J_d. This viscous coupling, which couples the damper inertia to the motor inertia, is usually a
magnetic coupling; in the past, fluid coupling was used. Most manufacturers
of small instrument servo motors have integral motor/damper units available.

Equations (10-45) and (10-46) are the simultaneous torque equations for the system of Fig. 10-21. Equation (10-47) is an inversion of Eq. (10-46).

$$T_m(s) = \theta_m(s)(J_m s^2 + B_m s) + [\theta_m(s) - \theta_d(s)]sB_d \qquad (10\text{-}45)$$

$$[\theta_m(s) - \theta_d(s)]sB_d = J_d\theta_d(s)s^2 \qquad (10\text{-}46)$$

or

$$\theta_m(s)B_d s = (J_d s^2 + B_d s)\theta_d(s) \qquad (10\text{-}47)$$

Equations (10-48) and (10-49) are the simultaneous equations derived from the previous ones. Using Cramer's rule, Eq. (10-50) is written as a solution for this set of simultaneous equations.

$$T_m(s) = \theta_m(s)(J_m s^2 + B_m s + B_d s) + \theta_d(s)(-B_d s) \qquad (10\text{-}48)$$

$$0 = \theta_m(s)(-B_d s) + \theta_d(s)(J_d s^2 + B_d s) \qquad (10\text{-}49)$$

$$
\begin{aligned}
\theta_m(s) &= \frac{T_m(s)(J_d s^2 + B_d s)}{(J_m s^2 + B_m s + B_d s)(J_d s^2 + B_d s) - (B_d s)^2} \\[2mm]
&= \frac{T_m(s)}{s[J_m s + B_m + B_d - B_d/(1 + sJ_d/B_d)]} \\[2mm]
&= \frac{T_m(s)[(J_d/B_d)s + 1]}{s\{J_m s[(J_d/B_d)s + 1] + (B_m + B_d)[(J_d/B_d)s + 1] - B_d\}} \\[2mm]
&= \frac{T_m(s)[(J_d/B_d)s + 1]}{s\{(J_m J_d/B_d)s^2 + J_m s + [(B_m + B_d)J_d/B_d]s + B_m + B_d - B_d\}} \\[2mm]
&= \frac{T_m(s)[(J_d/B_d)s + 1]}{B_m s\{(J_m J_d/B_d B_m)s^2 + (J_m/B_m)s + [(B_m + B_d)J_d/B_m B_d]s + 1\}}
\end{aligned}
$$
$$\qquad (10\text{-}50)$$

Substitution of Eqs. (10-51) and (10-52) results in Eq. (10-53). Equation (10-54) takes part of the denominator of Eq. (10-53) and puts it in a simpler form using the new parameter, ψ, which is defined in Eq. (10-55). Equation (10-56) restates Eq. (10-53) using the new parameter ψ.

$$\omega_m = \frac{B_m}{J_m} \qquad (10\text{-}51)$$

$$\omega_d = \frac{B_d}{J_d} \qquad (10\text{-}52)$$

$$
\begin{aligned}
\theta_m(s) &= \frac{T_m(s)(1 + s/\omega_d)}{B_m s[(s^2/\omega_d\omega_m) + (s/\omega_m) + (1 + B_d/B_m)(s/\omega_d) + 1]} \\[2mm]
&= \frac{T_m(s)(1 + s/\omega_d)}{(B_m s/\omega_d\omega_m)[s^2 + s\omega_d + s\omega_m + s(B_d/B_m)\omega_m + \omega_d\omega_m]}
\end{aligned}
$$
$$\qquad (10\text{-}53)$$

$$s\omega_d + s\frac{B_d}{B_m}\omega_m = s\frac{B_d}{J_d} + s\frac{B_d}{B_m} \times \frac{B_m}{J_m} = s\frac{B_d}{J_d} + s\frac{B_d}{J_m}$$

$$= sB_d\left(\frac{1}{J_d} + \frac{1}{J_m}\right) = sB_d\left(\frac{J_m + J_d}{J_m J_d}\right)$$

$$= \frac{sB_d}{J_d}\left(\frac{J_m + J_d}{J_m}\right) = s\omega_d\left(\frac{J_m + J_d}{J_m}\right)$$

$$= s\omega_d\left(1 + \frac{J_d}{J_m}\right) = \psi s\omega_d \tag{10-54}$$

where $\quad \psi = \dfrac{J_m + J_d}{J_m} = 1 + \dfrac{J_d}{J_m}$ $\hfill$ (10-55)

$$\theta_m(s) = \frac{T_m(s)(1 + s/\omega_d)}{(B_m s/\omega_d \omega_m)[s^2 + s\omega_m + \psi s\omega_d + \omega_d \omega_m]}$$

$$= \frac{T_m(s)(1 + s/\omega_d)}{(B_m s/\omega_d \omega_m)[s^2 + (\omega_d \psi + \omega_m)s + \omega_d \omega_m]} \tag{10-56}$$

Equation (10-57) describes a hypothetical situation where two poles are assumed at $\psi\omega_d$ and at ω_m/ψ; this convenient assumption by George Biernson* greatly simplifies the analysis. Note that the resulting quadratic is very close to that in the bracketed term in the denominator of Eq. (10-56).

$$(s + \psi\omega_d)\left(s + \frac{\omega_m}{\psi}\right) = s^2 + \left(\omega_d\psi + \frac{\omega_m}{\psi}\right)s + \omega_m\omega_d \tag{10-57}$$

Since the term $\psi\omega_d$ is much larger than ω_m (considering that ω_d is already larger than ω_m, and ψ must be appreciably greater than unity for the inertial damper to be of any great value), it follows that the $\psi\omega_d$ term is much larger than ω_m. Therefore, very little error results if ω_m is replaced by ω_m/ψ; this approximation is expressed in Eq. (10-58).

$$s^2 + (\omega_d\psi + \omega_m)s + \omega_m\omega_d \approx (s + \psi\omega_d)\left(s + \frac{\omega_m}{\psi}\right)$$

$$\text{for } \psi\omega_d \gg \omega_m, \ \omega_d > \omega_m \tag{10-58}$$

The net effect of this assumption is that the resulting pole positions are slightly inaccurate; but the error is insignificant and the resulting mathematical simplicity makes the substitution desirable. Once the substitution is made, Eq. (10-59) may be written; the system poles are then approximately at the two locations ω_m/ψ and $\psi\omega_d$. A Bode plot for this gain characteristic is given in Fig. 10-22.

---

* In his excellent paper, "Comparison Of Lead Network, Tachometer, and Damper Stabilization for Electric Servos," *IRE Transactions on Automatic Control*, Vol. AC-4, May 1959.

$$\theta_m(s) \approx \frac{T_m(s)(1 + s/\omega_d)}{(B_m s/\omega_d\omega_m)(s + \psi\omega_d)(s + \omega_m/\psi)}$$

$$= \frac{T_m(s)(s + \omega_d)}{J_m s(s + \omega_m/\psi)(s + \psi\omega_d)} \tag{10-59}$$

Observe that the shape of this characteristic (Fig. 10-22) is very similar to

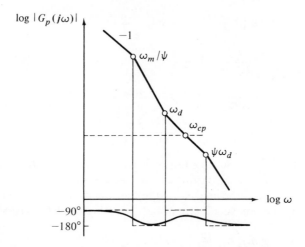

Figure 10-22. Bode plot of open-loop response of VCID servo.

that of the lead network system. The only difference is that the break frequencies are labeled differently. These two systems perform somewhat differently, however, even though their Bode plots are similar, for reasons given below.

10-9. the VCID servo position loop

For stability reasons, it is desirable to have ω_{cp} at the geometric mean between ω_d and $\psi\omega_d$. At this point the greatest variation in open-loop gain may be accommodated for a given degree of instability. The VCID system is conditionally stable, like the lead network system. Equation (10-60) states the gain crossover frequency in terms of the parameter ψ.

$$\omega_{cp} \approx \sqrt{\psi(\omega_d)^2} = \sqrt{\psi}\,\omega_d \tag{10-60}$$

Figure 10-23 shows the overall system, including the load and damper dynamics (in the rightmost block). Figure 10-24 is the VCID mechanical schematic diagram, and Fig. 10-25 is the VCID open-loop gain Bode plot. One effect of a damper that may be seen from the Bode plot is that it lowers the motor break frequency by ψ (the ratio of the total new inertia to the iner-

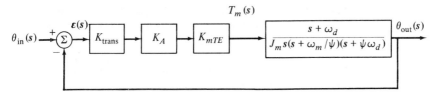

Figure 10-23.   Simplified block diagram of VCID servo.

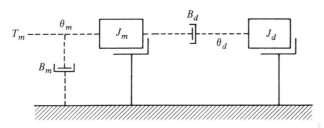

Figure 10-24.   Mechanical equivalent of motor and VCID.

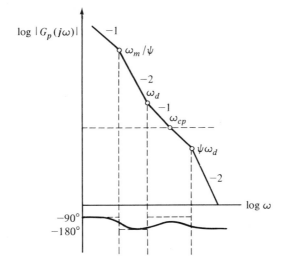

Figure 10-25.   Bode plot of the open-loop gain of a
VCID servo.

tia of the motor alone), where the "motor inertia" is the actual motor inertia
plus the reflected inertia of the load. Another effect of the damper is to provide a lead term which makes it possible to have a gain crossover frequency
appreciably above ω_m. The resulting VCID servo has an excellent velocity
constant K_v; the stiffness is also greatly improved over that of the simple

servo system, but at the cost of acceleration because of the added damper inertia. The primary application of VCID servos is in small ac instrument servos (mechanical power of 10 W or less) having relatively low inertia.

Example 10-2. Consider the Vernitron 08D4B-CCO-A1, VCID servo motor, which has the following specifications:

$$\begin{aligned}
T_{max} &= 0.3 \text{ in} \cdot \text{oz} \\
\Omega_{max} &= 6300 \text{ rpm} \\
J_{rotor} &= 0.48 \text{ g} \cdot \text{cm}^2 \\
J_d &= 5.0 \text{ g} \cdot \text{cm}^2 \\
B_d &= 200 \frac{\text{dyne} \cdot \text{cm}}{\text{rad/s}} \\
\omega_1 &= 6.0 \text{ rad/s} \\
\omega_2 &= 40 \text{ rad/s} \\
\omega_3 &= 500 \text{ rad/s} \\
\text{Max } K_v &= 3000 \text{ s}^{-1}
\end{aligned}$$

(a) Does $\omega_2 = \omega_d$?
(b) Solve for ψ.
(c) Does $\omega_3 = \psi\omega_d$?
(d) Solve for ω_m.
(e) Does $\omega_1 = \omega_m/\psi$?
(f) Solve for K_v.

solution

(a) $\omega_d = \dfrac{B_d}{J_d} = 200\dfrac{\text{dyne} \cdot \text{cm/rad/s}}{5 \text{ g} \cdot \text{cm}^2} = 40 \text{ rad/s}$

Therefore $\omega_2 = \omega_d$.

(b) $\psi = 1 + \dfrac{J_d}{J_m} = 1 + \dfrac{5}{0.48} = 11.4$

(c) $\psi\omega_d = 11.4 \times 40 = 456 \text{ rad/s}$

Therefore $\omega_3 \neq \psi\omega_d$ (but the manufacturer's data is not greatly different from the calculated value of $\psi\omega_d$).

(d) $\omega_m \approx \dfrac{T_{max}}{\Omega_{max}J_m} = \dfrac{0.3 \text{ in} \cdot \text{oz}}{6300 \text{ rpm}} \times \dfrac{1 \text{ rpm}}{0.105 \text{ rad/s}} \times \dfrac{70{,}000 \ (\text{rad/s}^2)/(\text{in} \cdot \text{oz} /\text{g} \cdot \text{cm}^2)}{0.48 \text{ g} \cdot \text{cm}^2}$

$= 66.1 \text{ rad/s}$

(e) $\dfrac{\omega_m}{\psi} = \dfrac{66.1}{11.4} = 5.8 \text{ rad/s} \approx 6.0 \text{ rad/s}$

Therefore $\omega_1 = \omega_m/\psi$.

(f) $\omega_{cp} = \omega_d\sqrt{\psi} \approx 40\sqrt{11.4} = 135 \text{ rad/s}$

$$K_v = \omega_{cp} \times \dfrac{\omega_d}{\omega_m/\psi} = 135 \times \dfrac{40}{5.8} = 930$$

For $K_v = 3000$,

$$\omega_{cp} = \dfrac{3000}{40/5.8} = 435 \text{ rad/s}$$

which is possible but might be a bit unstable.

10-10. VCID servo performance

Figure 10-26 is the VCID system diagram in transfer-function form. Equation (10-61) states the open-loop gain.

$$G_p(s) = \frac{K_{\text{trans}} K_A K_{mTE}(s + \omega_d)}{J_m s(s + \omega_m/\psi)(s + \psi\omega_d)} \tag{10-61}$$

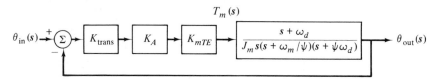

Figure 10-26.   Simplified block diagram of VCID servo.

For

$$\left(\frac{\omega_m}{\psi}\right) < \omega_d < \omega_{cp} < \psi\omega_d \tag{10-62}$$

$$|G_p(j\omega_{cp})| \approx \frac{K_{\text{trans}} K_A K_{mTE}\omega_{cp}}{J_m \omega_{cp}\omega_{cp}\psi\omega_d} = 1 \tag{10-63}$$

Therefore,

$$\omega_{cp} = \frac{K_{\text{trans}} K_A K_{mTE}}{J_m \psi\omega_d} \tag{10-64}$$

$$K_{\text{trans}} K_A K_{mTE} = J_m \psi\omega_d\omega_{cp} \tag{10-65}$$

Equation (10-62) is a statement of the highest acceptable region for the gain crossover frequency ω_{cp}. Equation (10-63) is a solution for the open-loop gain in the region of ω_{cp}. Equation (10-64) is a solution for the gain crossover frequency in terms of the loop gains; Equation (10-65) is an inversion of this equation to provide a simpler expression for the three gain blocks prior to the damper block. Figure 10-27 shows the overall VCID servo block diagram in terms of frequencies.

$$T_m(s) = \epsilon(s)J_m\psi\omega_d\omega_{cp} \tag{10-66}$$

$$\frac{\theta_{\text{out}}(s)}{T_{\text{dist}}(s)} = \frac{1}{J_m\psi\omega_{cp}\omega_d} G'_p(s) \tag{10-67}$$

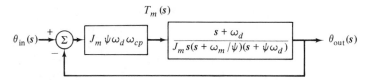

Figure 10-27.   Gain-frequency representation of VCID servo.

$$\frac{\theta_{\text{out}}(s)}{T_{\text{dist}}(s)} \approx \frac{1}{J_m \psi \omega_{cp} \omega_d} \frac{1}{1 + s/\omega_{cp}} \tag{10-68}$$

$$K_{T(\text{dc})} = J_m \psi \omega_{cp} \omega_d \tag{10-69}$$

Equation (10-66) gives the relationship between the output motor torque and a steady system error. Equation (10-67) is the torque disturbance gain of the system. Equation (10-68) is the statement of this torque error gain, and Fig. 10-28 is the Bode plot of this torque error. Equation (10-69) is a statement of

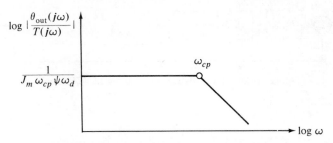

Figure 10-28.   Torque error gain of VCID servo.

the system dc torque stiffness. Observe that the torque stiffness at dc is appreciably greater than that for the simple servo because ψ is greater than 1, and both ω_{cp} and ω_d are greater than ω_m, the simple servo gain crossover frequency.

$$K_v = \frac{1}{\lim\limits_{s \to 0} s\{(1/s^2) \times 1/[1 + G_p(s)]\}} = \frac{1}{P} \tag{10-70}$$

$$
\begin{aligned}
P &= \lim_{s \to 0} \frac{1}{s[1 + G'_p(s)]} = \lim_{s \to 0} \frac{1}{s\{1 + [\omega_{cp}(s + \omega_d)]/[s(s + \omega_m/\psi)(1 + s/\psi\omega_d)]\}} \\
&= \lim_{s \to 0} \frac{s(s + \omega_m/\psi)(1 + s/\psi\omega_d)}{s[s(s + \omega_m/\psi)(1 + s/\psi\omega_d) + \omega_{cp}(s + \omega_d)]} \\
&= \lim_{s \to 0} \frac{(s + \omega_m/\psi)(1 + s/\psi\omega_d)}{s(s + \omega_m/\psi)(1 + s/\psi\omega_d) + \omega_{cp}(s + \omega_d)} \\
&= \frac{\omega_m/\psi}{\omega_{cp}\omega_d} = \frac{\omega_m}{\psi\omega_{cp}\omega_d} \tag{10-71}
\end{aligned}
$$

$$K_v = \psi\omega_{cp}\left(\frac{\omega_d}{\omega_m}\right) = \omega_{cp}\left(\frac{\psi\omega_d}{\omega_m}\right) = \frac{(\omega_d)^2 \psi^{3/2}}{\omega_m} \tag{10-72}$$

Equations (10-70), (10-71), and (10-72) solve for the velocity constant K_v. Figure 10-29 shows the graphical interpretation of the velocity constant; it is equal in value to the frequency of the intersection of the extension of the low-frequency -1 slope with the unity gain axis. This graphical technique for determining the velocity constant is valid for any of the servo configurations discussed in this book.

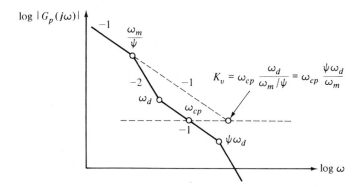

Figure 10-29.   VCID open-loop bode plot showing graphical interpretation of K_v.

Example 10-3. Given a VCID servomotor with $\omega_m = 7$ Hz, $J_m = 1.45$ g·cm²,
$J_d = 20$ g·cm², and $\omega_d = 1.5$ Hz.
(a) Calculate K_v.
(b) How much does K_v change if a 4000 g·cm² load is coupled to the motor shaft
through a 100:1 gear reduction?

solution

(a) $\psi = 1 + \dfrac{20}{1.45} = 14.8$

$\dfrac{\omega_m}{\psi} = \dfrac{7}{14.8} = 0.473$ Hz ≈ 3 rad/s

$\omega_d = 1.5$ Hz $= 9.4$ rad/s

$\psi\omega_d = 9.4 \times 14.8 = 139$ rad/s

$\omega_{cp} = \omega_d\sqrt{\psi} = 9.4\sqrt{14.8} = 36.2$ rad/s

$K_v = \omega_{cp}\left(\dfrac{\omega_d}{\omega_m/\psi}\right) = 36.2 \times \dfrac{9.4}{3} = 113.4$ s⁻¹

(b) $J_{\text{reflected}} = \dfrac{4000}{(100)^2} = 0.4$ g·cm²

$K_{v1} = \omega_{cp1}\dfrac{\omega_{d_1}\psi_1}{\omega_{m_1}} = \sqrt{\psi_1}\,\omega_{d_1}\dfrac{\omega_{d_1}\psi_1}{\omega_{m_1}} = \psi_1^{3/2}\dfrac{(\omega_{d_1})^2}{\omega_{m_1}}$

$\psi = 1 + \dfrac{J_d}{J_m} = \dfrac{J_m + J_d}{J_m}$

$\omega_m = \dfrac{T_{\max}}{J_m\Omega_{\max}}$

$\dfrac{\omega_{m_1}}{\omega_{m_2}} = \dfrac{J_{m_2}}{J_{m_1}}$

$\dfrac{K_{v_2}}{K_{v_1}} = \left(\dfrac{\psi_2}{\psi_1}\right)^{3/2}\left(\dfrac{\omega_{m_1}}{\omega_{m_2}}\right) = \left(\dfrac{1 + 20/1.85}{14.8}\right)^{3/2}\left(\dfrac{1.85}{1.45}\right) = \left(\dfrac{11.8}{14.8}\right)^{3/2}1.275$

$\quad = (0.797)^{3/2} \times 1.275 = 0.712 \times 1.275 = 0.908$

$K_{v_2} = 113.4 \times 0.908 = 103$ s⁻¹

10-11. summary

Lead network servos have excellent velocity constants, even greater than for tachometer-stabilized servos in many cases; the stiffness, however, is not as high as for a tachometer-stabilized servo. The velocity constant cannot be increased without limit, because there are limitations to $\gamma\omega_l$ and ω_l for stability reasons. However, by lowering ω_m, the velocity constant may be increased; ω_m may be lowered either by increasing the armature circuit resistance of a dc motor or by increasing the inertia. Either of these changes results in system losses; increasing inertia results in loss of peak acceleration capability. An increase in the armature circuit resistance results in less effective power output of the motor for a given power amplifier capability. (Armature circuit resistance is also increased by using a "constant current source" which has essentially infinite output impedance; this results in ω_m approaching zero and K_v approaching infinity.) The greatest advantage of lead network servos is that they are simple; they find many applications where simplicity is desired. They are used primarily with dc servos.

Viscous coupled inertial dampers (VCIDs) provide a convenient mechanical means of improving the performance of servomotors in position servos. The effect of the damper is to lower the motor break frequency by adding inertia and to add a lead (reduction in phase lag) due to the damper viscous coupling. Excellent K_v and stiffness are obtained at the cost of acceleration capability. The primary use of VCIDs is for ac instrument servos having low inertia.

problems

10-1. Design a lead network with a lead frequency of 6 Hz and a lag frequency of 54 Hz; use a 0.5-μF capacitor. Record the gain and phase at 80, 100, 120, 150, and 200 rad/s.

10-2. Select ω_{cp} for a lead network servo using the lead network of Problem 10-1 with $\omega_m = 3$ Hz and $\omega_e = 70$ Hz. Using a Nichols chart, estimate M_p and determine $G'(j\omega_{cp})$ by plotting the five frequencies of Problem 10-1.

10-3. Given a Kearfott R1310-2B VCID servo motor with the following characteristics:

> First lag frequency: 0.3 Hz
> Lead frequency: 1.2 Hz
> Second lag frequency: 28 Hz
> Find (a) a safe ω_{cp}, and (b) K_v.

10-4. Using the VCID motor of Example 10-3 (Vernitron 08D4B-CCO-A1), for a reflected load inertia of 0.3 g·cm² through a 10:1 gear train, find (a) the safest ω_{cp}, (b) K_v, and (c) K_T referred to the output shaft. (Use the manufacturers' data as much as possible.)

11

resonance, limits on ω $_{cp}$;
scaling, saturation, and
tracking systems

Previous chapters assumed certain limiting factors which restricted loop
bandwidths; these restrictions are now explored. In some cases these limitations are evident: namely, a position loop limited by the motor break frequency or possibly a rate loop limited by an electrical break frequency due
to a power amplifier or inductance in the motor. These limitations, however,
are not always the restricting ones; in larger systems, other factors may
limit the bandwidth. In such larger systems, because of these other limitations, it is often possible to estimate the limiting frequencies and from
these to determine the loop bandwidths. Knowing the bandwidths, the velocity constant and stiffness may be calculated.

11-1. analysis of load resonance

Resonance of a mechanical load often is the factor that limits the rate
loop or position loop bandwidth of power servos. Beginning simply, the
position loop bandwidth of a lead network servo with resonant load is examined. The motor and load part of this system are shown in Fig. 11-1. The
motor in this case is assumed to be a torque source by neglecting the damping
associated with the motor.

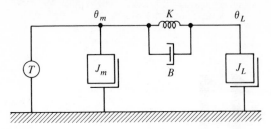

Figure 11-1. Motor mechanically coupled to resonant load.

$$T(s) = J_m\theta_m(s)s^2 + [\theta_m(s) - \theta_L(s)](Bs + K) \qquad (11\text{-}1)$$

$$[\theta_m(s) - \theta_L(s)](Bs + K) = J_L\theta_L(s)s^2 \qquad (11\text{-}2)$$

Equations (11-1) and (11-2) are the torque equations for this system; these relations are restated in Eqs. (11-3) and (11-4).

$$T(s) = \theta_m(s)(J_m s^2 + Bs + K) + \theta_L(s)(-Bs - K) \qquad (11\text{-}3)$$

$$0 = \theta_m(s)(-Bs - K) + \theta_L(s)(J_L s^2 + Bs + K) \qquad (11\text{-}4)$$

Equation (11-5) solves for the load position in terms of the applied torque;

$$\theta_L(s) = \cfrac{\begin{vmatrix} J_m s^2 + Bs + K & T(s) \\ -Bs - K & 0 \end{vmatrix}}{\begin{vmatrix} J_m s^2 + Bs + K & -Bs - K \\ -Bs - K & J_L s^2 + Bs + K \end{vmatrix}}$$

$$= \frac{T(s)(Bs + K)}{(J_m s^2 + Bs + K)(J_L s^2 + Bs + K) - (Bs + K)^2}$$

$$= \frac{T(s)(Bs + K)}{J_m J_L s^4 + (J_m + J_L)(Bs + K)s^2}$$

$$= \frac{T(s)[(B/J_L)s + K/J_L]}{J_m s^4 + [(J_m + J_L)Bs^3/J_L] + [(J_m + J_L)/J_L]Ks^2} \qquad (11\text{-}5)$$

$$= \frac{T(s)[2\zeta\omega_n s + (\omega_n)^2]}{J_m s^4 + (J_m + J_L)2\zeta\omega_n s^3 + (J_m + J_L)(\omega_n)^2 s^2} \qquad (11\text{-}6)$$

where

$$2\zeta\omega_n = \frac{B}{J_L}, \qquad (\omega_n)^2 = \frac{K}{J_L}$$

$$\frac{\theta_L(s)}{T(s)} = \frac{2\zeta\omega_n s + (\omega_n)^2}{J_m s^2[s^2 + (1 + J_L/J_m)2\zeta\omega_n s + (1 + J_L/J_m)(\omega_n)^2]} \qquad (11\text{-}7)$$

Equation (11-5) is simplified in Eq. (11-6). A further modification is given in Eq. (11-7). Examination of Eq. (11-7) shows that at low frequencies the system open-loop gain declines at a -2 slope. This negative slope continues to the resonant frequency, whereupon the denominator of Eq. (11-7) becomes very small and causes the gain to peak. The complete response of Eq. (11-7) is shown in Fig. 11-2.

Figure 11-3 shows a complete lead network servo with resonant load in standard form. Equation (11-8) is the general expression for the loop gain.

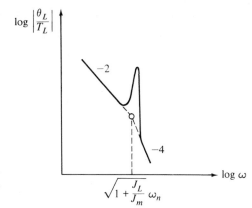

Figure 11-2. Bode plot of open position loop of servo motor coupled to resonant load.

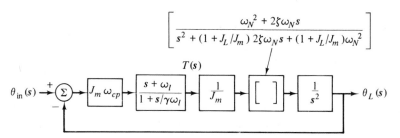

Figure 11-3.   Lead network servo with resonant load.

Equation (11-9) solves for the open-loop gain at the resonant frequency, $\omega_n\sqrt{1 + J_L/J_m}$ (where ω_n is the resonant frequency of the load by itself).

$$G(s) = J_m\omega_{cp}\left(\frac{s + \omega_l}{1 + s/\gamma\omega_l}\right)\left(\frac{1}{J_m s^2}\right)$$

$$\times\left[\frac{(\omega_n)^2 + 2\zeta\omega_n s}{s^2 + (1 + J_L/J_m)2\zeta\omega_n s + (1 + J_L/J_m)(\omega_n)^2}\right]$$

$$= \frac{\omega_{cp}(s + \omega_l)}{s^2(1 + s/\gamma\omega_l)}\left[\frac{(\omega_n)^2 + 2\zeta\omega_n s}{s^2 + (1 + J_L/J_m)2\zeta\omega_n s + (1 + J_L/J_m)(\omega_n)^2}\right] \quad (11\text{-}8)$$

$$G\left(j\omega_n\sqrt{1 + \frac{J_L}{J_m}}\right) = \frac{\omega_{cp}(j\omega_n\sqrt{1 + J_L/J_m} + \omega_l)}{(-1)(\omega_n)^2(1 + J_L/J_m)(1 + (j\omega_n\sqrt{1 + J_L/J_m}/\gamma\omega_l)}$$

$$\times\left[\frac{(\omega_n)^2}{(1 + J_L/J_m)2\zeta\omega_n j\omega_n\sqrt{1 + J_L/J_m}}\right]$$

$$\approx \frac{\omega_{cp}(j\omega_n\sqrt{1 + J_L/J_m}}{(-1)(\omega_n)^2(1 + J_L/J_m)(j\omega_n\sqrt{1 + J_L/J_m}/\gamma\omega_l)}$$

$$\times\left[\frac{1}{2\zeta j(1 + J_L/J_m)^{3/2}}\right]$$

$$= \frac{\omega_{cp}\gamma\omega_l}{-2j\zeta(\omega_n)^2(1 + J_L/J_m)^{5/2}} \quad (11\text{-}9)$$

For the parameter values indicated, Eq. (11-10) states the gain at resonance.
For $\omega_l = \omega_{cp}/3$, $J_L = J_m$, $\gamma = 10$, and $\zeta = 0.05$,

$$G\left(j\omega_n \sqrt{1 + \frac{J_L}{J_m}}\right) = \left|\frac{10\omega_{cp} \times \omega_{cp}/3}{(-j)2\zeta(\omega_n)^2(5.66)}\right| = \frac{10}{2 \times 3 \times 5.66} \times \frac{(\omega_{cp})^2}{(\omega_n)^2(0.05)}$$

$$= 5.88 \frac{(\omega_{cp})^2}{(\omega_n)^2} \qquad (11\text{-}10)$$

$$\omega_n = \sqrt{\frac{5.88(\omega_{cp})^2}{0.5}} = \sqrt{11.76}\,\omega_{cp} = 3.43\,\omega_{cp} \qquad (11\text{-}11)$$

Therefore

$$\omega_{cp} = \frac{\omega_n}{3.43} = 0.29\,\omega_n \qquad (11\text{-}12)$$

To assure that the servo will not oscillate at the resonant frequency, the gain
of Eq. (11-10) is made equal to $\frac{1}{2}$. Equation (11-11) uses this gain to solve for
the allowable maximum value of ω_{cp}, found as $0.29\omega_n$ in Eq. (11-12). Therefore, if ω_{cp} is approximately $\frac{1}{4}\omega_n$, a stable system results.

This simple example of the destabilizing effect of structural resonance
indicates the fact that it is a basic limitation in servos. Similar analysis indicates that rate loop bandwidths are limited by resonance and that the position loops closed around these rate loops are also limited by the resonance.

One might think that it would be possible to compensate for a resonance
by using a tuned electric filter and then closing the loop at a higher frequency.
This cannot be done because practical mechanical resonant loads have a
spectrum of resonant frequencies, all of which normally change somewhat as
a function of load angle. The first resonant frequency defines the lower boundary of this spectrum; it is this lower boundary that limits loop bandwidths.
In an antenna system, for instance, the lowest resonant frequency can be
accurately approximated by the total load inertia resonating with the gear
train spring rate.

Example 11-1. A lead network servo with resonant load is being designed;
a "current source" is used to drive the motor so that $\omega_m \longrightarrow 0$. Calculate ω_{cp}, given
$\zeta = 0.02$ and that the gain at $\omega_n\sqrt{1 + (J_L/J_m)}$ is 0.5, $J_L = 0.5J_m$, $f_n = 14$ Hz,
$\omega_{cp} = 4\omega_l$, and $\gamma = 16$.

solution $\zeta = 0.02$, $J_L/J_m = 0.5$, $f_n = 14$ Hz, $\omega_{cp} = 4\omega_l$, and $\gamma = 16$.

$$G\left(j\omega_n\sqrt{1 + \frac{J_L}{J_m}}\right) = \frac{\omega_{cp}\gamma\omega_l}{(-1)2j\zeta(\omega_n)^2(1 + (J_L/J_m)^{5/2})} \qquad \text{Eq. (11-9)}$$

$$0.5 = \frac{\gamma\omega_{cp}\omega_l}{2\zeta(\omega_n)^2((1 + (J_L/J_m)^{5/2})} = \frac{16\omega_{cp}(\omega_{cp}/4)}{2 \times 0.02(\omega_n)^2(1.5)^{5/2}}$$

$$= \frac{4(\omega_{cp})^2}{0.04(\omega_n)^2 \times 2.76} = \frac{100}{2.76} \times \frac{(\omega_{cp})^2}{(\omega_n)^2} \quad \text{or} \quad (\omega_{cp})^2 = \frac{1.38}{100}(\omega_n)^2$$

$$\omega_{cp} = 0.117\,\omega_n$$

$$\omega_n = 14 \times 2\pi = 88 \text{ rad/s}$$

Therefore,

$$\omega_{cp} = 0.117 \times 88 = 10.3 \, \text{rad/s}$$

11-2. bandwidth limits in general

Servo bandwidths are limited by a number of characteristics. These include transport lags, carrier frequency, load resonance, saturation effects, and backlash in gearing (causing limit cycles). In the case of transport lags, the longer the delay, the greater the phase lag at a particular gain crossover frequency; this is readily analyzed using frequency-response techniques. In the case of carrier frequency bandwidth limitations, the empirical information of Table 11-1 is useful; this table is discussed in the next section. Load resonance effects were discussed in the last section; usually, the rate loop or position loop bandwidth is limited to one-half or less of the resonant frequency. In the case of saturation effects, these are most noticeable for high-performance wide-bandwidth servos.

Often when a high amplifier gain follows some noise, quadrature, or harmonic producing device (such as a synchro or resolver), the amplifier may be saturated by one or more of these spurious voltages, thus effectively reducing gain and bandwidth (two other important saturation effects are discussed in sections 11-4 and 11-5). In the case of backlash as a factor limiting bandwidth, a general rule of thumb is that the backlash should be kept to a fraction of the resolution of the system or of the accuracy desired for the system. Chubb* points out that "the amount of backlash that a servo can withstand without sustained oscillation is proportional to the amount of load friction." This is perhaps the only definitive statement that may be made. It points out that for a given load characteristic there is a maximum allowable backlash; if the gears give more backlash, then more load friction must be added (this is practical for instrument servos).

11-3. empirical bandwidth data

Table 11-1 lists, in order of increasing rate loop bandwidth, a number of different servos characterized by mechanical output power and type of electrical drive system. It may be seen that the 60-Hz servos have the lowest bandwidth, 400-Hz servos have greater bandwidth, and dc servos have the widest bandwidth. This is to be expected, because a dc servo does not have a carrier lag effect due to the sampling of the carrier. Also observe that full-

---

* Bruce A. Chubb, *Modern Analytical Design of Instrument Servomechanisms* (Reading, Mass.: Addison-Wesley Publishing Company, 1967), p. 186.

wave systems provide greater bandwidths than half-wave systems; higher-power systems tend to have lower bandwidths than lower-power systems.

Table 11-1   typical values of rate loop bandwidth

motor type	mechan- ical power (W)	electrical drive	ω_{cr} (rad/s)	comments
2ϕ 60 Hz	several	half-wave mag. amp.	30	practical maximum
2ϕ 60 Hz	several	full-wave mag. amp.	60	practical maximum
2ϕ 400 Hz	750	full-wave mag. amp.	120	practical maxumum
dc torque motor	2400	motor generator	120	dc tachometer full-wave SCR field drive
2ϕ 400 Hz	several	half-wave mag. amp.	135	easily attainable
2ϕ 400 Hz	100	full-wave mag. amp.	180	care required
2ϕ 400 Hz	several	full-wave mag. amp.	270	easily attainable
2ϕ 400 Hz	12	full-wave mag. amp.	360	practical maximum
dc motor and tachometer	11	transistor linear	375	limited by load resonance and compliance between tachometer and motor

Table 11-1 is stated in terms of rate loop bandwidth limitations. Lead network servos would be limited in a similar manner; the lead network upper break frequency (lag) would be comparable to ω_{cr}.

Example 11-2. Using Table 11-1, estimate reasonable rate loop bandwidths for the following servos:

(a) 100 W mechanical power using a half-wave 60-Hz motor
(b) 100 W mechanical power using a full-wave 60-Hz motor
(c) 250 W mechanical power using a full-wave 400-Hz motor

solution

(a) $\omega_{cr} \approx (180 \times 0.8) \times \frac{60}{400} \times \frac{1}{2} = 10.8$ rad/s ≈ 11 rad/s

care / required — factor to make design more easily at- tainable — frequency ratio — half-wave versus full-wave

(b) $\omega_{cr} \approx 2 \times 11 = 22$ rad/s
(c) 400 Hertz full-wave, 750 W: $\omega_{cr} = 120$ rad/s (practical maximum)
400 Hertz full-wave, 100 W: $\omega_{cr} = 180$ rad/s (care required)
$\omega_{cr} \approx \frac{1}{3}(180 - 120) + 120$ rad/s ≈ 140 rad/s

The solutions in Example 11-2 are estimates; for design purposes, calculations should be based on the most recent empirical data available. The above calculations cannot be interpreted as being as exact as the equations seem to imply, because a slight change in 0.8 and 0.7 factors (which are estimated empirical experience factors) may make an appreciable change in the result.

11-4. scaling

Scaling is concerned with *saturation* of amplifiers in servos. Problems that may result from such saturation are limitations in maximum velocity or maximum torque. Consider a system with a required maximum velocity of $26.8°/s$ at the load and a gear ratio (motor to load) of 600. This is equivalent to a load velocity of 4.47 rpm and a motor velocity of 2680 rpm. Assuming a tachometer having an output of 3 V/1000 rpm, the maximum tachometer output is 8.05 V. If this system uses amplifiers that saturate at 6 V, then 6 V is the maximum command to the tachometer loop, thus limiting the maximum velocity to less than the desired amount. If equal-summing resistors (see Appendix A) are used from the tachometer to the summing point and from the position loop amplifier to the summing point, only a 6-V maximum is obtainable from the amplifier, and therefore the tachometer output voltage may never exceed 6 V.

Figure 11-4 demonstrates this situation. Given $R_2 = R_3$, then for the

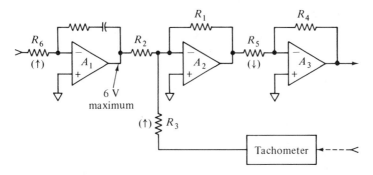

Figure 11-4.   Maximum rate of servo limited by amplifier saturation.

rate loop in equilibrium a 6-V output from A_1 is balanced by 6 V from the tachometer. Figure 11-5 is a block diagram equivalent to the circuit diagram of Fig. 11-4. To overcome amplifier saturation, it is possible to scale the tachometer output by a factor of one-half. This means that for a 6-V output from A_1, the tachometer requires an output of 12 V (which is greater than the required 8.05 V). Increasing R_3 by a factor of 2 effectively attenuates the

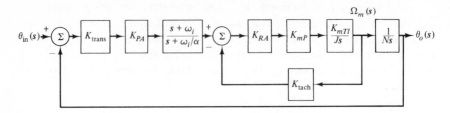

Figure 11-5.   Tachometer-stabilized integral network compensated servo.

tachometer output by a factor of 2; this change, however, descreases the rate loop gain by 2. This gain reduction can be compensated by decreasing R_5 by a factor of 2. These changes take care of the rate loop. Recalling that the external dc gain of a subloop is equal to the reciprocal of the feedback constant, it is apparent that reducing the feedback gain by a factor of 2 increases the effective forward loop gain of that loop; this requires a reduction in the position loop gain, and therefore R_6 must be increased by a factor of 2 to compensate for the increase in R_3. Perhaps an easier way to visualize this scaling technique is that if R_3 is increased, R_2 should be increased to keep the summing gain constant; but if R_2 is increased, then the scaling problem still exists and therefore another position loop resistor must be increased (R_6); a rate loop resistor must also be decreased (R_5) to keep the rate loop gain constant.

In general, scaling problems such as the one just described may be solved by considering the maximum voltages required out of transducers in the system and then assuring that voltages being summed against the transducer outputs always exceed those maximum values. If in a system a certain maximum velocity is required, it is always wise to scale the system to be certain that the command has an appreciable overspeed margin (perhaps even 100 per cent).

Example 11-3. A servomotor is stabilized by a C.P.P.C. DC-8-☐-7 tachometer as shown in Fig. E11-3a. (a) How should the circuit values be changed to assure a maximum speed of 4000 rev/min? (b) Draw a new diagram showing these new values.

solution

(a) $E_{\text{tach(max)}} = 4000 \text{ rev/min} \times \dfrac{5 \text{ V}}{1000 \text{ rev/min}} = 20 \text{ V}$

Scaling: if R_5 is increased to 20 kΩ, then R_4 must be increased to 102 kΩ ≈ 100 kΩ to keep the rate loop gain constant. Because an increase in R_5 is (normally) accompanied by an increase in R_3 (but this cannot be done for scaling

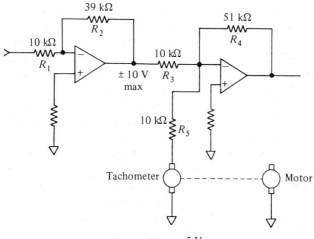

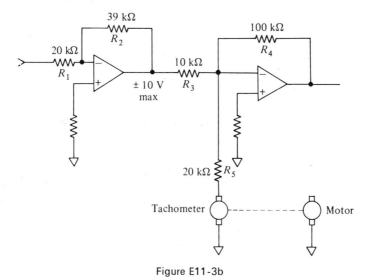

$$DC-8-\square -7: \quad K_{GE\Omega} = \frac{5\text{ V}}{1000\text{ rev/min}}$$

Figure E11-3a

reasons), R_1 must therefore be increased to $20\text{ k}\Omega$ (or R_2 decreased to $19.5\text{ k}\Omega$ $\approx 20\text{ k}\Omega$).

(b) New diagram:

Figure E11-3b

11-5. saturation

The technique of Section 11-4 is designed to prevent amplifier saturation; now the question of servo saturated performance is discussed. The discussion is based primarily on a paper by George Biernson.* Servo saturated performance in this section relates to servo velocity and acceleration saturation (which may be due to amplifier saturation). For instance, a power amplifier may supply a certain maximum current which gives a maximum motor torque, meaning that there is a maximum acceleration capability. The calculations discussed here relate maximum velocity and acceleration of a servo to the allowable maximum loop bandwidths. The maximum allowable bandwidth is such that any increase in bandwidth results in saturated instability, or saturated overshoots. Saturated overshoots are normally encountered immediately after a very large position change is commanded. At the time that the servo approaches zero error, the stored kinetic energy of the system may cause such overshoots. Saturated overshoots are undesirable because they consume time and cause a rather violent type of system instability. One possible solution is to reduce bandwidth automatically whenever a saturated step is commanded.

Figure 11-6 is a block diagram labeled for use in this discussion. Equa-

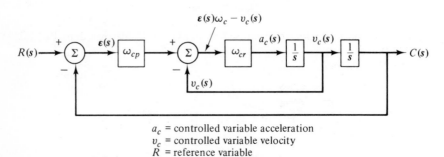

a_c = controlled variable acceleration
v_c = controlled variable velocity
R = reference variable
ε = error (actuating signal)
C = controlled variable

Figure 11-6. Tachometer-stabilized servo labeled for saturated response.

tion (11-13) defines the maximum velocity capability of this system, and Eq. (11-14) defines the maximum acceleration capability of this system. Equation (11-15) is the assumed rate loop open-loop gain expression, and Eq. (11-16) is the closed rate loop transfer function.

$$v_m = |v_c(t)|_{\max} \tag{11-13}$$

$$a_m = |a_c(t)|_{\max} \tag{11-14}$$

$$G_r(s) = \frac{\omega_{cr}}{s} \tag{11-15}$$

* George A. Biernson, "How the Bandwidth of a Servo Affects Its Saturated Response," *I.R.E. Transactions on Automatic Control*, Vol. PGAC-4, March 1958.

$$G'_r(s) = \frac{\omega_{cr}}{s + \omega_{cr}} = \frac{1}{1 + s/\omega_{cr}} \tag{11-16}$$

$$G_p(s) = \frac{\omega_{cp}}{s(1 + s/\omega_{cr})} \tag{11-17}$$

Equation (11-17) states the position loop open-loop gain transfer function. These equations will be referred to later in the analysis. Figure 11-7 shows the

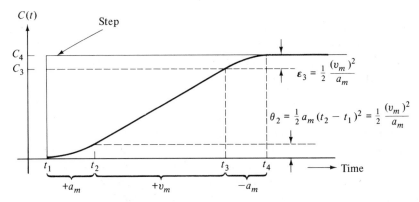

Figure 11-7.   Ideal saturated response.

ideal saturated response to a step input; it is ideal in the sense that the servo output takes the minimum possible time to reach its commanded input. The servo exhibits maximum acceleration at time t_1. Maximum acceleration continues until maximum velocity is reached at t_2; it runs at maximum velocity from t_2 to t_3, where it decelerates (at maximum negative acceleration) until it synchronizes at zero error at time t_4 (this does not consider the normal linear system settling time). Figure 11-7 is ideal in the sense that there are no overshoots, there is perfect synchronization, and the new position is reached in the minimum possible time for the system. Examining the various parts of this motion, it may be seen that the time from t_1 to t_2 is equal to the maximum velocity v_m divided by the maximum acceleration a_m as stated in Eq. 11-18, because the ideal system is assumed to be moving at maximum acceleration during this period.

Equation (11-18), as noted above, states the time $(t_2 - t_1)$ in terms of the maximum velocity and maximum acceleration:

$$t_2 - t_1 = \frac{v_m}{a_m} \tag{11-18}$$

$$\theta_2 = \frac{1}{2} a_m (t_2 - t_1)^2 = \frac{1}{2} \frac{(v_m)^2}{a_m} \tag{11-19}$$

Equation (11-19) expresses θ_2 in terms of $(t_2 - t_1)$ and v_m and a_m. The ideal transition point (where the system should go into full deceleration) as shown in Fig. 11-7 is ϵ_3; by symmetry this (ideal) value is the same as θ_2 as stated in Eq. (11-20). Therefore

$$\epsilon_3 = \frac{1}{2} \frac{(v_m)^2}{a_m} \tag{11-20}$$

From Fig. 11-6 the acceleration, in general, may be stated as in Eq. (11-21):

$$a_c = \omega_{cr}(\epsilon \omega_{cp} - v_c) \tag{11-21}$$

When the rate loop bandwidth is large, it can be seen that the acceleration is positive when $\epsilon \omega_{cp}$ is greater than v_c and negative when $\epsilon \omega_{cp}$ is less than v_c: In effect, there is a transition or "switch point" in acceleration that takes place at the point defined by Eq. (11-22).

$$\epsilon_s = \frac{v_c}{\omega_{cp}} \tag{11-22}$$

This states that the acceleration switches from a positive to a negative value when the error is equal to the velocity divided by the position loop bandwidth. Another way of saying this is that if the system runs at some velocity v_c, then the acceleration switches when the error is equal to v_c divided by ω_{cp}. Up to t_3, the velocity is v_m, and therefore the acceleration transition or switch point is as stated in Eq. (11-23) and (11-24):

$$\epsilon_s = \frac{v_c}{\omega_{cp}} = \frac{v_m}{\omega_{cp}} \tag{11-23}$$

$$\epsilon_s = \frac{v_m}{\omega_{cp}} \tag{11-24}$$

Now Eq. (11-20) states the ideal switch point for no overshoots, and Eq. (11-24) states the actual switch point; by setting the actual switching error of Eq. (11-24) greater than the ideal switch point of Eq. (11-20), Eq. (11-25) results. Restating this in Eq. (11-26) gives the actual bandwidth requirement for no saturated overshoots.

$$\frac{v_m}{\omega_{cp}} \geq \frac{(v_m)^2}{2a_m} \tag{11-25}$$

$$\omega_{cp} \leq \frac{2a_m}{v_m} \tag{11-26}$$

Equation (11-26) is very important because it gives the value of the position loop bandwidth that prevents saturated overshoots. It shows that the greater the available acceleration, the greater the allowable position loop bandwidth. It also shows that the lower the saturated velocity, the greater the allowable position loop bandwidth. From Eq. (11-26) it is now clear that in a wideband system having limited acceleration there is a severe danger of saturated overshoots. If a saturated error ever does take place, despite scaling, then it is important to reduce the position loop gain (temporarily but immediately) so that the system comes smoothly to its final position. Whenever the error falls below some specified amount, (a fraction of the saturated error), then the system is switched to its full gain again to allow smooth synchronization.

Equation (11-27) gives the possible number of saturated overshoots whenever the bandwidth exceeds the critical value stated in Eq. (11-26).

$$N = \frac{v_m \omega_{cp}}{2a_m} - 1 \tag{11-27}$$

A general expression for bandwidth in terms of acceleration, velocity, and number of overshoots is given in Eq. (11-28).

$$\omega_{cp} = \frac{2a_m}{v_m}(N+1) \tag{11-28}$$

$$t_s = \frac{v_m}{a_m}(2+N) \tag{11-29}$$

Equation (11-29) gives the settling time for a system displaying saturated overshoots; not included in this equation is the time that it takes for the system to synchronize after the saturated overshoots are completed (this time is proportional to the reciprocal of ω_{cp}).

The previous analysis is based on the assumption of Eq. (11-30), which states that the rate loop bandwidth is relatively wide compared to the magnitude of maximum acceleration over maximum velocity.

$$\omega_{cr} \gg \frac{a_m}{v_m} \tag{11-30}$$

Equation (11-31) is a modified version of Eq. (11-26) to consider the effect of finite rate loop bandwidth.

$$\omega_{cp} \leq \frac{2a_m}{v_m}\left(1 - \frac{\omega_{cp}}{4\omega_{cr}}\right) \tag{11-31}$$

For $\omega_{cr} = 3\omega_{cp}$,

$$\omega_{cp} \approx \frac{2a_m}{v_m}\left(1 - \frac{\omega_{cp}}{12\omega_{cp}}\right) = \frac{2a_m}{v_m}(0.92) \tag{11-32}$$

Equation (11-32) restates Eq. (11-31) for the case where the rate loop bandwidth is equal to three times the position loop bandwidth (a reasonable ratio); it may be seen that the value of the position loop bandwidth is not greatly different from the value that emerges from the simpler Eq. (11-26).

Given a lead network system, an expression for the lead break frequency may be determined in terms of velocity, acceleration, and overshoots. This is stated in Eq. (11-33); it is based on a lead network as described in Eq. (11-34) and shown in Fig. 11-8.

$$\omega_l = \frac{2a_m}{v_m}(N+1) \qquad \text{for } \omega_{cp} > \omega_l \tag{11-33}$$

$$G(s)_{\text{lead network}} = \frac{s + \omega_l}{s + \gamma\omega_l} \tag{11-34}$$

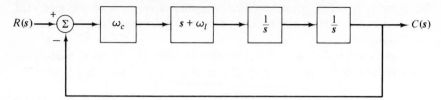

Figure 11-8. Simplified lead network servo block diagram.

It is assumed that the ratio between the lead and lag frequencies is quite large.

Example 11-4.

Given:

$$\ddot{\theta}_{\max} = 40°/s^2 = a_m$$
$$\dot{\theta}_{\max} = 20°/s = v_m$$
$$\omega_{cp} = 11\frac{\text{rad}}{\text{s}}$$

(a) Are there any saturated overshoots, and if so, how many?
(b) Calculate the saturated settling time.
(c) Graph the response to a 60° step.

solution

(a) $\dfrac{2a_m}{v_m} = \dfrac{2 \times 40°/s^2}{20°/s} = 4\ s^{-1} = 4\ \text{rad/s}$

$\omega_{cp} = \dfrac{2a_m}{v_m}(N+1)$

$11 = 4(N+1)$

$N+1 \approx 2.75$ or $N = 1.75 \approx 2$

(b) Settling time $= t_s = \dfrac{v_m}{a_m}(N+2) = \dfrac{1}{2}(3.75) = 1.875\ s$

(c) For a 60° step input, a graph of servo time response for $\omega_{cp} = 11$ is shown in Fig. E11-4.

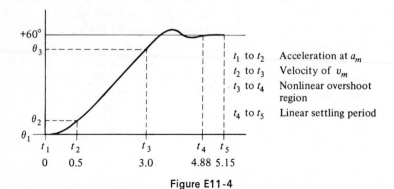

Figure E11-4

$$t_2 - t_1 = \frac{v_m}{a_m} = 0.5 \text{ s}$$

$$\theta_2 - \theta_1 = \tfrac{1}{2}a_m(t_2 - t_1)^2 = \tfrac{1}{2} \times 40(0.5)^2 = 5° \quad \text{or} \quad \theta_2 = 5°$$

$$\theta_3 = 60 - 5° = 55°$$

$$\theta_3 - \theta_2 = 55 - 5 = 50°$$

$$t_3 - t_2 = \frac{50°}{20°/\text{s}} = 2.5 \text{ s} \quad \text{and} \quad t_3 = 3 \text{ s}$$

In Biernson's analysis, θ_3 is the starting point for the saturated settling time.

$$t_s = t_4 - t_3 = \frac{v_m}{a_m}(N + 2) = \frac{20}{40}(3.75) = 1.88 \text{ s}$$

$$t_4 = 3.0 + 1.88 = 4.88 \text{ s}$$

Let the linear settling time $= 3/\omega_{cp}$.

$$\frac{3}{\omega_{cp}} = \frac{3}{11} = 0.27 \text{ s}$$

$$\text{Total time} = 4.88 + 0.27 = 5.15 \text{ s}$$

11-6. introduction to automatic tracking systems

Tracking systems use radar, radio, optical, or other (transduced) information as error data to cause a servo to follow some "target" motion automatically. A great deal of development work was done on such systems during World War II, much of it related to gun-aiming from radar tracking antennas. The following sections are concerned with problems peculiar to automatic tracking systems.

11-7. secant correction

Secant correction is necessary in many automatic tracking systems. This forward loop gain correction modification is provided because elevation-over-azimuth tracking antennas have an inherent reduction in gain in the azimuth loop with increasing elevation angles. The gain reduction is proportional to the cosine of the elevation angle because the error between the antenna position and the target is measured in the deflection plane (the plane determined by the boresight axis of the antenna and an intersecting horizontal line), whereas the antenna is moved about an axis normal to the azimuth plane.

Figure 11-9 shows a diagram of the line-of-sight distance r to a target and the projection of this distance in the horizontal plane (labelled x_h). Figure 11-10 shows the same information as Fig. 11-9, and also shows a target motion of Δs in time Δt. Figure 11-11 combines the two previous diagrams to show a hemisphere whose center is at the tracking antenna and whose radius r is the radial distance to the target.

Equation (11-35) expresses the target motion Δs in terms of the geometric

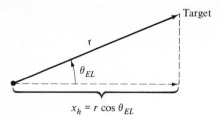

Figure 11-9. Two-dimensional representation of tracking situation.

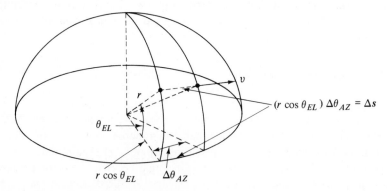

v = target linear velocity
Δt = small increment in time
Δs = linear target motion in time Δt

Figure 11-10. Target motion in tracking situation.

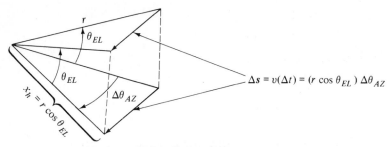

Figure 11-11. Hemisphere coverage of azimuth-over-elevation tracking antenna.

parameters; Eq. (11-36) expresses the target's linear velocity v in terms of these geometric parameters.

$$\Delta s = (r \cos \theta_{EL}) \Delta\theta_{AZ} \tag{11-35}$$

$$v = \lim_{\Delta s \to 0} \frac{\Delta s}{\Delta t} = \lim_{\Delta s \to 0} \frac{(r \cos \theta_{EL}) \Delta\theta_{AZ}}{\Delta t}$$

$$= \lim_{\Delta\theta_{AZ} \to 0} \left(r \cos \theta_{EL}\left(\frac{\Delta\theta_{AZ}}{\Delta t}\right)\right) = r(\cos \theta_{EL})\dot\theta_{AZ} \tag{11-36}$$

or

$$\dot{\theta}_{AZ} = \frac{v}{(r \cos \theta_{EL})} \tag{11-37}$$

By solving Eq. (11-36) for the azimuth angular rate, Eq. (11-37) results. Examination of this last equation shows that the azimuth rate of the antenna is directly related to the target linear velocity and inversely related to a cos θ_{EL} term, causing the azimuth velocity to go to infinity when the elevation angle is 90°. This means, for a constant target velocity v, that as the elevation angle of the target from the antenna approaches 90°, the antenna azimuth velocity required to maintain track approaches infinity. Naturally, there is a maximum azimuth velocity that any given system can provide, and this limits the elevation angle for a given target velocity. It should be noted in Eq. (11-37) that the term v/r is the target angular rate in the deflection plane; this is the same as the azimuth angular velocity for the target in the horizontal plane at the same line-of-sight range. The deflection plane is important because tracking antennas have their angular error sensors attached to the moving antennas, and therefore sense error in the deflection plane. If it were possible to sense the target error directly in the azimuth plane, there would be no geometric gain problem. But since the target error is detected in this deflection plane, a problem results. Equation (11-38) shows the relationship between the target angular rate in the deflection plane and the target angular rate in the azimuth plane.

$$\dot{\theta}_D = \dot{\theta}_{AZ} \cos \theta_{EL} \tag{11-38}$$

$$G_p(s) = \frac{\cos \theta_{EL} \, \omega_{cp}}{s(1 + s/\omega_{cr})} \tag{11-39}$$

Figure 11-12 shows the servo loop considering the geometric effect (shown as

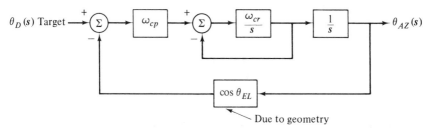

Figure 11-12.   Diagram showing gain reduction due to elevation-over-azimuth geometry.

the feedback gain in this diagram). Equation (11-39) is the open-loop gain expression for this system; it can be seen that as the elevation angle θ_{EL} increases, the loop gain drops. This characteristic is very undesirable in any system and totally unacceptable in a conditionally stable system (most tracking systems are conditionally stable because of the integral network com-

pensation normally used in the position loop). As a consequence, a gain correction is normally used to keep the loop gain relatively constant: Fig. 11-13

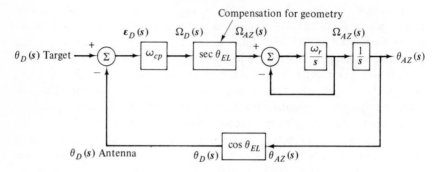

Figure 11-13.   Secant-corrected elevation-over-azimuth tracking antenna.

shows this, the correction consisting of a sec θ_{EL} gain in the forward loop.
There is a limit to the angle to which correction can be fully applied. A typical limiting elevation angle is 84°, where the secant takes on a value of approximately 10. The actual limitations are due to the azimuth velocity capability,
the expected target angular motion in the deflection plane, and the angular
range of the secant function.

The secant correction may be generated by a specially shaped potentiometer, a cosine potentiometer in a feedback loop, or a resolver in an ac
feedback loop.

Example 11-5. A target is moving at 600 mi/h at a line-of-sight range of 1 mi
from a tracking radar. Calculate the maximum azimuth velocity for (a) $\theta_{EL} = 0°$,
(b) $\theta_{EL} = 30°$, (c) $\theta_{EL} = 60°$, and (d) $\theta_{EL} = 85°$.

solution

(a) At $\theta_{EL} = 0°$:

$$\theta_{AZ} = \frac{600 \text{ mi/h}}{1 \text{ mi}} \times \frac{1 \text{ h}}{60 \text{ min}} \times \frac{1 \text{ min}}{60 \text{ s}} = 0.167 \frac{\text{rad}}{\text{s}} = 9.57°/\text{s}$$

(b) At 30°:

$$\theta_{AZ} = \left(9.57 \frac{\text{deg}}{\text{s}}\right) \times \sec 30° = 9.55 \times \frac{1}{0.866} = 11.05°/\text{s}$$

(c) At 60°:

$$\theta_{AZ} = \left(9.57 \frac{\text{deg}}{\text{s}}\right) \times \sec 60° = 9.57 \times \frac{1}{0.5} = 19.15°/\text{s}$$

(d) At 85°:

$$\theta_{AZ} = \left(9.57 \frac{\text{deg}}{\text{s}}\right) \times \sec 85° = 9.55 \times \frac{1}{0.0872} = 109.5°/\text{s}$$

11-8. manual position follow-up servo

Another pertinent consideration for automatic tracking systems is a problem resulting from manual positioning followed by target acquisition and automatic tracking. The fact that a problem can result is shown by the following situation. An antenna operator manually positions an antenna to the location of the expected target and then sets the system so that once the target is acquired, automatic tracking is initiated. After target acquisition, if tracking is lost, the system automatically returns to manual control. Without proper provisions, the antenna automatically returns to the position that the manual controls were at when the target was first acquired. This type of operation, however, is completely unacceptable. The usual solution to the problem is that once automatic tracking is initiated, the manual positioning controls are simultaneously caused to track the antenna position such that if antenna track is lost, the antenna holds its last position. This technique is known as *manual position follow-up*.

Figure 11-14 shows a system having both manual control and automatic

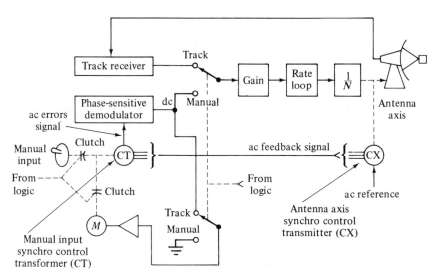

Figure 11-14.   Manual position follow-up in a tracking system.

tracking capabilities. The logic which switches from manual to (automatic) tracking control is not shown, but this normally relates to the AGC level of the tracking receiver or to lock-up of the receiver phase-locked local oscillator. Figure 11-14 shows the manual input connected through a mechanical clutch to a manual input synchro control transformer (CT), which is the primary positioning reference device for the manual loop. For the system in manual mode, the angular difference between this synchro control transformer

(CT) and the antenna axis synchro control transmitter (CX) is represented as an ac error signal out of the manual input synchro control transformer. This error voltage is applied to a phase-sensitive demodulator, the output of which is a bipolar dc signal representing the system error magnitude and sign. In the manual mode the dc error is applied via the gain block to the rate loop and through the gear ratio to the antenna axis, thus causing the antenna to follow any manually commanded input. Whenever the system "acquires" the target, the logic causes the system to switch from Manual to Track, causing the tracking receiver to control the antenna position, as shown in Fig. 11-14. In this automatic mode, the output of the phase-sensitive demodulator drives a servo motor whose load is the control transformer rotor. The CT rotor thus automatically tracks the antenna control transmitter (CX). As a consequence, in the automatic track mode, the manual CT accurately follows the antenna position; thus, if there is a tracking loss, the antenna is held at the position where the target was last tracked. This system is called as manual position follow-up servo.

11-9. rate memory

An alternative technique sometimes used in the event of loss of target in automatic tracking systems is to store the last known target velocity and continue to drive the antenna at that rate (continuing from the last known target position). One way to accomplish this is to use voltages stored in the integral networks to command antenna velocities in both azimuth and elevation. Thus, whenever track is lost, if the input to an integral network is opened, the integral network circuit stores the voltage on its capacitor; this continues to command the antenna to operate at its previous (or last) velocity until automatic tracking is acquired and resumed. The effect of this *rate memory system* is to minimize chances of losing the target and to reduce reacquisition transients when the target signal reappears. The rate memory system is effected by opening the input to the integral network, using a relay (see Fig. 11-15) or field-effect transistor (FET).

For good rate storage, the integrator network operational amplifier, shown in Fig. 11-15, should have low bias input current. Typically, in a system having a rate memory mode, it is common to set a time limit on how long the rate memory mode is held. If the target is not reacquired within this given time, the system reverts to the manual mode. The manual position is the last antenna position before switching out of rate memory, if manual position follow-up is used.

Example 11-6. An operational amplifier integral network with $\alpha = 50$ and $\omega_i = 10$ rad/s is to be used in a rate memory mode. Using an operational amplifier with a maximum input current of 50 nA, specify the feedback elements R_2, R_1, and C (in Fig. 11-15) so that the circuit has only a 5 per cent error in 20 s of a 4-V stored signal.

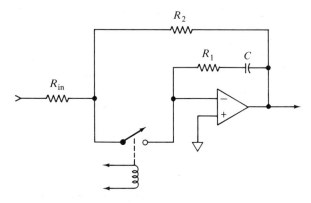

Figure 11-15.   Rate memory circuit.

solution

Since $dE/dt = i/C$,

$$C = \frac{i}{(dE/dt)} = \frac{50 \times 10^{-9} \text{ A}}{0.01 \text{ V/s}} = 5000 \times 10^{-9} \text{ F} = 5 \mu\text{F}$$

Since $R_1 C = 1/\omega_i$ and $\alpha = (R_1 + R_2)/R_1$,

$$R_1 = \frac{1}{5 \times 10^{-6} \times 10} = 20 \text{ k}\Omega$$

$$R_2 = R_1(\alpha - 1) = 20 \text{ k}\Omega \times 49 = 980 \text{ k}\Omega \approx 1 \text{ M}\Omega$$

11-10. scanners

Also used in some tracking systems are *automatic scanning generators* that command the antenna to follow spiral or rectangular patterns. In following the scanning pattern, the required antenna velocities are sometimes quite high. In such a case it is possible that the antenna moves past the target rather rapidly and fails to acquire tracking instantly because of the momentum of the antenna system. For this type of situation, it is possible to use a position memory system which uses a synchro to store the position of the target at the time that it was first detected and hold it until the antenna can move to that stored position, using the synchro position as a reference command, and then lock on to the target.

11-11. summary

A simple analysis of resonance effects on servos was presented; the particular approach may be extended to investigate tachometer-stabilized servos or any other configuration. Empirical bandwidth data was presented; this information is useful as a guide in the early stages of design.

Scaling is concerned with the design considerations that prevent amplifier saturation from degrading servo performance. When saturation effects cannot be avoided, it is possible to make correcting provisions; in particular, for a servo with a certain maximum velocity, the allowable position loop bandwidth for no saturated overshoot is proportional to the maximum acceleration capability.

Systems using servos for automatic tracking sometimes require special provisions, including secant correction for elevation-over-azimuth systems, manual position followup servos, rate memory, and scanners.

problems

11-1. Assuming $\omega_m = 0$, calculate a reasonable ω_{cp} for a lead network servo with a resonant load for $\zeta = 0.05$, $J_L = J_m$, $f_n = 6$ Hz, $\omega_{cp} = 3\omega_l$, and $\gamma = 9$.

11-2. Calculate the open- and closed-loop gain and phase for Problem 11-1 at ω_{cp}.

11-3. For the servo design given in Fig. P11-3:

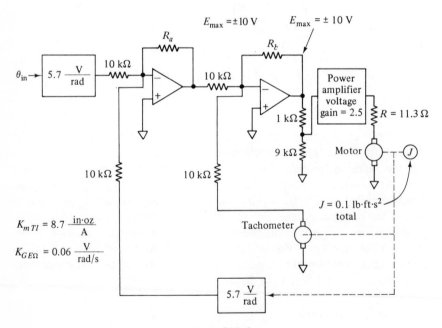

Figure P11-3

(a) Can a maximum acceleration at stall of $40°/s^2$ be obtained? If not, how should the circuit values be changed?

(b) Is the scaling acceptable for a maximum velocity of 300 rad/s? If not, how should the circuit values be changed?

11-4. Given $\ddot{\theta}_{max} = 20$ rad/s², $\dot{\theta}_{max} = 30$ rpm. If the position loop uses an operational amplifier with a 100 -kΩ feedback resistor and has an ω_{cp} of 6 Hz, to what value should the 100-kΩ resistor be changed to provide no saturated overshoots?

11-5. In Problem 11-4, if the original configuration remained, estimate the total settling time from the time that the servo starts to decelerate.

11-6. At what rate will an integral network drift in the rate memory mode if the storage capacitor is 2.0 μF and the amplifier bias current is 0.1 μA?

12

error budgets

To describe properly the overall error of a servo-system, it is necessary to combine a number of different contributing errors. In this chapter an approach to error budgets is presented, and a tabulation of antenna tracking servo-system errors is given. This listing is not intended to cover all possible servo errors, but it does indicate many of the common ones.

Table 12-1 is an outline of an error budget. Note that the errors are

Table 12-1   error budget outline

one-axis error budget	pointing	tracking
static errors		
1. static friction	√	√
2. motor starting error	√	√
3. tachometer noise	√	√
4. component errors	√	√
5. transducer errors	√	—
6. instrument gearing	√	—
7. structural deflections	√	—
8. steady torques	√	√
9. wind gusts	√	√
dynamic errors		
10. tachometer ripple	√	√
11. target motion	√	√
12. tracking noise	—	√

listed in two parts: *static* and *dynamic*. Static errors are independent of antenna motion; dynamic errors involve motion. A second division of Table 12-1 is by *pointing* and *tracking* errors. Pointing systems are commanded from a manual, computer, or other external source of information; an example is an antenna commanded by an operator's control. Pointing errors cause the antenna to point in a direction different from the commanded direction. In the case of a ground-based antenna, the command is given in earth coordinates, and the antenna position is measured relative to local earth coordinates. A schematic of elevation angle sensing given in Fig. 12-1 shows that

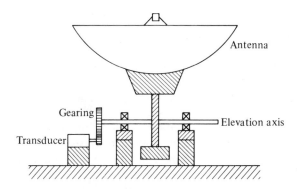

Figure 12-1. Pointing system elevation axis.

transducer, instrument gearing, and structural deflection errors are all present as parts of the pointing error.

In tracking systems, an error sensor is attached to the moving part of the antenna; the error is measured between the antenna boresight and the target position. Therefore certain errors which are included in the pointing error are *not* included in the tracking error. As shown in Table 12-1, items 5, 6, and 7 in particular are *not* included in the tracking error because they relate only to pointing accuracy. Item 12, tracking noise, is not present for the pointing system: it relates to tracking receiver noise.

Figure 12-2 is a diagram of the elevation error in relation to the azimuth error; these errors are orthogonal to each other and therefore must be combined to give a total pointing error defined in Eq. (12-1):

$$\epsilon_{\text{total}} = \sqrt{(\epsilon_{AZ})^2 + (\epsilon_{EL})^2} \qquad (12\text{-}1)$$

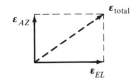

Figure 12-2. Combining elevation and azimuth errors

12-1. disturbance errors

Before discussing the individual error contributors in detail, a general approach to various disturbance errors is discussed in some detail. This approach was introduced previously in Sections 7-5 and 9-5.

$$\frac{\theta(s)}{T(s)} = \frac{1}{BA} \times \frac{\theta(s)}{\alpha(s)} \tag{12-2}$$

Figure 12-3 is a diagram of a tachometer-stabilized servo. Equation

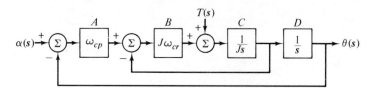

Figure 12-3. Tachometer-stabilized servo with torque disturbance.

(12-2) states the "shortcut" relation between the output angle and the torque disturbance. The "shortcut" approach consists of dividing the disturbance input $T(s)$ by the gain from the input summing point (AB), and multiplying this quantity by the system closed-loop gain. Equation (12-3) gives the system closed-loop gain, and Eq. (12-4) gives the error disturbance gain.

$$\frac{\theta(s)}{\alpha(s)} = \frac{ADBC/(1 + BC)}{1 + ADBC/(1 + BC)} = \frac{ABCD}{1 + BC + ABCD} \tag{12-3}$$

$$\frac{\theta(s)}{T(s)} = \frac{1}{BA} \times \frac{ABCD}{1 + BC + ABCD} = \frac{CD}{1 + BC + ABCD} \tag{12-4}$$

To prove that this "shortcut" method is correct, the disturbance input $T(s)$ is considered to be the system input and the normal input $\alpha(s)$ is taken as zero; by solving this, the correct output is determined and compared to the "shortcut" result. Figure 12-4 is the modified block diagram considering the

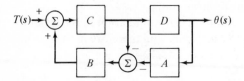

Figure 12-4. Modified diagram showing disturbance as system input.

input to be the disturbance. Figure 12-5 is a simplification of Fig. 12-4: the solution of this diagram is given in Eq. (12-5).

$$\frac{\theta(s)}{T(s)} = \frac{C}{1 + CB(1 + DA)} \times D = \frac{CD}{1 + BC + ABCD} \tag{12-5}$$

Observe that this result is identical to that given in Eq. (12-4).

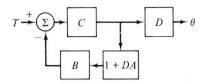

Figure 12-5. Reduced diagram.

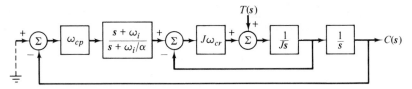

Figure 12-6. Tachometer-stabilized integral network compensated servo with torque disturbance.

Figure 12-6 is a general case of a system that has a position loop integral network and assumed zero position command; this will also be solved by the shortcut approach. Equations (12-6) through (12-8) give the shortcut solution. Equation (12-9) is a simpler statement of the error using an approximation for the closed-loop gain.

$$G'_r(s) = \frac{\omega_{cr}}{s + \omega_{cr}} \tag{12-6}$$

$$G'_p(s) = \frac{\omega_{cp}\omega_{cr}(s + \omega_i)/s(s + \omega_{cr})(s + \omega_i/\alpha)}{1 + \omega_{cp}\omega_{cr}(s + \omega_i)/s(s + \omega_{cr})(s + \omega_i/\alpha)}$$

$$= \frac{\omega_{cp}\omega_{cr}(s + \omega_i)}{s(s + \omega_{cr})(s + \omega_i/\alpha) + \omega_{cp}\omega_{cr}(s + \omega_i)} \tag{12-7}$$

$$\frac{C(s)}{T(s)} = \frac{G'_p(s)}{J\omega_{cp}\omega_{cr}} \times \frac{1}{(s + \omega_i)/(s + \omega_i/\alpha)}$$

$$= \frac{\omega_{cp}\omega_{cr}(s + \omega_i)}{s(s + \omega_{cr})(s + \omega_i/\alpha) + \omega_{cp}\omega_{cr}(s + \omega_i)} \times \frac{s + \omega_i/\alpha}{J\omega_{cp}\omega_{cr}(s + \omega_i)}$$

$$= \frac{s + \omega_i/\alpha}{J(s^3 + s^2(\omega_i/\alpha) + s^2\omega_{cr} + s\omega_{cr}\omega_i/\alpha + \omega_{cp}\omega_{cr}s + \omega_{cp}\omega_{cr}\omega_i)} \tag{12-8}$$

$$= \frac{s + \omega_i/\alpha}{J\omega_{cr}\omega_{cp}(s + \omega_i)} \times G'_p(s)$$

$$\approx \frac{s + \omega_i/\alpha}{J\omega_{cr}\omega_{cp}(s + \omega_i)} \times \frac{1}{(1 + s/\omega_{cp})(1 + s/\omega_{cr})} \tag{12-9}$$

If a step function in torque is assumed, the previous result can be used to determine the resulting transient error by taking the inverse Laplace transformation. The step-function transform is stated in Eq. (12-10); the resulting output motion is given in Eq. (12-11).

$$T(s) = \frac{T}{s} \tag{12-10}$$

$$C(s) = \frac{T}{s} \times \frac{s + \omega_i/\alpha}{J\omega_{cr}\omega_{cp}(s + \omega_i)} G'_p(s) \tag{12-11}$$

Because this equation is fairly complicated, so the inverse transform would be somewhat difficult to obtain, some assumptions may be made to simplify the solution while obtaining a result sufficiently accurate for engineering design purposes. The frequency characteristic of the error torque transfer function is shown in Fig. 12-7. If it is assumed that the transfer-function fre-

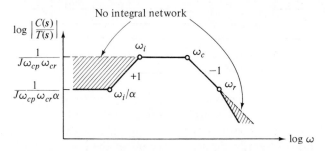

Figure 12-7. Torque error gain characteristic of tachometer-stabilized servo with and without an integral network.

quency response has greater gain than as shown, a pessimistic transient error result should be provided. The crosshatched sections of Fig. 12-7 will be added to the transfer function of Eq. (12-11). This is equivalent to eliminating the integral network (thus reducing dc stiffness). Therefore, by filling in this area the resulting calculated error magnitude should be pessimistic, because there is greater error energy transmitted. (Actually, eliminating the integral network reduces the peak error somewhat, because the servo becomes more stable and thus has a lower overshoot transient response.) By assuming that the error gain response includes the crosshatched areas, the inverse transformation of the resulting simpler expression is determined in Eq. (12-12); the resulting maximum transient torque error is given in Eq. (12-13).

$$\mathcal{L}^{-1}C(s) \leq \mathcal{L}^{-1}\left[\frac{T}{s} \times \frac{1}{J\omega_{cr}\omega_{cp}} \times \frac{1}{1 + s/\omega_{cp}}\right]$$

$$= \mathcal{L}^{-1}\left[\frac{T}{s} \times \frac{1}{J\omega_{cr}\omega_{cp}} \times \frac{1}{1 + s/\omega_{cp}}\right]$$

$$= \mathcal{L}^{-1}\left[\frac{T}{s} \times \frac{1}{J\omega_{cr}\omega_{cp}} \times \frac{\omega_{cp}}{s + \omega_{cp}}\right]$$

$$= \mathcal{L}^{-1}\left[\frac{T}{J\omega_{cr}} \times \frac{1}{s} \times \frac{1}{s + \omega_{cp}}\right] = \mathcal{L}^{-1}\left[\frac{T}{J\omega_{cr}} \times \left(\frac{1/\omega_{cp}}{s} - \frac{1/\omega_{cp}}{s + \omega_{cp}}\right)\right]$$

$$= \frac{T}{J\omega_{cr}} \times \frac{1}{\omega_{cp}}(1 - e^{-\omega_{cp}t}) \tag{12-12}$$

Therefore

$$C(t)_{\max} = \frac{T}{J\omega_{cr}\omega_{cp}} \tag{12-13}$$

The above result can be somewhat optimistic because of the peaking error due to integral network response; by increasing the value by 50 per cent, a conservative error is obtained. For the actual case with the integral network, this maximum would last for a short period and then would be reduced by the effect of the integral network. Therefore 1.5 times the result of Eq. (12-13) is a somewhat pessimistic result that may be used safely for engineering purposes for stable systems.

The particular contributors to the error budget given in Table 12-1 are now discussed individually.

12-2. static friction error (static)

Figure 12-8 is a diagram of the static and Coulomb friction effects. Consider a shaft supported by a bearing and initially at rest. As torque applied

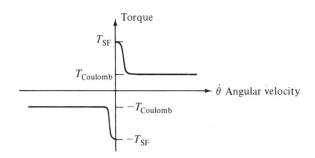

Figure 12-8. Static and Coulomb friction.

to the shaft is increased from zero, no motion results until the torque reaches a value sufficient to overcome the static friction torque, T_{SF}. At this point the shaft starts to turn and, as the angular velocity increases a small amount above zero, the friction torque drops to the magnitude of the Coulomb friction, T_{Coulomb}. The drop from T_{SF} to T_{Coulomb} takes place at a very low angular velocity, normally much less than 1 rev/min. Therefore there is an abrupt reduction in friction torque once motion starts. For a servo, an error must be developed initially to overcome the static friction and allow motion to begin; once this motion has started, there is a negative torque step equal to the difference between T_{SF} and T_{Coulomb}. Conservatively, it may be assumed that a step function equal in magnitude to the static friction is applied to the system; the resulting error transient magnitude may then be used as a contributor to the error budget.

Figure 12-9 shows the static friction torque T_{SF} applied at the proper

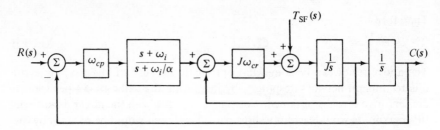

Figure 12-9. Equivalent diagram for determining the effect of static friction.

point in the system diagram. Equation (12-14) states the transfer function for the output motion due to this torque.

$$\frac{C(s)}{T(s)} = \frac{1}{J\omega_{cr}\omega_{cp}(s + \omega_i)/(s + \omega_i/\alpha)} \times \frac{C(s)}{R(s)} = \frac{(s + \omega_i/\alpha)}{J\omega_{cr}\omega_{cp}(s + \omega_i)} G'_p(s)$$

(12-14)

Figure 12-10 is the frequency-response plot of this torque error gain. Since

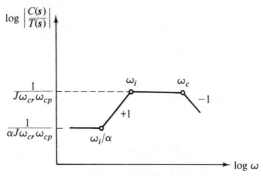

Figure 12-10. Torque error gain of tachometer-stabilized integral network compensated servo.

there is no system input $R(s)$, the resulting system output $C(s)$ is all due to error. As the last section showed, the integral network causes a slight increase over the peak transient error for the system without an integral network; as a result the static friction error may be conservatively evaluated by Eq. (12-15).

$$E_{SF} = \frac{1.5T_{SF}}{J\omega_{cr}\omega_{cp}}$$

(12-15)

12-3. motor starting voltage error (static)

The same general approach is used in determining the errors due to motor starting voltage. Figure 12-11 shows a system block diagram that in-

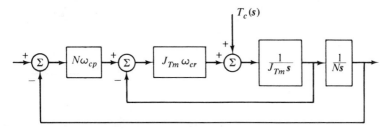

Figure 12-11. Equivalent diagram for determining motor starting voltage error.

cludes a rate loop and the motor starting torque, $T_c(s)$. Equation (12-16) states the relationship between T_c and the motor starting voltage; Eq. (12-17) gives the resulting system error.

$$T_c = e_{\text{start}} \times \frac{T_{\max}}{e_{\max}} = e_{\text{start}}K_{mTE} = \text{starting torque} \tag{12-16}$$

$$\epsilon_{ms} = \frac{T_c}{NJ_{Tm}\omega_{cr}\omega_{cp}}G'_p(j\omega) = \frac{e_{\text{start}}K_{mTE}}{NJ_{Tm}\omega_{cr}\omega_{cp}}G'_p(j\omega) \tag{12-17}$$

12-4. tachometer noise error (static)

Tachometer noise is analyzed in a similar fashion. In this case, however, the disturbance is not applied as a torque, but as an equivalent rate input as defined in Eq. (12-18). The error due to tachometer noise is stated in Eq. (12-19).

$$\Omega_N = \text{tachometer noise} = \frac{e_{N(\text{tach})}}{K_{GE\Omega}} \tag{12-18}$$

$$|\epsilon_N| = \left| \frac{\Omega_N}{N\omega_{cp}}G'_p(j\omega) \right| \approx \frac{\Omega_N}{\omega_{cp}N} = \frac{e_{N(\text{tach})}}{\omega_{cp}NK_{GE\Omega}} \tag{12-19}$$

where $e_{N(\text{tach})}$ is the tachometer output noise voltage and $K_{GE\Omega}$ is the tachometer gain constant.

12-5. component errors (static)

There are many potential component errors due to electronic, electromechanical, or other components. These contribute to the overall error of a servo system; two of these are discussed here. Figure 12-12 is the block diagram of a tachometer-stabilized servo system. Figure 12-13 shows two noise contributions due to two of the components in the system. The first contribution is N_{trans}, which is noise associated with a transducer; the second is N_{AVRO}, which is the output noise of the rate loop voltage amplifier.

Equation (12-20) gives the approximate open-loop position loop gain

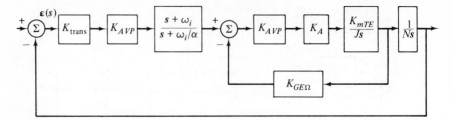

Figure 12-12. Servo block diagram showing hardware blocks.

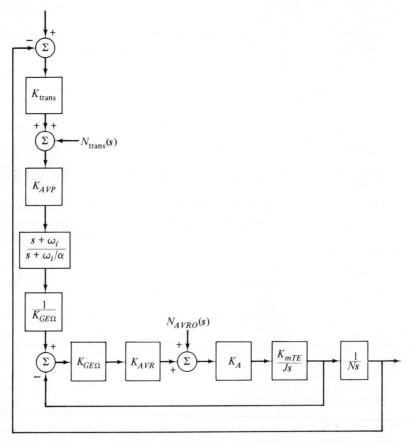

Figure 12-13. Modified hardware block diagram showing component noise.

of this system; from this the expression for the position loop gain crossover frequency ω_{cp} is determined as expressed in Eq. (12-21).

$$G_p(s) = \frac{K_{trans}K_{AVP}(s + \omega_i)/(s + \omega_i/\alpha)}{NsK_{GE\Omega}} \tag{12-20}$$

$$\omega_{cp} = \frac{K_{trans}K_{AVP}}{NK_{GE\Omega}} \tag{12-21}$$

$$\frac{\dot{\theta}_c(s)}{\epsilon(s)} = \frac{K_{trans}K_{AVP}(s + \omega_i)/(s + \omega_i/\alpha)}{K_{GE\Omega}} = N\omega_{cp}\frac{(s + \omega_i)}{(s + \omega_i/\alpha)} \tag{12-22}$$

Equation (12-22) states the relationship between the command angular velocity $\dot{\theta}_c$ and an equivalent input error signal (not the actual system error). From this, Fig. 12-14 is drawn; the system error due to the rate loop voltage amplifier noise is stated in Eq. (12-23).

$$\epsilon_{NAVRO}(s) = \frac{N_{AVRO}}{K_{AVR}K_{GE\Omega}} \times \frac{1}{N\omega_{cp}(s + \omega_i)/(s + \omega_i/\alpha)} \tag{12-23}$$

At low frequencies $$\epsilon_{NAVROL} = \frac{N_{AVRO}}{K_{GE\Omega}K_{AVR}N\omega_{cp}\alpha} \tag{12-24}$$

At medium frequencies (near ω_{cp}) $$\epsilon_{NAVROM}(s) = \frac{N_{AVRO}}{K_{GE\Omega}K_{AVR}N\omega_{cp}}$$
$$\tag{12-25}$$

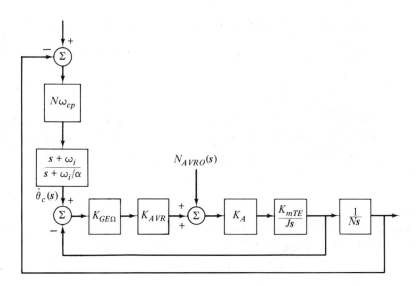

Figure 12-14. Modified diagram with position loop gain in bandwidth form.

The Bode plot for this equation is given in Fig. 12-15. Equation (12-24) gives the low-frequency error, and Eq. (12-25) gives the maximum error for the band from ω_i to ω_{cp}. The high-frequency error is given in Eq. (12-26).

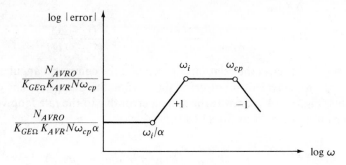

Figure 12-15. Error gain frequency response for rate loop amplifier noise.

At high frequencies $(|s| > \omega_{cp})$

$$\epsilon_{NAVROH}(s) = \frac{N_{AVRO}}{K_{GE\Omega}K_{AVR}N\omega_{cp}} \times \frac{1}{1 + s/\omega_{cp}} \qquad (12\text{-}26)$$

12-6. transducer errors (static)

Transducer noise referred to the input is stated in Eq. (12-27).

$$N_{transI} = \frac{N_{transO}}{K_{trans}} = \text{transducer noise referred to the input} \qquad (12\text{-}27)$$

$$\epsilon_{NtransI}(s) = \frac{N_{transO}}{K_{trans}} \times G'_p(s) = N_{transI} \times \frac{1}{1 + s/\omega_{cp}} \qquad (12\text{-}28)$$

Equation (12-28) gives the error expression for an input transducer such as a potentiometer, synchro, or resolver. As an example, consider a synchro control transformer which serves as the input error sensor of a servo. The transducer gain constant is stated in Eq. (12-29).

$$K_{trans} = 0.4 \frac{V}{deg} \qquad (12\text{-}29)$$

For an assumed transducer error as stated in Eq. (12-30), the equivalent system error is given in Eq. (12-31).

$$N_{transO} = 10_{mV} = 0.01 \text{ V} \qquad (12\text{-}30)$$

$$\epsilon_{transI} = \frac{0.01 \text{ V}}{0.4 \text{ V/deg}} = 0.025° \qquad (12\text{-}31)$$

12-7. gearing errors (static)

Instrument gearing is frequently a significant error contributor. It is possible to analyze gearing errors by knowing the characteristics of the gears in the instrumentation. Figure 12-16 shows the error characteristic of an

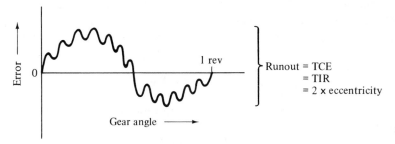

Figure 12-16. Instrument gear error plot for one gear revolution.

instrument gear; the error is shown as a function of the gear's angular position. The general character of this error curve is sinusoidal. There are also many little sine waves superimposed on the larger, longer period sine wave. The smaller sine waves are due to errors in the shape of the individual teeth; this error, therefore, is called *tooth-to-tooth* error. The total combined error magnitude is called the *total composite error* (TCE) or *total indicated runout* (TIR).

A valid model from which the characteristics of gearing may be determined analytically is shown in Fig. 12-17. Consider a perfect gear of the same

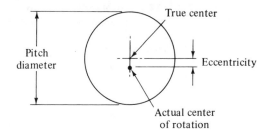

Figure 12-17. Gear model to visualize runout error.

diameter as the one shown in Fig. 12-17 and mated with that gear; also consider that the angular position of the perfect gear is controlled by the angular position of the first gear (because of the mating of the teeth). The error is then the difference between the position of the perfect gear and the position of the input of the first imperfect gear. Because of imperfections of the gear being considered, the position of the perfect gear is not an accurate representation of the input position to the first gear. The angular position error is given by Eq. (12-32). This is a practical equation to define the instantaneous error (in radians) of any particular gear.

$$\text{Error(rad)} = \frac{\text{TIR}}{\text{PD}}[\sin\theta + \tan\phi(1 - \cos\theta)] \qquad (12\text{-}32)$$

where TIR is the total indicated runout (in inches), and PD is the pitch diameter (in inches). To find the maximum error, Eq. (12-32) is differentiated and the result is allowed to go to zero as in Eq. (12-33); it is found that the error curve is a maximum when $\tan\theta$ is equal to the negative reciprocal of $\tan\phi$.

$$\frac{dE}{d\theta} = \frac{\text{TIR}}{\text{PD}}(\cos\theta + \tan\phi\sin\theta) \longrightarrow 0 \qquad (12\text{-}33)$$

For a 20° pressure angle (the most common value for instrument gears), the maximum errors occur at $+110°$ and at $-70°$. The largest peak error is at 110°. The error at 110° is 1.422 TIR/PD; the error at $-70°$ is -0.71 TIR/PD. The average of these two is 1.06 TIR/PD. Using the slightly larger value of 1.1TIR/PD, Eq. (12-34) is written to express the "peak" gearing error of one gear.

$$E_{\text{gear}} = 1.1\frac{\text{TIR}}{\text{PD}} \qquad (12\text{-}34)$$

This expression gives conservative results for average errors, but does not consider worst-case peak errors (those having a low probability of occurrence, particularly for trains of more than two gears).

Table 12-2 gives the total composite error (or TIR) for Precision 1, 2,

Table 12-2   total indicated runout (TIR) three precision gear classes

precision class	total indicated runout (TIR) (in)
1	0.001
2	0.0005
3	0.00025

and 3 gears; "Precision" grades are the standard ratings of gear accuracy. Consider a gear with a 1-in pitch diameter having Class 1 Precision. Equation (12-35) calculates the "peak" error as approximately 3.8′ of arc for such a gear.

$$\text{Error} = 1.1 \times \frac{0.001}{1} \times 57.3 = 0.063° \approx 3.8' \qquad (12\text{-}35)$$

12-8. deflection errors (static)

Figure 12-18 is a mechanical schematic of a tracking antenna on a pedestal that is caused to deflect by wind force. The resulting *deflection angle*

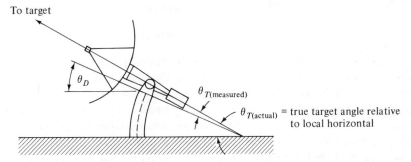

Figure 12-18. Model for visualizing error due to structural deflection.

of this pedestal is θ_D. Because of this deflection angle θ_D, the measured elevation angle of the antenna (θ_T) is reduced by that amount. This is expressed in Eq. (12-36).

$$\theta_{T(\text{actual})} = \theta_{T(\text{measured})} + \theta_D \qquad (12\text{-}36)$$

The error due to these structural deflections is a direct contributor to an antenna's pointing error; this error is given in Eq. (12-37).

$$\text{Error} = \theta_D = \frac{T}{K} \qquad (12\text{-}37)$$

12-9. steady torque errors (static)

Various steady torque errors contribute to system pointing or tracking error; Table 12-3 lists four of these potential contributors. All of these are

Table 12-3   tabulation of typical steady torques found in antenna systems

1. unbalance T_{UB}
2. steady wind T_w
3. ice loading T_{ice}
4. cable torques T_{cable}

steady torques, and therefore the servo's dc torque stiffness is used to calculate the errors. Equation (12-38) gives the resulting error for a tachometer-stabilized servo system with integral network compensation.

$$\epsilon = \frac{T}{J_T \omega_{cr} \omega_{cp} \alpha} \tag{12-38}$$

$$J_T \approx J_A \quad \text{(hydraulic)} \tag{12-39}$$

$$\approx N^2 J_M \quad \text{(electric)} \tag{12-40}$$

Equations (12-39) and (12-40) state the approximate total inertia that would normally be used in Eq. (12-38) for hydraulic and electric systems. The distinction between hydraulic and electric systems is based on the fact that the inertia of hydraulic motors is usually small compared to the reflected load inertia, and electric motor inertias are usually large compared to the reflected load inertia. Equation (12-41) gives a useful general expression for wind torque; if the torque at a single wind velocity is known, it is possible to calculate the torque at other velocities using this relation.

$$T_w = Kv^2 \quad (v = \text{wind velocity}) \tag{12-41}$$

12-10. wind gust errors (static)

Figure 12-19 shows a wind torque input to a tachometer-stabilized,

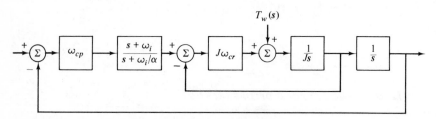

Figure 12-19. Tachometer-stabilized integral network compensated servo with wind torque disturbance.

integral network compensated servo. Equations (12-42) and (12-43) are the error transfer functions for hydraulic and electric systems.

$$\frac{\epsilon_w(s)}{T_w(s)} \approx \frac{s + (\omega_i/\alpha)}{J_A \omega_{cr} \omega_{cp}(s + \omega_i)(1 + s/\omega_{cp})} \quad \text{(hydraulic)} \tag{12-42}$$

$$\frac{\epsilon_w(s)}{T_w(s)} \approx \frac{s + (\omega_i/\alpha)}{N^2 J_M \omega_{cr} \omega_{cp}(s + \omega_i)(1 + s/\omega_{cp})} \quad \text{(electric)} \tag{12-43}$$

Figure 12-20 gives the Bode plot for these expressions. If it is assumed that the spectrum of a wind gust is largely in the frequency band from ω_i to ω_{cp},

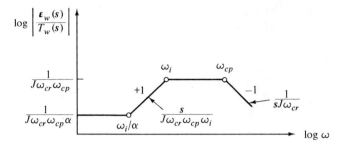

Figure 12-20. Torque error gain of tachometer-stabilized integral network compensated servo.

then the gust error is given in Eq. (12-44); the assumption for this expression is similar to that used for static friction.

$$\epsilon = 1.5 \frac{T_{\text{gust}}}{J\omega_{cr}\omega_{cp}} \qquad (12\text{-}44)$$

This way of determining the gust error is probably pessimistic; if, for instance, an appreciable part of the gust spectrum occurs at frequencies below ω_i, then the error would be lower than that assumed. If, however, the gust is assumed to have a 1-s rise time, it is possible to make the assumption that the gust has a shape as shown in Fig. 12-21; this shape is that of a half-sine

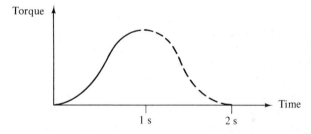

Figure 12-21. Assumed wind gust shape.

wave for the rise time; therefore the period of the sine wave is 2-s and its analytical expression is given in Eq. (12-45). Let

$$T_{\text{wind}}(t) = \frac{T_{\text{max}}}{2} \sin \frac{2\pi t}{2} = \frac{T_{\text{max}}}{2} \sin \pi t \qquad (12\text{-}45)$$

Then

$$|\epsilon_w| = \frac{T}{G} = \frac{T_{w(\text{max})}/2}{|\epsilon_w(j\omega)/T_w(j\omega)|} \qquad (12\text{-}46)$$

The frequency of this sine wave is $\frac{1}{2}$ Hz (π rad/s); the error due to wind is stated in Eq. (12-46). If ω_i (the integral network upper break frequency) is above the frequency of the sine wave ($\frac{1}{2}$ Hz), Eq. (12-47) defines the error gain at that frequency for $\omega_i = \omega_{cp}/4$. This result leads to Eq. (12-48) (for the gust frequency between ω_i/α and ω_i).

$$\left|\frac{\epsilon_w(j\pi)}{(T_N(j\pi))}\right| = \left|\left[\frac{s}{J\omega_{cr}\omega_{cp}\omega_i}\right]_{s=j\pi}\right| \quad \text{for } \frac{\omega_i}{\alpha} < \pi < \omega_i$$

$$= \frac{\pi}{J\omega_{cr}\omega_{cp}\omega_i} \approx \frac{\pi}{J\omega_{cr}\omega_{cp}(\omega_{cp}/4)} = \frac{4\pi}{J\omega_{cr}(\omega_{cp})^2} \quad \text{for } \omega_i = \frac{\omega_{cp}}{4}$$

$$\tag{12-47}$$

$$|\epsilon_w| = \frac{T_{w(\max)}}{2} \times \frac{4\pi}{J\omega_{cr}(\omega_{cp})^2} = \frac{2\pi T_{w(\max)}}{J\omega_{cr}(\omega_{cp})^2} \tag{12-48}$$

12-11. tachometer ripple error (dynamic)

Tachometer ripple is due to variations in the magnitude of the tachometer output voltage for a given constant output shaft velocity. This ripple introduces an ac signal into the rate loop summing point; as a result there is a system error at that frequency. For this ripple expressed as a voltage, the gain constant of the tachometer must be divided into the voltage to provide the ripple in angular rate. Direct current tachometers usually have ripple specified as a *ripple factor*. This ripple factor may be used in Eq. (12-49) to determine the resulting error.

$$\epsilon = \frac{\Omega_{\max} \times \text{ripple factor}}{N\omega_{cp}} \times \frac{G(j\omega_{\text{ripple}})}{1 + G(j\omega_{\text{ripple}})} \tag{12-49}$$

The first part of this equation gives the error which is introduced into the servo; this is the ripple factor times the angular velocity of the servo divided by the gear ratio times the position loop bandwidth. Examination of Fig. 12-14 shows the reason for inclusion of the gear ratio; this diagram also shows that the integral network gain would have to be included for low ripple frequencies. The second (dynamic) part of Eq. (12-49) defines the closed-loop system gain at the ripple frequency. If the velocity is very low, the dynamic part is unity, and the integral network gain reduces the error. The frequency of the ripple is determined by the design of the tachometer; for dc tachometers it is the angular velocity times the number of commutator bars.

12-12. target motion error (dynamic)

There are many ways to analyze errors due to target motion; some of these are discussed in this section. The simplest characterization of target motion is to assume that the target moves at a constant velocity equal to its average velocity; the error is then given in Eq. (12-50) for an integral network compensated servo.

$$\epsilon = \frac{\Omega_{max}}{Kv} = \frac{\Omega_{max}}{\alpha\omega_{cp}} \qquad (12\text{-}50)$$

This is the simplest way to determine target motion error.

Another approach is to define target motion by its maximum velocity and maximum acceleration. Given these two values, it is possible to postulate a sine wave of such amplitude and frequency that its maximum velocity and maximum acceleration are the same as those for the target. Consider Eqs. (12-51), (12-52), and (12-53), which are sinewave position, velocity, and acceleration expressions, respectively.

$$\theta = A \sin \omega_s t \qquad (12\text{-}51)$$

$$\dot{\theta} = A\omega_s \cos \omega_s t \qquad (12\text{-}52)$$

$$\ddot{\theta} = -A(\omega_s)^2 \sin \omega_s t \qquad (12\text{-}53)$$

The maximum angular velocity is given by Eq. (12-54) and the maximum angular acceleration is given in Eq. (12-55).

$$\dot{\theta}_{max} = A\omega_s \qquad (12\text{-}54)$$

$$\ddot{\theta}_{max} = A(\omega_s)^2 \qquad (12\text{-}55)$$

Dividing Eq. (12-55) by Eq. (12-54), the sine wave's angular frequency is determined [Eq. (12-56)]. The amplitude of the sine wave is determined in Eq. (12-57).

$$\omega_s = \frac{\ddot{\theta}_{max}}{\dot{\theta}_{max}} \qquad (12\text{-}56)$$

$$A = \frac{\dot{\theta}_{max}}{\omega_s} = \frac{(\dot{\theta}_{max})^2}{\ddot{\theta}_{max}} \qquad (12\text{-}57)$$

Therefore it is possible to determine a sine wave as defined in Eq. (12-51) that will have a given maximum angular velocity and a given maximum acceleration.

If one assumes a tachometer-stabilized servo with a high α position loop integral network, then the open-loop gain is as shown in Fig. 12-22. The magnitude of the gain at a frequency ω_s below ω_i but above ω_i/α is given in

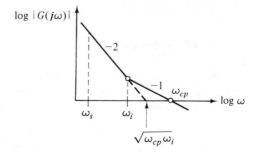

Figure 12-22.   Open position loop with high α integral network.

Eq. (12-58). Using Eqs. (12-57), (12-58), and (12-56), Eq. (12-59) can be written to give a simple and interesting result.

$$|G(j\omega_s)| \approx \frac{\omega_{cp}}{\omega_s} \times \frac{\omega_i}{\omega_s} = \frac{\omega_{cp}\omega_i}{(\omega_s)^2} \tag{12-58}$$

$$|\text{Error}| = \left| \frac{A}{1 + G(j\omega_s)} \right| \approx \frac{A}{G(j\omega_s)} = \frac{(\dot{\theta}_{max})^2}{\ddot{\theta}_{max}} \times \frac{(\omega_s)^2}{\omega_{cp}\omega_i}$$

$$= \frac{(\dot{\theta}_{max})^2}{\ddot{\theta}_{max}} \times \frac{(\ddot{\theta}_{max})^2}{(\dot{\theta}_{max})^2 \omega_{cp}\omega_i} = \frac{\ddot{\theta}_{max}}{\omega_{cp}\omega_i} \tag{12-59}$$

This result in Eq. (12-59) is valid only for the sine wave frequency above ω_i/α and below ω_i. As an example, consider a target maximum acceleration of $10°/s^2$, a maximum velocity of $2°/s$, a position loop bandwidth of 40 rad/s, and an integral network upper break frequency of 10 rad/s; then the error magnitude is defined in Eq. (12-60). To check this, ω_s may be calculated [Eq. (12-61)], and the magnitude of the assumed sine wave can be calculated [Eq. (12-62)].

$$|\text{Error}| = \frac{10°/s^2}{(40 \text{ s}^{-1}) \times 10 \text{ s}^{-1}} = 0.025° \tag{12-60}$$

$$\omega_s = \frac{10°/s^2}{2°/s} = \frac{5 \text{ rad}}{s} \tag{12-61}$$

$$A = \frac{2°/s}{5 \text{ rad/s}} = 0.4° \tag{12-62}$$

$$G(j5) \approx \frac{40}{5} \times \frac{10}{5} = 8 \times 2 = 16 \tag{12-63}$$

$$|\text{Error}| = \frac{0.4°}{16} = 0.025° \tag{12-64}$$

The gain at the sine wave frequency is stated in Eq. (12-63), and the resulting error is determined in Eq. (12-64) [identical to that previously determined in Eq. (12-60)]. It should be emphasized that the open-loop gain transfer function has a -2 slope in the region of the ω_s for the preceding analysis. In general, given a maximum velocity and maximum acceleration, a sine wave may be calculated that exhibits these maximum values; then a system error calculated, given the servo's open-loop gain characteristic.

12-13. error constants

Most practical servos are "Type 1" servos. Type 1 means that there is one *pure integration* in the open-loop characteristic. Equation (12-65) is the open-loop transfer function of a Type 1 servo.

$$G(s) = \frac{\omega_{cp}(s + \omega_i)}{s(s + \omega_i/\alpha)(1 + s/\omega_{cr})} \tag{12-65}$$

It will be noted from the general form of this equation that this could be an integral network compensated servo, a lead network servo, or a VCID servo. The significant characteristic of this gain equation is that there is one pure integration in the denominator, thereby making it the general open-loop gain expression for a Type 1 servo.

Continuing in the study of errors, Eq. (12-66) defines the error as a function of the input and the system gain. Equation (12-67) is a statement of the final value theorem. Equation (12-68) uses the final value theorem to determine the steady-state error (as time approaches infinity) of the Type 1 system of Eq. (12-65).

$$\epsilon(s) = \frac{R(s)}{1 + G(s)} \tag{12-66}$$

Final value theorem $$\lim_{t \to \infty} f(t) = \lim_{s \to 0} sF(s) \tag{12-67}$$

Therefore

$$\epsilon(t) = \lim_{t \to \infty} \frac{sR(s)}{1 + G(s)} = \lim_{s \to 0} \frac{sR(s)}{1 + \omega_{cp}(s + \omega_i)/[s(s + \omega_i/\alpha)(1 + s/\omega_{cr})]}$$

$$= \lim_{s \to 0} \frac{sR(s)}{1 + \alpha\omega_{cp}/s} = \frac{s^2 R(s)}{s + \alpha\omega_{cp}} \tag{12-68}$$

By substituting a step function [Eq. (12-69)] for $R(s)$ in Eq. (12-68), zero error is found by Eq. (12-70).

Step input $$R(s) = \frac{1}{s} \tag{12-69}$$

$$\epsilon(\infty) = \frac{s}{s + \alpha\omega_{cp}}\bigg|_{s=0} = 0 \tag{12-70}$$

Ramp $$R(s) = \frac{1}{s^2} \tag{12-71}$$

For a ramp input [Eq. (12-71)] there is a constant system steady-state error as determined in Eq. (12-72); this error is related to the velocity constant as defined in Eq. (12-73).

$$\epsilon(\infty) = \frac{1}{s + \alpha\omega_{cp}}\bigg|_{s=0} = \frac{1}{\alpha\omega_{cp}} \tag{12-72}$$

$$\alpha\omega_{cp} = K_v \tag{12-73}$$

Steady acceleration input $$R(s) = \frac{2}{s^2} \tag{12-74}$$

$$\epsilon(\infty) = \frac{2}{s(s + \alpha\omega_{cp})}\bigg|_{s=0} = \infty \tag{12-75}$$

For a steady acceleration input [Eq. (12-74)], the error goes to infinity as shown in Eq. (12-75). It is clear, therefore, that (theoretically) a Type 1 servo has zero steady-state error for a step input, a constant steady-state error for a velocity (ramp) input, and infinite steady-state error for a constant acceleration input. It is necessary, therefore, to consider acceleration inputs in a different way.

Consider an input command signal $R(t)$ that has most or all components of its acceleration spectrum below the position loop crossover frequency ω_{cp}. It is then reasonable to approximate the spectrum by Eq. (12-76). The magnitude of the equivalent velocity sine wave is then defined in Eq. (12-77) and that of the position sine wave is defined in Eq. (12-78).

$$\ddot{R}(t) = A \sin \omega_A t = |\ddot{R}|_{\max} \sin \omega_A t \tag{12-76}$$

$$|\dot{R}(t)|_{\max} = \frac{A}{\omega_A} \tag{12-77}$$

$$|R(t)|_{\max} = \frac{A}{(\omega_A)^2} \tag{12-78}$$

Consider Fig. 12-23, which defines the gain at this angular frequency ω_A (below ω_{cp} and ω_i).

$$G_A = \frac{\omega_{cp}}{\omega_A} \times \frac{\omega_i}{\omega_A} = \frac{\omega_{cp}\omega_i}{(\omega_A)^2} \tag{12-79}$$

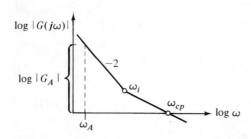

Figure 12-23. Open position loop gain at ω_s (below ω_c and ω_i).

Therefore

$$\text{Error} = \frac{|R(t)|_{\max}}{G_A} = \frac{A/(\omega_A)^2}{\omega_{cp}\omega_i/(\omega_A)^2} = \frac{A}{\omega_{cp}\omega_i} = \frac{|\ddot{R}|_{\max}}{\omega_{cp}\omega_i} \tag{12-80}$$

Equation (12-79) states the gain at that frequency; the error for the sine wave of Eq. (12-78) can now be determined by Eq. (12-80). This is the same result as had been determined in the last section; of interest is the fact that the extension of the -2 slope intersects the unity gain line at a frequency equal to the square root of the denominator of the last part of Eq. (12-80) (see Fig. 12-24). This denominator quantity $\omega_{cp}\,\omega_i$ is sometimes improperly called the *acceleration constant*; it is not truly an acceleration constant because that implies a similarity to the velocity constant, which is related to a constant applied velocity. The so-called acceleration constant is *not* related to a constant input acceleration, because this situation leads to an infinite error for a Type 1 servo; rather, it is related to input spectra which lie in the frequency region of the -2 slope below ω_i. This constant would be better labeled a

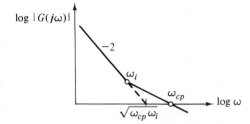

Figure 12-24. Geometric interpretation of second derivative constant.

second derivative constant, because it relates to the second derivative of the input signal.

The discussion to this point has been concerned with Type 1 systems, those with a single pure integration in the open-loop characteristic. It is possible to make Type 2 systems, those with two pure integrations in the open-loop characteristic. Torque motors driven by constant current sources inside position loops approximate Type 2 systems. Because of the two integrations, Type 2 servos can follow constant acceleration inputs with a constant error. Because Type 1 systems are the most commonly used servos, they are the principal subject of this book. The techniques of this book, however, can be extended to Type 2 systems by careful construction of block diagrams and the proper use of gain/bandwidth expressions.

Consider now an angular rate input at a frequency ω_x as shown in Fig. 12-25. For the angular rate defined in Eq. (12-81), the magnitude of a posi-

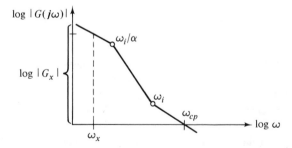

Figure 12-25. Open position loop with integral network.

tion sinewave having that velocity characteristic is given in Eq. (12-82). Let

$$\dot{R}(t) = |\dot{R}|_{\max} \sin \omega_x t \qquad (12\text{-}81)$$

Then

$$|R(t)|_{\max} = \frac{|\dot{R}|_{\max}}{\omega_x} \qquad (12\text{-}82)$$

The gain at the frequency ω_x is given in Eq. (12-83), and the resulting system error is given in Eq. (12-84).

$$G_x = \frac{\alpha\omega_{cp}}{\omega_x} \quad \text{for } \omega_x < \frac{\omega_i}{\alpha} \tag{12-83}$$

$$\text{Error} = \frac{|\dot{R}|_{max}/\omega_x}{\alpha\omega_{cp}/\omega_x} = \frac{|\dot{R}|_{max}}{\alpha\omega_{cp}} \tag{12-84}$$

It will be noted that the denominator of Eq. (12-84) is the same as K_v; therefore the *first derivative constant* is the same as the normal velocity constant (recall that K_v errors are related to constant input velocities, whereas this development relates to a sinusoidally varying velocity—in effect a one-line spectrum).

12-14. passing track method

A useful technique for analyzing target motion errors is the "passing track" technique.* In this analysis it is assumed that the target is moving in a straight line and that the servo is tracking this target. Some analyses consider this a problem in both azimuth and elevation; for the sake of simplicity, only azimuth motion is considered here. In Fig. 12-26, the distance between

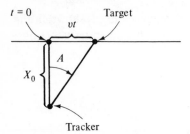

Figure 12-26. The passing track situation in two dimensions.

the tracker and the target at its point of closest approach is X_0, and the target is moving at a linear velocity v. For the analysis, consider a point at a distance vt from the point of closest approach; this point is at an angle A from the X_0 line. The relationship between position, velocity, and acceleration as a function of time is shown in Fig. 12-27. The position curve starts from the third quadrant, comes through zero and goes up in the first quadrant to the upper right-hand corner. The first derivative (velocity) reaches its maximum value at the point of closest approach (chosen as the crossing between the ordinate and the abscissa of this plot at $t = 0$). The acceleration starts at a low value, goes to a peak before the velocity reaches a peak, drops through

* Harold Chestnut and Robert W. Mayer, *Servomechanisms and Regulating System Design,* Vol. II (New York: John Wiley & Sons, Inc., 1955), pp. 44–49.

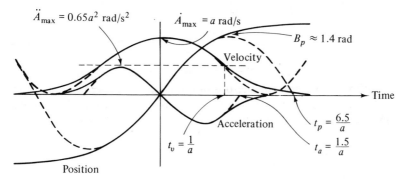

Figure 12-27. Position, velocity, and acceleration time functions for the passing track situation.

zero at the point where the velocity is a maximum, increases to a negative maximum, and then slopes off again in the fourth quadrant.

In the analysis to follow, the curves of Fig. 12-27 are approximated as sine waves; using three sine waves, a reasonable approximation of the target motion spectrum is obtained. Position is approximated by a sine wave that has a magnitude of 1.4 rad. The magnitude of the velocity and acceleration sine waves are related to the constant a, defined as the maximum angular rate at the point of closest approach. The magnitude of the maximum angular acceleration is $0.65a^2$, as noted in Fig. 12-27. These magnitudes are used to define the sine waves characterizing the position, velocity, and acceleration of the target. The frequencies of the sine waves are different, as shown in Fig. 12-27, and are related to the crossover points of the various sine waves. For instance, the crossover point (half-period) of the position sinusoid is t_p, which is equal to $6.5/a$; this is used to determine the position sine wave frequency. Similarly, t_v is the crossover point (one-fourth period) of the velocity sinusoid, and t_a is equal to one-half the period of the acceleration sinusoid.

A general sine wave is assumed in Eq. (12-85) to determine the constants B and T for each of the three sine waves.

$$\theta = B \sin 2\pi f t = B \sin \frac{2\pi t}{T} \qquad (12\text{-}85)$$

$$T_p = 2t_p = \frac{2 \times 6.5}{a} = \frac{13}{a} \qquad (12\text{-}86)$$

Consider Eq. (12-86), which gives the period of the position sine wave (twice the value of t_p); the resulting period is $13/a$. The frequency of the position sine wave is given in Eq. (12-87). The magnitude of the position sine wave is given in Eq. (12-88).

$$f_p = \frac{a}{13} \qquad (12\text{-}87)$$

$$B_p = 1.4 \text{ rad} \tag{12-88}$$

$$\theta_p = 1.4 \sin \frac{2\pi a}{13} t = 80° \sin 0.48at \tag{12-89}$$

$$\omega_p = 0.48a \tag{12-90}$$

The resulting expression for the position angle, θ_p, is given in Eq. (12-89). The angular velocity of this sine wave is given in Eq. (12-90). Similarly, Eqs. (12-91) through (12-100) define the parameters of the velocity and acceleration sinusoids.

$$T_v = 4t_v = \frac{4}{a} \tag{12-91}$$

$$f_v = \frac{a}{4} \tag{12-92}$$

$$B_v = \frac{\dot{A}_{max}}{2} = \frac{a}{2} \tag{12-93}$$

$$\dot{\theta}_v = \frac{a}{2} \sin \frac{2\pi a}{a} t = \frac{a}{2} \sin 1.57at \tag{12-94}$$

$$\omega_v = 1.57a \tag{12-95}$$

$$T_a = 2t_a = \frac{3}{a} \tag{12-96}$$

$$f_a = \frac{a}{3} \tag{12-97}$$

$$B_a = \ddot{A}_{max} = 0.65a^2 \tag{12-98}$$

$$\ddot{\theta} = 0.65a^2 \sin \frac{2\pi a}{3} t = 0.65a^2 \sin 2.1at \tag{12-99}$$

$$\omega_a = 2.1a \tag{12-100}$$

The position sine wave is restated in Eq. (12-101).

$$\theta_p = 80° \sin 0.48at \tag{12-101}$$

To express the velocity sine wave as a servo input, it must be an expression of position command, not angular velocity as is Eq. (12-94). Therefore Eq. (12-94) must be integrated to obtain an equivalent position input; this is done in Eq. (12-102). Similarly, Eq. (12-103) takes the double integral of Eq. (12-99) to obtain a position sine wave input that is equivalent to the acceleration function given in Eq. (12-99).

$$\theta_v = \int \dot{\theta}_v dt = \int \frac{a}{2} \sin 1.57at \, dt = \frac{-a}{2 \times 1.57a} \cos 1.57at$$

$$= -0.32 \cos 1.57at = -17.3° \cos 1.57at \tag{12-102}$$

$$\theta_A = \int\int \ddot{\theta}_A \, dt = \int\int 0.65a^2 \sin 2.1at \, dt = -\frac{0.65a^2}{(2.1a)^2} \sin 2.1at$$

$$= -0.148 \sin 2.1at = -8.5° \sin 2.1at \tag{12-103}$$

In summary, the shapes of the position, velocity, and acceleration curves as a function of time were approximated by sketched sine waves. The peak values of these three sinusoids define maximum position, maximum velocity, and maximum acceleration. Consequently, these three equations are time functions of angular position, velocity, and acceleration. To get all three equations in the required position-input form, the last two were integrated once and twice, respectively.

In effect, a three-line spectrum for the motion of the passing track target was determined; based on this spectrum there are three frequency components as stated in Eqs. (12-101), (12-102), and (12-103). Given these frequency components, the resulting errors may be calculated from the servo's open-loop gain characteristic.

Consider the following example. For a target linear velocity of 200 knots and a closest approach distance of 500 yd, Eq. (12-104) calculates the linear velocity in yards per second; from this information, the value of a is calculated in Eq. (12-105) (a is the maximum angular velocity at the point of closest approach of the target). From this, ω_p is calculated in Eq. (12-106).

$$v = 200 \frac{\text{nm}}{\text{h}} \times 2000 \frac{\text{yd}}{\text{nm}} \times \frac{1 \text{ h}}{3600 \text{ s}} = 112 \frac{\text{yd}}{\text{s}} \tag{12-104}$$

$$a = \frac{112}{500} = 0.224 \frac{\text{rad}}{\text{s}} \tag{12-105}$$

$$\omega_p = 0.224 \times 0.48 = 0.107 \frac{\text{rad}}{\text{s}} \tag{12-106}$$

$$\omega_v = 1.57 \times 0.224 = 0.351 \frac{\text{rad}}{\text{s}} \tag{12-107}$$

$$\omega_a = 2.1 \times 0.224 = 0.47 \frac{\text{rad}}{\text{s}} \tag{12-108}$$

ω_v is calculated in Eq. (12-107), and ω_a is calculated in Eq. (12-108). For an assumed ω_{cp} of 8 rad/s and ω_i of 2 rad/s, the system performance is calculated as shown below.

To determine the system open-loop gains at the three frequencies, consider Fig. 12-28; the gain at ω_x is given as G_x in Eq. (12-109). Equations (12-110), (12-111), and (12-112) use this result to determine the system open-loop gain at the three sine wave frequencies.

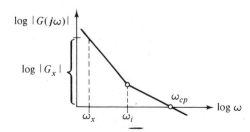

Figure 12-28. Open-loop gain at ω_x (below ω_i and above ω_i/α).

$$G_x = \frac{\omega_{cp}}{\omega_i} \times \left(\frac{\omega_i}{\omega_x}\right)^2 = \frac{\omega_{cp}\omega_i}{(\omega_x)^2} \tag{12-109}$$

$$G(j\omega_p) = \frac{\omega_{cp}\omega_i}{(\omega_p)^2} = \frac{8 \times 2}{(0.107)^2} = 1390 \tag{12-110}$$

$$G(j\omega_r) = \frac{16}{(0.351)^2} = 130 \tag{12-111}$$

$$G(j\omega_a) = \frac{16}{(0.47)^2} = 73 \tag{12-112}$$

From these values, the system errors for position, velocity, and acceleration are determined in Eqs. (12-113), (12-114), and (12-115). A conservative total error is obtained by directly summing these three errors in Eq. (12-116).

$$\epsilon_p = \frac{B_p}{|G(j\omega_p)|} = \frac{80°}{1390} = 0.058° \tag{12-113}$$

$$\epsilon_v = \frac{17.3°}{130} = 0.134° \tag{12-114}$$

$$\epsilon_a = \frac{8.5}{73} = 0.116° \tag{12-115}$$

$$\epsilon_{\text{total}} = \epsilon_p + \epsilon_v + \epsilon_a = 0.058° + 0.134° + 0.116° = 0.308° \approx 0.31° \tag{12-116}$$

12-15. tracking noise (dynamic)

For tracking systems, the angular error detector provides unwanted noise into the servo; this results in an angular noise error. A simplified expression for tracking noise error is stated in Eq. (12-117).

$$\epsilon_N = \frac{k\theta_B}{\sqrt{s/N}} \tag{12-117}$$

This expression is a first-order approximation of the noise error in a tracking system (for more accurate formulas, refer to literature concerning system design).* For Eq. (12-117), given a beam width of 0.5°, a signal-to-noise ratio of 20 dB, and $k = 1$ (a reasonable value), Eq. (12-118) gives the resulting 0.05° error, the rms angular error due to receiver noise.

$$\epsilon_N = \frac{1 \times 0.5°}{\sqrt{100}} = 0.05° \text{ rms} \tag{12-118}$$

Example 12-1. Find the root-sum-square pointing error and tracking error for the following single-axis servo.

$$\omega_{cp} = 10 \text{ rad/s}$$
$$\omega_{cr} = 50 \text{ rad/s}$$

---

* David K. Barton, *Radar System Analysis* (Englewood Cliffs, N.J.: Prentice-Hall, Inc., 1964), Chapters 9 and 10.

$$J_{\text{total}} = 1 \text{ lb} \cdot \text{ft} \cdot \text{s}^2$$
$$T_{\text{static friction}} = 2 \text{ lb} \cdot \text{ft}$$
Position transducer error $= 0.2°$
Tracking noise error $= 0.1°$

solution

$$K_T = J\omega_{cr}\omega_{cp} = 1 \times 50 \times 10 \frac{\text{lb} \cdot \text{ft}}{\text{rad}} = 500 \frac{\text{lb} \cdot \text{ft}}{\text{rad}}$$

$$\epsilon_{SF} = \frac{2 \text{ lb} \cdot \text{ft}}{500 \text{ lb} \cdot \text{ft/rad}} \times 57.3 \frac{\text{deg}}{\text{rad}} = 0.2292°$$

	pointing		tracking	
	ϵ	ϵ^2	ϵ	ϵ^2
static friction	0.2292	0.052533	0.2292	0.052533
transducer	0.2000	0.040000		
tracking noise error			0.1000	0.010000
		0.092533		0.062533
root-sum-square error	0.3042°		0.2501°	

Example 12-2. Develop the error budget for the tracking system in Fig. E12-2a.

$$\omega_{cr} = 160 \text{ rad/s} \qquad \omega_{cp} = 40 \text{ rad/s} \qquad \omega_i = 8 \text{ rad/s} \qquad \alpha = 20$$

motor	T1352	tachometer	TG-1312
$T_{\max}$	20 in·oz	$\Omega_{\max}$	63 rad/s
$\Omega_{\max}$	400 rad/s		
R_{arm}	11.3 Ω		
K_{mTI}	8.7 $\frac{\text{oz} \cdot \text{in}}{A}$		
$K_{mv\Omega}$	0.06 $\frac{V}{\text{rad/s}}$	$K_{GE\Omega}$	0.235 $\frac{V}{\text{rad/s}}$
L	4 mH		
J_{arm}	8.8×10^{-4} oz·in·s^2	J_{arm}	10×10^{-4} oz·in·s^2
T_{friction}	0.7 in·oz	T_{friction}	1.0 in·oz
Ripple torque	0.07 T_{motor}	Ripple voltage	0.07 E_{tach}
Ripple frequency	31 c/rev	Ripple frequency	31 c/rev

load		target	
J_{load}	0.187 oz·in·s^2	$\Omega_{\max}$ 24°/s	
static friction	1.4 in·oz	$\dot{\Omega}_{\max}$ 120°/s^2	
steady torque	8 in·oz		
transient torque	4 in·oz		

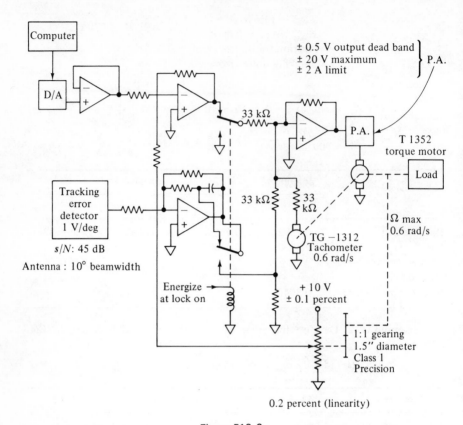

Figure E12-2a

Determine the following errors:

(a) static friction
(b) motor starting
(c) tachometer noise
(d) component errors
(e) transducer errors
(f) instrument gearing
(g) structural deflection
(h) steady torques
(i) wind gusts
(j) tachometer ripple
(k) target motion
(l) tracking noise

solution

$$J_{total} = 0.187 + 2(0.00088) = 0.189 \ \text{oz} \cdot \text{in} \cdot \text{s}^2$$

$$T_{friction} = 0.7 + 1 + 1.4 = 3.1 \ \text{oz} \cdot \text{in}$$

$$K_T = 0.189 \times 40 \times 160 \ \frac{\text{oz} \cdot \text{in}}{\text{rad}} = 1210 \ \frac{\text{oz} \cdot \text{in}}{\text{rad}}$$

$$= 21.1 \ \frac{\text{oz} \cdot \text{in}}{\text{deg}}$$

(a) $\epsilon_{SF} = \dfrac{1.5 \times 3.1}{21.1} = 0.22°$

(b) Not applicable

(c) Not applicable

(d) Component error: power amplifier deadband

$$\epsilon_{deadband} = \frac{0.5 \ \text{V}}{11.3 \ \Omega} \times \frac{8.7 \ \text{oz} \cdot \text{in}/\text{A}}{21.1 \ \text{oz} \cdot \text{in}/\text{deg}} = 0.0175°$$

(e) $\epsilon_{trans} = 0.3 \times 10^{-2} \times 350° = 1.05°$

(f) $\epsilon_{gear} = \dfrac{2 \times 1.1 \times 0.001}{1.5} \times 57.3 = 0.084°$

(g) Not applicable

(h) $\epsilon_{\text{steady torque}} = \dfrac{8}{21.1} \times \dfrac{1}{20} = 0.019°$

(i) $\epsilon_{transient} = \dfrac{4}{21.1} = 0.19°$

(j) Tachometer ripple:

$$e_{ripple} = 0.07 e_{tach}$$

$$\text{Rate error} = 0.07 \ \Omega_{tach}; \quad 31 \ \frac{\text{c}}{\text{rev}}$$

$$\omega_{ripple} = 2\pi \times 31 \ \frac{\text{rad}}{\text{rev}} \times \Omega_m \ \frac{\text{rad}}{\text{s}} \times \frac{1 \ \text{rev}}{2\pi \ \text{rad}}$$

$$= 31 \ \Omega_m \ \frac{\text{rad}}{\text{s}}$$

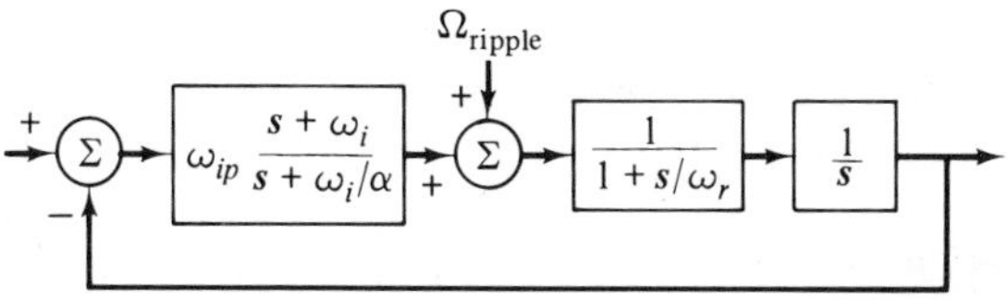

Figure E12-2b

$$\epsilon_{ripple} = \frac{\Omega_{ripple}}{\omega_{cp}(s + \omega_i)/(s + \omega_i/\alpha)} \times \frac{1}{1 + s/\omega_{cp}} = \frac{\Omega_{ripple}(s + \omega_i/\alpha)}{\omega_{cp}(s + \omega_i)(1 + s/\omega_{cp})}$$

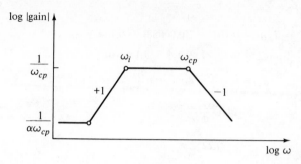

Figure E12-2c

Max rate $= 24°/\text{s}$

$$\omega_{\text{ripple(max)}} = \frac{31 \times 24}{57.3} = 13\frac{\text{rad}}{\text{s}}$$

$$\omega_i < 13 < \omega_{cp} \quad \text{therefore} \quad \left|\frac{\epsilon}{\Omega}\right| = \frac{1}{\omega_{cp}}$$

$$\epsilon_{\text{ripple}} = \frac{0.07 \times 24°/\text{s}}{40\ \text{s}^{-1}} = 0.042°$$

(k) Target motion:

$$K_v = 800\ \text{s}^{-1}$$

$$\text{``}K_\alpha\text{''} = 8 \times 40 = 320\ \text{s}^{-2}$$

$$\epsilon_{K_v} = \frac{24}{800} = 0.03°$$

$$\epsilon_{\text{``}K_\alpha\text{''}} = \frac{120}{320} = 0.375°$$

$$A = \frac{(\dot{\theta}_{\max})^2}{\ddot{\theta}_{\max}} = \frac{(24/57.3)^2}{(120/57.3)} \times 57.3 = \frac{24^2}{120} = 4.8°$$

$$\omega_s = \frac{\ddot{\theta}_{\max}}{\dot{\theta}_{\max}} = \frac{120}{24} = 5\frac{\text{rad}}{\text{s}}$$

$$G(j\omega_s) = \frac{\omega_{cp}(s + \omega_i)}{s^2} = \frac{40(j5 + 8)}{25} = -8(j + 1.6)$$

$$= -12.8 - j8$$

$$|1 + G(j\omega_s)| = |-11.8 - j8| = \sqrt{11.8^2 + 8^2} = 14.3$$

$$\epsilon = \frac{4.8°}{14.3} = 0.336°$$

Therefore use $\epsilon_{K_v} + \epsilon_{\text{``}K_\alpha\text{''}} = 0.405°$ (larger, more conservative).

(l) Tracking noise:

$$\epsilon = \frac{\theta_{Bw}}{\sqrt{s/n}}$$

$$45 \text{ dB} = 10^4 \, (\log_{10}^{-1} 0.5) = 31{,}600$$
$$\sqrt{31{,}600} = 178$$
$$\frac{10°}{178} = 0.056°$$

single-axis error budget (deg)

static	pointing ϵ	pointing ϵ^2	tracking ϵ	tracking ϵ^2
static friction	0.220	4.84×10^{-2}	0.220	4.84×10^{-2}
component errors	0.018	0.03×10^{-2}	0.018	0.03×10^{-2}
transducer	1.050	110.25×10^{-2}	—	—
gearing error	0.084	0.71×10^{-2}	—	—
steady torque	0.019	0.04×10^{-2}	0.019	0.04×10^{-2}
wind gusts	0.190	3.61×10^{-2}	0.190	3.61×10^{-2}
sum square		119.48×10^{-2}		8.52×10^{-2}
direct sum	1.581		0.447	
dynamic				
tachometer ripple	0.042	0.18×10^{-2}	0.042	0.18×10^{-2}
target motion	0.405	16.40×10^{-2}	0.405	16.40×10^{-2}
tracking noise	—	—	0.056	0.31×10^{-2}
sum square		16.58×10^{-2}		16.89×10^{-2}
direct sum	0.447		0.503	
total sum square		136.06×10^{-2}		25.41×10^{-2}
direct sum total	2.028		0.950	
root sum square		1.166		0.504

12-16. summary

An approach to error budgets for a servo system was presented. Various error contributors were discussed and approximate formulas (good enough for most design work) were developed. The passing track method of approximating one type of target motion for tracking systems was described.

problems

12-1. By means of an error budget, determine the worst-case values for azimuth and elevation errors for the pointing system defined below.

ω_{cr}: 100 rad/s

ω_{cp}: 20 rad/s

ω_1: 5 rad/s

α: 10

$\Omega_{target(max)}$: 20°/s

$\dot{\Omega}_{target(max)}$: 40°/s²

Tach ripple: 5%, 25 cycles/rev

Transducer error: 0.1° (each)

J_{total}: 0.4 slug·ft² (reflected to load)

Static friction: 2.5 lb·ft

Instrument gearing to transducer: four gears, Class 1 Precision, all 0.8-in. pitch diameter

$T_{unbalance}$: 20 lb·ft

12-2. For a TV camera tracking a racing car, if the car velocity is 240 mi/h and the camera is 100 ft from the track, for $\omega_{cp} = 40$ Hz, $\omega_{cr} = 100$ Hz, $\omega_i = 10$ Hz, $\alpha = 100$, and $J_L = 1.2$ lb·ft·s², find:

(a) the maximum accelerating torque required

(b) a reasonable estimate for the maximum error in tracking; compare this with K_v and "K_α" errors

(c) How low transient torque must be kept so as not to add more than 20 per cent to the error.

12-3. In a servo using an ac tachometer directly coupled to the motor, the in-phase null voltage is 0.2 V, the gear ratio is 20:1 (motor to load), the tachometer generates 2.4 V/1000 rpm, and $\omega_{cp} = 4$ Hz. What is the position error due to the tachometer null voltage?

13

electrohydraulic servos

Electrohydraulic servos have some distinct advantages over electric servos for certain applications. One advantage is that they have excellent torque stiffness. In machine tool control, hydraulic servos are popular because of their very high acceleration capability, which allows rapid motion of the tool (or work piece) from one position to the next. The electronics associated with hydraulic servos can be relatively simple compared to the electronics required for an all-electric motor-driven servo of equal mechanical power. A disadvantage of hydraulic systems, however, is that they require oil at relatively high pressure; leaks can develop, and in cases where fire is a potential hazard, special oils have to be used. It is also necessary to filter the oil continually to prevent damage to the servo valves and other hydraulic components.

13-1. basic relations

To develop the subject of hydraulic servos, the simple but representative valve-controlled actuator model shown in Fig. 13-1 is used. In the lower part of this figure is shown a *four-way spool valve*, which is capable of *porting* supply oil to either side of the actuator piston and returning oil from the other side. If one side of the piston is getting supply oil from the valve, oil from the other side is being ported to Return. The *control spool position* is defined as x; for positive values of x, oil is ported to the left side of the piston, thus resulting in a clockwise angular velocity, Ω_m of the output shaft. In this diagram the effective moment arm r_m of the motor varies as a function of angular position; in actual fixed-displacement rotary hydraulic servo mo-

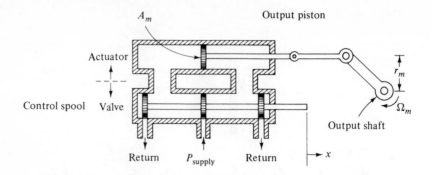

x = control spool position
A_m = effective motor piston area
r_m = effective motor moment arm
P_m = motor differential pressure (piston)
Q_m = motor flow (into, or out of motor)

Figure 13-1. Hydraulic valve-controlled actuator.

tors, the effective moment arm remains constant. The operation of fixed-displacement motors is similar to that suggested by Fig. 13-1.

To develop the characteristics of this basic hydraulic system, the torque and velocity expressions are now derived. Equation (13-1) gives the expression for output torque in terms of the parameters of Fig. 13-1.

$$P_m\left(\frac{\text{lb}}{\text{in}^2}\right) \times A_m(\text{in}^2) \times r_m(\text{in}) = \text{torque (lb}\cdot\text{in)} \qquad (13\text{-}1)$$

It will be noted that the left half of the left side of this expression is the piston force and that quantity times the moment arm gives the output torque. Equation (13-2) is the expression for the output angular velocity.

$$Q_m\left(\frac{\text{in}^3}{\text{s}}\right) \times \frac{1}{A_m(\text{in}^2)} \times \frac{1}{r_m(\text{in})} = \Omega_m(\text{rad/s}) \qquad (13\text{-}2)$$

It will be noted that in both of these equations, $A_m r_m$ appear together; this combination of constants is commonly known as the *motor displacement per radian* or D_m as defined in Eq. (13-3).

$$A_m r_m = D_m = \text{motor displacement per radian} \qquad (13\text{-}3)$$

It is possible to rewrite Eqs. (13-1) and (13-2) using D_m; these important expressions are given in Eqs. (13-4) and (13-5).

$$P_m D_m = T_m \qquad (13\text{-}4)$$

$$\frac{Q_m}{D_m} = \Omega_m \qquad (13\text{-}5)$$

Power in rotary systems is normally expressed as torque times angular velocity; in hydraulic systems it is expressed as pressure times flow. Equation (13-6) is an expression for power in horsepower in terms of pressure in pounds per square inch (psi) and flow in gallons per minute (gpm); pounds per square inch and gallons per minute are the usual units for pressure and flow in hydraulic systems.

$$\text{Horsepower} = \frac{PQ}{1714} \qquad (P \text{ in psi, } Q \text{ in gpm}) \qquad (13\text{-}6)$$

As an example, if a load is being driven by a hydraulic actuator that has 2000 psi across it, and 10 gpm is flowing into the actuator, the power is found as 11.65 hp in Eq. (13-7).

$$\text{Power} = \frac{2000 \text{ psi} \times 10 \text{ gpm}}{1714(\text{psi} \cdot \text{gpm/hp})} = 11.65 \text{ hp} \qquad (13\text{-}7)$$

In hydraulic servos, two-stage electrohydraulic servo valves are the most commonly used controlling devices. These valves consist of a torque motor device which operates a small flapper valve (or other low-flow valve); this in turn controls the position of the spool (shown schematically in Fig. 13-1). It is called a two-stage valve because the first stage is the flapper–nozzle combination and the second stage is the spool. Examples of two-stage electrohydraulic servo valves manufactured by Sanders Associates are given in Table 13-1. The specifications for flow in gallons per minute are normally

Table 13-1   sanders associates two-stage electrohydraulic servo valves (flapper–nozzle first stage)

Q_m (gpm)	f_n 90° phase lag (Hz)	weight (lb)
0.25	90	1
2.5	90	1.25
16	55	3.7
55	35	8
170	15	40

given for a pressure drop of 1000 psi across the valve; this is necessary because as the pressure varies, the amount of flow varies for a given orifice; this characteristic is discussed below. The natural frequency f_n for these valves relates to the resonant frequency of the valve and indicates the effective limit in bandwidth of the valve's ability to respond to input signals. The weight of these valves indicates the excellent weight efficiency of these devices; it was seen in a previous example that 10 gpm at 2000 psi represents approximately 12 hp. Therefore the third valve, weighing less than 4 lb, can control more than 12 hp (not considered is the weight and volume of the required hydraulic power supply).

To understand properly the operation of electrohydraulic servos, it is necessary to understand the operation of a *servo valve*, which is the heart of these systems. Figure 13-2 shows the basic characteristic of a servo valve;

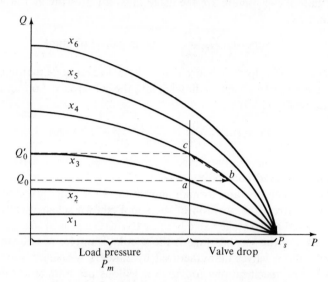

Figure 13-2. Hydraulic spool valve characteristic.

Eq. (13-8) describes the valve characteristic in analytical form.

$$Q_v = Cx\sqrt{P_s - P_L} \tag{13-8}$$

The above equation states that the flow through the valve is equal to a constant C times spool position x times the square root of the difference between the supply pressure P_s and the load pressure P_L. Because of the square root, the curves are parabolic; also, the flow is zero if the load pressure equals the supply pressure (because there must be a pressure across the valve to result in flow through it). Along the abscissa of the figure are shown two regions; P_m is the load pressure drop; the valve pressure drop is shown to the right of P_m. A valve's maximum flow is rated at a particular pressure across the valve (usually 1000 psi). At one-third of the supply pressure drop across the valve, the maximum possible power goes to the motor. This can be proved quite readily by considering Eqs. (13-9) and (13-10). Equation (13-9) expresses the motor flow in terms of the constants of the valve and the pressure across the valve. Equation (13-10) states the power to the load (motor).

$$Q_m = Cx\sqrt{P_s - P_m} \tag{13-9}$$

$$\text{Power} = H = P_m Q_m = P_m Cx\sqrt{P_s - P_m} \tag{13-10}$$

If the derivative of Eq. (13-10) is set equal to zero, it is found that the motor pressure for maximum motor power is two-thirds of the supply pressure [Eq. (13-11)].

$$P_m = \frac{2}{3} P_s \quad \text{for} \quad \frac{dH}{dP_m} = 0 \tag{13-11}$$

For a 1000-psi supply, the maximum load power point would be for a motor pressure of approximately 667 psi; this implies a valve drop of 333 psi. By taking the square root of one-third and multiplying this by the 1000-psi flow rating of the valve, the flow at the maximum power point is then determined. There are lower limits to the valve's supply pressure determined by the amount of pressure required by the valve's first stage; for high-quality valves, this pressure can be 150 psi or even lower. For less expensive valves, the pilot (first) stage requires a higher pressure for proper operation. Manufacturer's data on valves will supply this information.

Example 13-1. Find two values of D_m from the motor data of Table 13-2.

solution

(a) From displacement data,

$$D_m = \frac{0.76 \text{ in}^3}{\text{rev}} \times \frac{1 \text{ rev}}{2\pi \text{ rad}} = 0.12 \frac{\text{in}^3}{\text{rad}}$$

(b) From torque data,

$$T_m = P_m D_m$$

$$D_m = \frac{T_m}{P_m} = \frac{12 \text{ in} \cdot \text{lb}}{100 \text{ lb/in}^2} = \frac{12 \text{ in}^3}{100}$$

$$= 0.12 \text{ in}^3 = 0.12 \frac{\text{in}^3}{\text{rad}}$$

Table 13-2   significant characteristics of a hydraulic servomotor

maximum speed	3600 rev/min
displacement	0.76 in³/rev
torque	12 in·lb/100 psi
volume under compression	0.85 in³
weight	16.75 lb

Example 13-2. By two methods, verify the output power expected for 800 psi across the motor of Table 13-2 operating at 1000 rev/min.

solution

(a) 800 psi; 1000 rev/min.

$$P = \Omega_m T_m = \frac{PQ}{1714}$$

$$Q = 1000 \frac{\text{rev}}{\text{min}} \times \frac{0.76 \text{ in}^3}{\text{rev}} \times \frac{\text{gal}}{231 \text{ in}^3} = 3.29 \text{ gpm}$$

$$\text{Power}_1 = \frac{3.29 \times 800}{1714} = 1.535 \text{ hp}$$

(b) $\text{Power}_2 = \Omega_m T_m = 1000 \frac{\text{rev}}{\text{min}} \times \frac{2\pi \text{ rad}}{\text{rev}} \times 800 \frac{\text{lb}}{\text{in}^2} \times \frac{0.12 \text{ in}^3}{\text{rad}}$

$$= 604,000 \frac{\text{in} \cdot \text{lb}}{\text{min}}$$

$$= 604,000 \frac{\text{in} \cdot \text{lb}}{\text{min}} \times \frac{\text{ft}}{12 \text{ in}} \times \frac{\text{hp}}{33,000 \text{ lb} \cdot \text{ft/min}}$$

$$= 1.52 \text{ hp}$$

Example 13-3

(a) Calculate the maximum valve flow for a Moog 73-103 servo valve for a supply pressure of 1800 psi. The 73-103 valve is rated at 10 gpm at 1000-psi drop across the valve.
(b) Calculate the maximum power this valve provides to a load when supplied by a 1800-psi power supply pressure.

solution

(a) For $P_{\text{supply}} = 1800$ psi, $Q_{\max} = 10 \text{ gpm} \times \sqrt{\frac{1800}{1000}} = 13.4 \text{ gpm}$

This calculated maximum flow is for zero load pressure, or in other words, for valve flow directly back to the power supply return.

$$Q_{\max \text{ power}} = 10 \text{ gpm} \times \sqrt{\frac{\frac{1}{3} \times 1800}{1000}} = 7.75 \text{ gpm}$$

(b) maximum power $= \dfrac{1200 \text{ psi} \times 7.75 \text{ gpm}}{1714} = 5.42 \text{ hp}$

13-2. motor–valve analysis

The general expression for flow in an electrohydraulic servo system is given in Eq. (13-12); this equates the valve flow to the sum of the flows to the motor, to leakage and to oil compressibility (due to the effective spring rate of the fluid).

$$Q_{\text{valve}} = Q_{\text{motor}} + Q_{\text{leakage}} + Q_{\text{compressibility}} \qquad (13\text{-}12)$$

This equation is restated in Eq. (13-13) in incremental form.

$$\Delta Q_{\text{valve}} = \Delta Q_m + \Delta Q_L + \Delta Q_c \qquad (13\text{-}13)$$

Initially, to simplify the analysis, only one of the terms from the right-hand side of this equation will be considered.

Equation (13-14) describes the valve performance in terms of the partial derivatives of the valve characteristic.

$$\Delta Q_{\text{valve}} = \left(\frac{\partial Q_m}{\partial x}\right) \Delta x + \left(\frac{\partial Q_m}{\partial P_m}\right) \Delta P_m \qquad (13\text{-}14)$$

These partial derivatives relate flow to spool position and to load (motor) pressure. This equation is an incremental equation; if one considers that at any time for relatively small signals the valve is working at some operating point, it is then possible to eliminate the deltas and Eq. (13-15) results. For simplification, two new constants are defined in Eqs. (13-16) through (13-18).

$$Q_v = \left(\frac{\partial Q_m}{\partial x_m}\right)x + \left(\frac{\partial Q_m}{\partial P_m}\right)P_m \tag{13-15}$$

Let

$$\frac{\partial Q_m}{\partial x} = K_v \tag{13-16}$$

$$\left|\frac{\partial Q_m}{\partial P_m}\right| = F_v \tag{13-17}$$

$$\frac{\partial Q_m}{\partial P_m} = -F_v \tag{13-18}$$

It will be noticed that the flow gain of the valve is called K_v; this should not be confused with a servo's K_v (velocity constant), which is quite different from this flow gain. The derivative of flow with respect to pressure is a negative value, because a motor pressure increase implies a decrease in valve pressure drop, and for a constant spool position, decreased flow results. The motor flow is given in Eq. (13-19) in terms of the displacement constant and angular velocity of the motor. It is now possible to write Eq. (13-20) as a general expression for the valve flow.

$$Q_{\text{motor}} = D_m\Omega_m \tag{13-19}$$

$$Q_v(s) = K_v x(s) - F_v P_m(s) = Q_m(s) = D_m\Omega_m(s) \tag{13-20}$$

In order to get a solution from this equation, it is necessary to find a relationship between the motor pressure and flow. For an inertial load, Eq. (13-21) can be written; when transposed, Eq. (13-22) results, which relates pressure to velocity.

$$T(s) = Js\Omega_m(s) = D_m P_m(s) \tag{13-21}$$

$$P_m(s) = \frac{Js\Omega_m(s)}{D_m} \tag{13-22}$$

Substituting this into Eq. (13-20) gives Eq. (13-23); Eq. (13-24) follows from this. The final expression relating output velocity to input spool position is given in Eq. (13-25).

$$Q_{\text{valve}}(s) = K_v x(s) - \frac{F_v Js\Omega_m(s)}{D_m} = D_m\Omega_m(s) \tag{13-23}$$

$$K_v x(s) = \left(\frac{F_v Js}{D_m} + D_m\right)\Omega_m(s) \tag{13-24}$$

$$\frac{\Omega_m(s)}{x(s)} = \frac{K_v}{(F_v Js/D_m) + D_m} = \frac{K_v/D_m}{1 + (F_v J/D_m^2)s} \tag{13-25}$$

This result implies that there is a simple time constant (low-pass filter action) associated with a servo valve working into a fixed displacement motor with an inertial load. This effect can be visualized by examining Fig. 13-2. Given the steady-state operating point shown at a, which implies a constant load velocity (constant Q_0) and a constant load torque (constant P_m), if a step function in x is applied to the system (x_3 to x_4), because of conservation of momentum, the instantaneous operating point moves from a to b, thus providing an increased load pressure drop. The excess pressure provides a torque to the inertial load, causing it to accelerate. It will accelerate along the x_4 curve from b to c, where a new equilibrium flow of Q_0' is reached. This point is on the x_4 spool position curve and at the initial load pressure (which assumes a constant load torque). The equations and the discussion just given are not intended to provide a quantitative means of calculating hydraulic system performance, but rather to show the physical mechanism of system operation when leakage and compressibility can be neglected. Equation (13-25) is valid, but to be used in practice the fact that the damping F_v varies must be considered.*

The system just described can be represented as a conceptual loop. The basic equations are given in Eqs. (13-26) and (13-27).

$$Q_m = K_v x - F_v P_m \tag{13-26}$$

$$K_v x - Q_m = F_v P_m \tag{13-27}$$

Figure 13-3 shows the conceptual loop; examination of this figure indicates

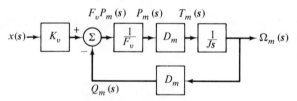

Figure 13-3. Conceptual loop of spool valve driving fixed-displacement actuator and inertia load.

that it meets the conditions of the two equations. This loop is solved in Eq. (13-28), which gives the correct result.

$$\frac{\Omega_m(s)}{x(s)} = K_v \left[\frac{D_m/F_v Js}{1 + (D_m)^2/F_v Js} \right] = \frac{K_v D_m}{F_v Js + (D_m)^2} = \frac{K_v/D_m}{1 + [F_v J/(D_m)^2]s} \tag{13-28}$$

* For an excellent reference on electrohydraulic servos which also covers the nonlinear aspects of these servos, see Allen C. Morse, *Electrohydraulic Servomechanisms* (New York: McGraw-Hill Book Company, Inc., 1963).

13-3. leakage flow

Another physical reality which must be considered in a model of this type is *leakage flow*: flow that is proportional to the pressure drop across the motor. It is not considered to be leakage out of pipes or oil dripping on the floor, but rather it is "resistive" flow that goes from the high-pressure line back to the return line around the motor, through seals, or through other similar conducting regions (or intentionally through needle valves to provide added damping). Leakage flow is defined in Eq. (13-29); it is incorporated in the system in Eq. (13-30), which is similar to Eq. (13-20) but now includes leakage flow. Equation (13-31) is a restatement of this expression. Equation (13-32) gives the motor flow to spool position transfer function.

$$Q_{leakage} = LP_m \tag{13-29}$$

$$\underbrace{K_v x(s) - F_v P_m(s)}_{Q_{valve}} = \underbrace{LP_m(s)}_{\text{leakage flow}} + \underbrace{D_m \Omega(s)}_{\text{motor flow}} \tag{13-30}$$

$$K_v x(s) = (F_v + L)P_m(s) + D_m \Omega(s)$$
$$= (F_v + L)\frac{Js\Omega_m(s)}{D_m} + D_m \Omega_m(s) \tag{13-31}$$

$$\frac{\Omega_m(s)}{x(s)} = \frac{K_v}{(F_v + L)Js/D_m + D_m} = \frac{K_v/D_m}{1 + [J(F_v + L)/(D_m)^2]s} \tag{13-32}$$

This is similar to Eq. (13-28) except that the valve damping term F_v is increased by the leakage term L. Equation (13-32) indicates that an increased damping term due to leakage flow increases the time constant of that equation; therefore, the more leakage that is present, the more sluggish the system becomes. Figure 13-4 gives the conceptual loop for the system considering leakage flow.

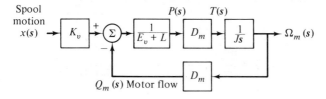

Figure 13-4. Conceptual loop of spool valve and load considering leakage flow.

13-4. compressibility flow: hydraulic resonance

Another characteristic that must be considered in writing equations for a hydraulic system is *oil compressibility*. Oil has a finite spring constant;

if a column of oil is subjected to compression, its volume is reduced by some small finite amount. Therefore, if the pressure on it changes, the volume also changes. This is shown schematically in Fig. 13-5, indicating that for

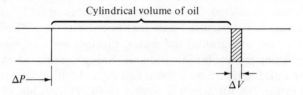

Figure 13-5. Volume change of oil under compression.

a slight change in pressure ΔP, there is a slight change in volume ΔV. This is defined in Eq. (13-33), where K_c is the compressibility constant.

$$\Delta V = K_c \, \Delta P \tag{13-33}$$

$$V(s) = K_c P(s) \tag{13-34}$$

In Laplace form, this is expressed in Eq. (13-34). Considering the fact that flow is the derivative of volume, Eq. (13-35) can be written; this result can be substituted into the general equation for the valve and load, resulting in Eq. (13-36).

$$Q(s) = sV(s) = sK_c P(s) \tag{13-35}$$

$$K_v x(s) = (F_v + L)P_m(s) + D_m\Omega(s) + sK_c P_m(s)$$

Let $F_v + L = F$. Then

$$K_v x(s) = (F + sK_c)P_m(s) + D_m\Omega(s)$$

$$= (F + sK_c)\frac{Js\Omega(s)}{D_m} + D_m\Omega(s) \tag{13-36}$$

Motor flow, therefore, is defined in Eq. (13-37), and the overall system spool-position to velocity transfer function is given in Eq. (13-38).

$$K_v x(s) = \left(D_m + \frac{JsF}{D_m} + \frac{Js^2 K_c}{D_m}\right)\Omega(s) \tag{13-37}$$

$$\frac{\Omega(s)}{x(s)} = \frac{K_v}{(Js^2 K_c/D_m) + (JsF/D_m) + D_m} = \frac{K_v/D_m}{1 + [JF/(D_m)^2]s + [JK_c/(D_m)^2]s^2} \tag{13-38}$$

$$K_c = \frac{V_{eq}}{\beta}\frac{\text{in}^3}{\text{lb}} \tag{13-39}$$

Equation (13-39) defines the compressibility constant in terms of the bulk modulus of the oil (which is its compressibility constant) and the oil volume of the system. Equations (13-40) and (13-41) define the natural frequency of this quadratic equation. Equations (13-42) and (13-43) define the system damping constant, ζ.

$$(\omega_n)^2 = \frac{(D_m)^2}{JK_c} \tag{13-40}$$

$$\omega_n = \frac{D_m}{\sqrt{JK_c}} \tag{13-41}$$

$$\frac{2\zeta}{\omega_n} = \frac{JF}{(D_m)^2} \tag{13-42}$$

$$\zeta = \frac{\omega_n JF}{2(D_m)^2} = \frac{D_m}{2\sqrt{JK_c}} \times \frac{JF}{(D_m)^2} = \frac{F}{2D_m}\sqrt{\frac{J}{K_c}} \tag{13-43}$$

Equation (13-41) defines ω_n, which is normally referred to as the hydraulic resonant frequency; this effect can be important in some systems. Very much as structural resonance limits the bandwidth of servos in general, this hydraulic resonance limits the bandwidth of hydraulic servos. Note in Eq. (13-38) that increased leakage tends to dampen the hydraulic resonant characteristic. Another means of damping hydraulic resonance is to use *pressure feedback*; this is not discussed in this book but is covered in some of the literature.* Pressure feedback may be accomplished by using electrical differential pressure transducers across the motor ports to measure the differential pressure and feeding this back to create a loop around the valve, or by using a pressure-compensated valve (which has internal pressure feedback).

The conceptual loop for this hydraulic servo with leakage and compressibility effects is given in Fig. 13-6. Equation (13-44) solves this loop; it can be

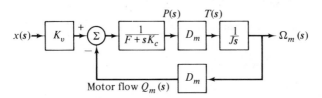

Figure 13-6. Conceptual loop of valve driving load considering leakage and compressibility.

seen that this result is the same as Eq. (13-38).

$$\frac{\Omega_m(s)}{x(s)} = K_v\left[\frac{D_m/(F + sK_c)Js}{1 + (D_m)^2/(F + sK_c)Js}\right] = \frac{K_vD_m}{(F + sK_c)Js + (D_m)^2}$$

$$= \frac{K_vD_m}{(D_m)^2 + FJs + K_cJs^2} = \frac{K_v/D_m}{1 + [FJ/(D_m)^2]s + [K_cJ/(D_m)^2]s^2} \tag{13-44}$$

Example 13-4. A Moog 73-103 valve is used to control the motor of Table 13-2, and the following additional information is known:

* A. C. Morse, *op. cit.*

Total inertia: 0.3 slug·ft²
Power supply pressure: 2000 psi
Load directly coupled to motor
Total volume of oil under compression: 7.5 in³
β = bulk modulus of oil = 250,000 psi

Calculate:
(a) how much leakage would have to be provided across the motor to damp the hydraulic resonance to $\zeta = 1$
(b) a reasonable value of ω_{cp}

solution

$$\text{Moog } 73\text{--}103 \qquad Q1000 \text{ psi} = 10 \text{ gpm}$$

$$\text{Motor} \qquad D_m = 0.12 \frac{\text{in}^3}{\text{rad}} = 0.754 \frac{\text{in}^3}{\text{rev}}$$

(a) $\zeta = \dfrac{F}{2D_m}\sqrt{\dfrac{J\beta}{V_{eq}}} = 1$

Therefore

$$F = 2D_m\sqrt{\frac{V_{eq}}{J\beta}} = 2 \times 0.12 \frac{\text{in}^3}{\text{rad}}\sqrt{\frac{7.5 \text{ in}^3}{0.3 \text{ lb·ft·s}^2 \times 0.25 \times 10^6 \text{ lb/in}^2}}$$

$$= 0.24 \frac{\text{in}^3}{\text{rad}}\sqrt{10^{-4}\frac{\text{in}}{(\text{lb}^2)\text{ ft·s}^2} \times \frac{\text{ft}}{12 \text{ in}}}$$

$$= 0.24 \frac{\text{in}^3}{\text{rad}}\sqrt{0.0833 \times 10^{-4}\frac{\text{in}^4}{(\text{lb·s})^2}}$$

$$= 0.24 \frac{\text{in}^3}{\text{rad}} \times 0.289 \times 10^{-2}\frac{\text{in}^2}{\text{lb·s}} = 0.069 \times 10^{-2}\frac{\text{in}^3/\text{s}}{\text{lb/in}^2}$$

$$= 0.000694 \frac{\text{in}^3/\text{s}}{\text{lb·in}^2}$$

$$F = \frac{0.000694 \text{ in}^3/\text{s/lb·in}^2}{3.86 \text{ in}^3/\text{s/gpm}} = 0.00018 \frac{\text{gpm}}{\text{psi}} = \frac{0.18 \text{ gpm}}{1000 \text{ psi}}$$

(b) $\omega_n = D_m\sqrt{\dfrac{\beta}{JV_{eq}}} = 0.12\dfrac{\text{in}^3}{\text{rad}}\sqrt{\dfrac{0.25 \times 10^6 \text{ lb/in}^2}{0.3 \text{ lb·ft·s}^2 \times 7.5 \text{ in}^3}}$

$$= 0.12 \frac{\text{in}^3}{\text{rad}} \times \sqrt{\frac{250,000 \times 1 \text{ ft}/12 \text{ in}}{2.25 \text{ ft·s}^2 \cdot \text{in}^3}} = 0.12\sqrt{\frac{250,000}{27.00}\frac{1}{\text{in}^6 \cdot \text{s}^2}}$$

$$= 0.12 \frac{\text{in}^3}{\text{rad}} \times 96.3 \frac{1}{\text{in}^3 \cdot \text{s}} = 11.55 \frac{\text{rad}}{\text{s}} \approx 12 \frac{\text{rad}}{\text{s}}$$

To be conservative, let $\omega_{cp} \approx \dfrac{\omega_n}{3} \cong 4 \dfrac{\text{rad}}{\text{s}}$

Example 13-5. If a load motion of 380° clockwise followed by 380° counterclockwise in a total of 0.2 s is required at a maximum repetition rate of 20 per minute, and the drive motor of Table 13-2 is directly coupled to the load, calculate:
(a) the flow rate during the active part of the cycle
(b) the average flow

(c) the servo valve flow rating if the load torque during the active part of the cycle is 15 lb·ft and there is a 2000-psi power supply.

solution

(a) $D_m = 0.12 \dfrac{\text{in}^3}{\text{rad}}$

$$Q_{\text{active}} = \frac{380°}{57.3°/\text{rad}} \times 0.12 \frac{\text{in}^3}{\text{rad}} \times \frac{1}{0.1\ \text{s}}$$

$$= 7.96 \frac{\text{in}^3}{\text{s}} \times \frac{1\ \text{gpm}}{3.86\ \text{in}^3/\text{s}} = 2.06\ \text{gpm (peak)}$$

(b) $Q_{\text{average}} = 2.06\ \text{gpm} \times \dfrac{0.2\ \text{s}}{3\ \text{s}} = 0.1375\ \text{gpm}$

(c) $T_{\text{max}} = P_m D_m = 2000 \dfrac{\text{lb}}{\text{in}^2} \times 0.12 \dfrac{\text{in}^3}{\text{rad}} \times \dfrac{1\ \text{ft}}{12\ \text{in}} = 20\ \text{lb·ft}$

Load torque $= 15\ \text{lb·ft}$; the pressure available across the valve to cause valve flow is

$$\frac{(20 - 15)\ \text{lb·ft}}{D_m} = \frac{5\ \text{lb·ft} \times 12\ \text{in/ft}}{0.12\ (\text{in}^3/\text{rad})\ \text{ft}} = 500\ \text{psi}$$

The valve rating $= 1000$ psi flow. Since

$$Q = K\sqrt{\Delta P}$$

$$\frac{Q_2}{Q_1} = \sqrt{\frac{\Delta P_2}{\Delta P_1}}$$

$$\frac{Q_{1000}}{2.06\ \text{gpm}} = \sqrt{\frac{1000}{500}}$$

Therefore

$$Q_{1000} = 2.06\sqrt{2} = 2.92\ \text{gpm} \approx 3\ \text{gpm}$$

13-5. hydraulic servo systems

In an actual system, the spool is normally driven by hydraulic pressure derived from a pilot stage. This pilot stage is usually controlled by an electric torque motor. Figure 13-7 shows an overall electrohydraulic servo system,

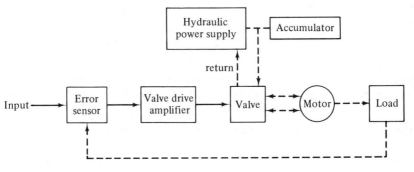

Figure 13-7

where the output of an amplifier is fed into the servo valve. A hydraulic power supply normally consists of a pump (which produces the necessary hydraulic flow at the required pressure) with a drive motor, a reservoir, filters, and a pressure control. The output of this pump is normally coupled through tubing to the valve. Often an accumulator is used near the valve and load; this acts as a hydraulic "capacitor" effectively to maintain the line pressure fairly constant under transient loads.

13-6. summary

The material of this chapter developed a direct technique for analyzing the linear phenomena of electrohydraulic servos. These servos are quite straightforward to design from a system standpoint as long as good quality components are used and they are operated well within their ratings. Care should be taken to check the hydraulic resonant frequency so that it is well above the desired ω_{cp}. By minimizing the path length from the valve to the load, the resonant frequency is maximized.

problems

Given the following valve and motor:

Sanders Associates SV-136 servo valve rated at 2.5 gpm at 1000-psi drop
Vickers MF-2003-A-23-12-20 motor
3600-rpm maximum
$D_m = 0.76 \text{ in}^3/\text{rev} = 0.121 \text{ in}^3/\text{rad}$
$J = 4.8 \times 10^{-3} \text{ lb} \cdot \text{in} \cdot \text{s}^2$
$V_{eq} = 0.85 \text{ in}^3$

13-1. Calculate the maximum power that the valve can supply to a load; the hydraulic power supply pressure is 3000 psi.

13-2. Calculate the output torque at maximum power.

13-3. Find the maximum acceleration of the unloaded motor at the maximum power point.

13-4. Calculate the rated flow motor velocity when driven by the valve.

13-5. If the total effective volume of oil under compression is seven times that of the motor alone, the total inertia is five times that of the motor alone, and $\beta = 250,000$ psi, find the hydraulic resonant frequency.

13-6. (a) How much leakage is required for $\zeta = 1$? (b) Find a reasonable value of ω_{cp}.

14

design—an approach; system performance comparison

Normally, four steps are taken to reach a final servo design. First the drive must be selected; this involves selection of the drive motor and the power gear train (if used). Second, the system bandwidths must be determined from the characteristics that are imposed on the system, including load resonance. Third, system errors must be calculated to assure that the system meets the specified performance; if not, modifications must be made in design. And finally, the saturated performance of the system must be examined to assure that this will not be a problem.

14-1. drive power

Two important elements of drive power are the power applied to the load and the power applied to the motor inertia. In hydraulic drives, the motor inertia is normally quite small; consequently, most of the power goes to the load. In the case of electric drives, because they have higher inertia than hydraulic drives for the same power, it is necessary to consider the power consumed in accelerating and decelerating this motor inertia. Equation (14-1) states the maximum power that a motor is required to provide, including both load and motor effects.

$$P_{\max} \leq (T_{\text{load(max)}})(\Omega_{\text{load(max)}}) + \Omega_{\text{motor(max)}}\ddot{\theta}_{\text{motor(max)}}(J_{\text{motor}} + J_{\text{gear}})$$
$$+ T_{\text{friction}}\Omega_{\max} \qquad (14\text{-}1)$$

It should be noted that in many cases this equation provides a very conservative result, because the load torque and the acceleration torque do not necessarily peak at the same time. It is sometimes necessary to make a torque and speed tabulation to evaluate properly a worst case for the system. However, from a simple first-cut basis Eq. (14-1) gives a valid worst possible power; for many systems, this equation must consider gear train efficiency, bearing losses, and so on. The gear ratio in the system must be set to provide the required maximum load torque and the required maximum load velocity. A useful technique is (a) to calculate the required load power, (b) to select a motor for this power, and then (c) to calculate the required gear ratio. This gear ratio gives the proper load torque and velocity unless the motor requires appreciable accelerating torque; if that is the case, a larger size motor is required.

14-2. system bandwidths

Because a servo's bandwidths are the most important factors in determining its static and dynamic performance, their determination is of great importance. If there are no structural resonance problems (normally true for low-power servos), bandwidth determinations are quite simple. For low-power ac servos, Eq. (14-2) defines the usual limiting bandwidths that can be attained for instrument servos (10 W mechanical power or less).

$$\omega_{cr} \leq \frac{\omega_{\text{carrier}}}{6} \qquad (14\text{-}2)$$

In higher-power systems, load resonance must always be examined; if it is a limiting problem, assumed bandwidths must take resonance effects into consideration. Figure 14-1 is the Bode plot for a simple servo with a resonant load. Figure 14-2 shows the diagram of a motor with resonant load (the damping shown is due to friction and lubrication). Figure 14-3 is the Bode plot of a rate loop with resonant load; it can be seen that the resonant

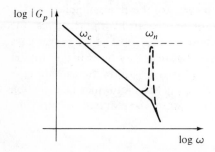

Figure 14-1. Bode plot of an open position loop whose closed-loop bandwidth is limited by structural resonance.

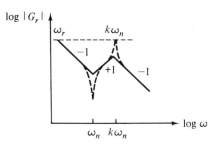

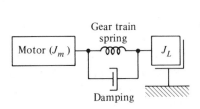

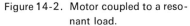

Figure 14-2. Motor coupled to a resonant load.

Figure 14-3. Bode plot of open rate loop
with resonant load.

peaking at $k\omega_n$ imposes a limit on the rate loop bandwidth. Equation (14-3)
defines k.

$$k = \sqrt{\frac{J_L}{J_m}} \qquad (14\text{-}3)$$

The usual assumption for a rate loop is to assume that its bandwidth will
not exceed one-half the natural frequency of resonance ω_n. In some cases,
particularly in electrical drive systems, the rate loop bandwidth can actually
be equal to or slightly greater than the natural frequency 'ω_n. A good initial
approximation, however, is to assume a rate loop bandwidth of one-half the
natural frequency of the load; for a simple uncompensated servo, ω_{cp} may be
assumed to be one-fourth of the natural frequency. The technique for a more
accurate analysis of resonance is merely an extension of the approach shown
previously in Section 11-1; it involves writing the equations for the motor–
load combination and determining from these the limiting rate loop bandwidth; from this the position loop bandwidth can be determined by calculation or by use of a Nichols chart. The position loop bandwidth is normally
one-fourth to one-third of the rate loop bandwidth.

14-3. performance calculation

System errors must be calculated; normally, there are five significant
error contributors. The velocity error is given in Eq. (14-4); this is the maximum reference velocity divided by K_v.

$$\text{Velocity error} = \frac{\Omega_{\max}}{K_v} \qquad (14\text{-}4)$$

The steady torque error is given in Eq. (14-5); the transient torque error is
given in Eq. (14-6) (this is the worst-case calculation).

$$\text{Torque error} = \frac{T_{\max}}{K_T} \qquad (14\text{-}5)$$

$$\text{Transient torque error} = \frac{T_{\text{transient}}}{K_{T(\min)}} \qquad (14\text{-}6)$$

Equation (14-7) gives the static friction error in terms of the servo's transient stiffness.

$$\text{Static friction error} = \frac{T_{SF}}{K_{T(\text{transient})}} \tag{14-7}$$

Various techniques can be used to model the reference variable input motion including the use of a sine wave with particular values of peak velocity and peak acceleration, or the passing track approximation can be used. The technique of combination of these errors is important; direct summing gives a worst-case error, while root-sum squaring may be optimistic.

14-4. saturation

Saturated performance must be considered to assure that the system will not become unstable for large reference variable changes. Equation (14-8) is an approximate expression for the position loop bandwidth in terms of maximum acceleration, maximum velocity, and the number of saturated overshoots.

$$\omega_{cp} = \frac{2A_{\max}}{V_{\max}}(N + 1) \tag{14-8}$$

where

$$A_{\max} = \text{maximum acceleration}$$
$$V_{\max} = \text{maximum velocity}$$
$$N = \text{number of saturated overshoots}$$

If N in this equation is set equal to zero, then the expression defines the maximum value for the position loop bandwidth for no saturated overshoots (which implies smooth synchronization for large step commands). The approximate saturated overshoot settling time is given in Eq. (14-9) for the case where ω_{cp} is greater than the optimum value.

$$T_{\text{setting}} = \left(\frac{V_{\max}}{A_{\max}}\right)(N + 2) \tag{14-9}$$

When the requirements in these four areas of drive power, bandwidths, system errors, and saturated performance have been met, then an acceptable servo design has been achieved. Normally, in the actual process of design, more than one characteristic is found to be unacceptable; it is then necessary to return to an earlier step to modify either the servo design or some external characteristic.

14-5. system performance comparison

In an attempt to compare quantitatively various servo designs, Fig. 14-4 is drawn to represent the open-loop gain characteristics of various

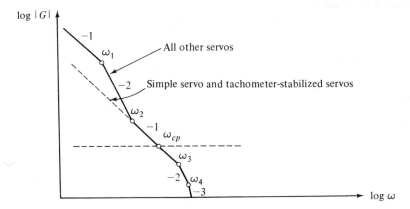

Figure 14-4. Composite open position loop Bode plot.

servo configurations. The dashed part of this curve is for simple and tacho-meter-stabilized servos; the solid line is for the other servo types. The break frequency ω_4 is an assumed limiting frequency such as the motor drive amplifier upper frequency limit or the motor electrical break frequency ω_e. The other three break frequencies and ω_{cp} in this diagram are defined for the five servo designs in Table 14-1. To simplify the comparison, ω_3 is chosen as $\omega_{4/2}$ in all cases except the simple servo where $\omega_3 = \omega_m$.

Table 14-1   significant frequencies for five servo configurations

servo type	bode plot frequencies (Fig. 14-4)			
	ω_1	ω_2	ω_{cp}	ω_3
simple servo	—	—	$\sim \omega_m$	ω_m
lead network	ω_m	$\omega_l = \omega_3/\gamma$	$\sim \sqrt{\gamma}\,\omega_l = \gamma\omega_l/\sqrt{\gamma}$	$\gamma\omega_l = \omega_4/2$
tachometer loop	—	—	$\omega_{cr}/k_1{}^a$	$\omega_{cr} = \omega_4/2$
VCID	ω_m/ψ	$\omega_d = \omega_3/\psi$	$\sim \sqrt{\psi}\,\omega_d = \psi\omega_d/\sqrt{\psi}$	$\psi\omega_d = \omega_4/2$
tachometer loop and integral network	ω_i/α	ω_i	$\omega_{cr}/k_2{}^a$	$\omega_{cr} = \omega_4/2$

[a] k_1 and k_2 are normally in the range of 2 to 5. The value of k_2 should be greater than k_1 to account for the destabilizing effect of the integral network; values of 2 and 3 for k_1 and k_2, respectively, would be reasonable first estimates.

Table 14-2 restates Table 14-1 for particular assumed values of γ, ψ, α, k_1, and k_2; the values of these constants are listed below Table 14-2. Most of the significant break frequencies are expressed in terms of ω_4, which allows direct performance comparison of the five servo types.

Table 14-3 gives formulas for four basic performance characteristics for

Table 14-2   bode plot frequencies for system comparison[a]

servo type	bode plot frequencies			
	ω_1	ω_2	ω_{cp}	ω_3
simple servo	—	—	$\sim \omega_m$	ω_m
lead network	ω_m	$\omega_3/10 = \omega_4/20$	$\omega_3/3 = \omega_4/6$	$\omega_4/2$
tachometer loop	—	—	$\omega_3/2 = \omega_4/4$	$\omega_4/2$
VCID	$\omega_m/20$	$\omega_3/20 = \omega_4/40$	$\omega_3/4 = \omega_4/8$	$\omega_4/2$
tachometer loop and integral network	$\omega_i/\alpha = \omega_4/400$	$\omega_i \approx \omega_3/10$ $= \omega_4/20$	$\omega_3/3 = \omega_4/6$	$\omega_4/2$

[a] $\gamma = 10, \psi = 20, \alpha = 20, \omega_4 =$ upper frequency limit. $k_1 = 2, \sqrt{\gamma} \approx 3, \sqrt{\psi} \approx 4$, $k_2 = 3$.

the five servo types. These formulas are based on the significant break frequencies for each servo type.

Table 14-4 is the performance rating for the five servo configurations based on the previous three tables.

ω_{cp} for the tachometer-stabilized servo (the third design listed) is the highest because this configuration has no open position loop low-frequency lags. The integral network adds phase lag at ω_{cp}, so ω_{cp} for this design is lowered somewhat. The lead network servo can be expected to have about the same ω_{cp} as the tachometer loop servo with integral network. The VCID servo has the lowest ω_{cp} of all (except for the simple servo), because its low-frequency lag at $\omega_{m/\psi}$ is lower than for the others and therefore contributes more phase lag at ω_{cp}. The lead frequency ω_2 for each servo is determined from ω_3 using γ, ψ, and a factor of ten in the case of the tachometer loop and integral network; the assumed values of γ, ψ, and α are listed again in a footnote to Table 14-4.

In Table 14-4 the servos are rated according to their performance in various categories. The highest rating is 5 and the lowest rating is 1. A simple servo, for instance, has the smallest velocity constant of any of the servo types and so it has a 1 rating; for complexity, however, it gets a 5 rating because it is the least complex and therefore the most desirable from this standpoint. Some of the rating numbers are equal for different servo types; for instance, ω_{cp} for the lead network servo and the tachometer loop with integral network servo are both given $3\frac{1}{2}$ because they are equally good in this performance characteristic. The reason that there are other than integer ratings is to make the total of all the servo ratings of one particular characteristic equal 15. The horizontal sum of the rating numbers is the rating for the particular servo type; the servos are listed starting from the top for the lowest rating and moving down to the highest rating.

The performance measures given in Table 14-4 are a good indication of

Table 14-3 servo performance formulas

servo type	ω_{cp}	K_v	$K_{T(dc)}/J$	$K_{T(transient)}$
			performance characteristics	
simple servo	$\sim \omega_m$	$\omega_{cp} \approx \omega_m$	$J\omega_{cp}\omega_m \approx J(\omega_m)^2$	$J\omega_{cp}\omega_m = J(\omega_m)^2$
lead network	$\omega_l\sqrt{\gamma}$	$\omega_{cp}(\omega_l/\omega_m) = (\omega_l)^2\sqrt{\gamma}/\omega_m$	$J\omega_{cp}\omega_l = J(\omega_l)^2\sqrt{\gamma}$	$J\omega_{cp}\omega_l = J(\omega_l)^2\sqrt{\gamma}$
tachometer loop	ω_{cr}/k_1^a	$\omega_{cp} \approx \omega_{cr}/k_1^a$	$J\omega_{cp}\omega_{cr} = J(\omega_{cr})^2/k_1^a$	$J\omega_{cp}\omega_{cr} = J(\omega_{cr})^2/k_1^a$
VCID	$\omega_d\sqrt{\psi}$	$\omega_{cp}(\psi\omega_d/\omega_m) = (\omega_d)^2\psi^{3/2}/\omega_m$	$J\psi\omega_{cp}\omega_d = J(\omega_d)^2\psi^{3/2}$	$J\psi\omega_{cp}\omega_d = J(\omega_d)^2\psi^{3/2}/k_1^a$
tachometer loop and integral network	ω_{cr}/k_2^a	$\alpha\omega_{cp} = \alpha\omega_{cr}/k_2^a$	$J\alpha\omega_{cp}\omega_{cr} = J\alpha(\omega_{cr})^2/k_2^a$	$J\omega_{cp}\omega_{cr} = J(\omega_{cr})^2/k_2$

[a] k_1 and k_2 are normally in the range of 2 to 5. The value of k_2 should be greater than k_1 to account for the destabilizing effect of the integral network; values of 2 and 3 for k_1 and k_2, respectively, would be reasonable first estimates.

Table 14-4 performance ratings of five different servo configurations[a]

servo type	ω_{cp}	K_v	$K_{T(dc)}/J$	complexity	rating
simple servo	ω_m (1)	$\omega_{cp} = \omega_m$ (1)	$\omega_m\omega_{cp} = (\omega_m)^2$ (1)	(5)	8
lead network	$\omega_4/6$ $(3\frac{1}{2})$	$\omega_{cp}(\omega_2/\omega_1) = (\omega_4)^2/120\omega_m$ (3)	$\omega_2\omega_{cp} = (\omega_4)^2/120$ (2)	(3)[b]	11.5
tachometer loop	$\omega_4/4$ (5)	$\omega_{cp} = \omega_4/4$ (2)	$\omega_3\omega_{cp} = (\omega_4)^2/8$ (4)	(2)	13
VCID	$\omega_4/8$ (2)	$\omega_{cp}(\omega_2/\omega_1) = \psi(\omega_4)^2/320\omega_m = (\omega_4)^2/16\omega_m$ (4)	$\omega_3\omega_{cp} = (\omega_4)^2/16$ (3)	(4)	13
tachometer and integral network	$\omega_4/6(3.5)$	$\omega_{cp}\alpha = 10\omega_4/3$ (5)	$\alpha\omega_i\omega_{cp} = (\omega_4)^2/6$ (5)	(1)	14.5

[a] $\omega_4 > 30\omega_m$, $\gamma = 10$, $\psi = 20$, $\alpha = 20$.
[b] The lead network configuration complexity rating is based on the assumption of a dc system.

operating characteristics. ω_{cp} is the closed-loop bandwidth and defines the servo's information-transmitting capability. K_v is an important constant for servos that are required to drive a load at any appreciable velocity. The second-to-last rating, $K_{T(dc)}/J$ is a measure of steady-state torque stiffness; the expressions given are the dc stiffnesses with J factored out, where J is the total inertia. These expressions follow directly from the frequencies given in the previous tables. The lead network servo is rated higher for K_v than the tachometer loop servo, because it is assumed that ω_4/ω_m is greater than 30. This rating chart is only a semiquantitative comparison because of the various assumptions made. For different assumed values of γ, ψ, and α, the results could be different. Also, the best value of ω_3 for each of the four servos would probably be slightly different from $\omega_{4/2}$; this common value was used to make a simple comparison possible. Further, the lead network servo is rated third highest in complexity based on the assumption of a dc servo.

14-6. servo configuration performance comparison example

As an example, consider the motor and drive of Fig. 14-5. Table 14-5 lists ω_{cp}, K_v, and $K_{T(dc)}/J$ for five servo configurations using this motor. The

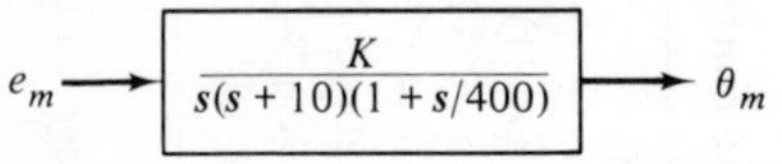

$$e_m \longrightarrow \boxed{\frac{K}{s(s+10)(1+s/400)}} \longrightarrow \theta_m$$

Figure 14-5. Motor and drive for servo comparison example.

"calculated" numbers were obtained using the analytical expressions of Table 14-3. The "actual" numbers were obtained by adjusting the "calculated" position loop gains to give an M_p of 2 dB for each case. Note that all the *calculated* values are conservative relative to the 2-dB peaking values.

Table 14-5   servo configuration performance comparison example[a]

servo type	$\omega_{cp}(\text{s}^{-1})$		$K_v(\text{s}^{-1})$		$[K_{T(dc)}/J](\text{s}^{-2})$	
	calcu-lated	actual	calcu-lated	actual	calcu-lated	actual
simple servo	10	12	10	12	100	120
lead network	67	107	133	214	1,330	2,140
tachometer loop	100	155	100	155	20,000	31,000
VCID	50	54	1000	1080	10,000	10,800
tachometer loop and intagral network	67	100	1333	2000	267,000	400,000

[a] $\omega_m = 10$, $\omega_{cp} = 400$, $\psi = 20$, $\alpha = 20$, $\gamma = 10$.

Therefore Table 14-3 gives reasonably accurate performance formulas. These formulas are valuable for initial system comparison and system performance calculation. More accurate performance figures result when using bandwidths obtained from Nichols charts, from analog or digital computer simulation, or from actual hardware when possible.

In support of the choice of values for ψ, γ, and α, a ψ of 20 was typical for VCID servomotors in catalog data available to the author. The values of γ for the lead network servo could be somewhat larger for improved stability at the expense of increased input noise, but a significant increase would lower K_v, $K_{T(\text{dc})}$, and ω_{cp} appreciably. In effect the VCID and lead network servos have been shown in a fairly good light. By choosing a value of only 20 for α, the tachometer-stabilized integral network compensated servo performance was conservatively presented. In summary, the relative positions of the various servos in the performance rating table (Table 14-4) seem reasonable.

problems

Which servo configuration is the best one to use for each of the following situations for the motor parameters and other constants listed below? Briefly state why it is the best choice.

servomotor or VCID motor (unloaded)		other specifications	
ω_m	20 rad/s	J_L	250 g·cm²
J_m	4 g·cm²	N	10:1
γ	9	ω_l	40 rad/s
ψ	16	ω_{cr}	400 rad/s
ω_d	40 rad/s		

14-1. A servo with a maximum steady load torque of 4 in·oz and an allowable error of 0.5°.

14-2. A servo that must hold the same error as in Problem 14-1, but for an input velocity of 150 rev/min (no load torque).

14-3. A servo that must hold the same error as in Problem 14-1, but for both the load torque and the input velocity.

14-4. A servo that must hold an error of 0.1° for a maximum input velocity of 10 rev/min and a maximum acceleration of 10°/s².

appendix A

operational amplifiers

By using operational amplifiers, the task of designing many circuits becomes simple and routine. Because the gain A and the input impedance of operational amplifiers are very high, it is possible to make some simplifying assumptions for design purposes. Figure A-1 is a convenient representation of an

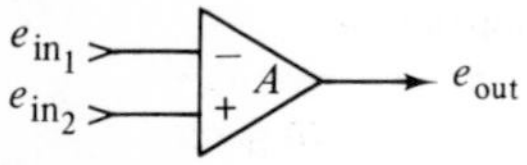

Figure A-1. Operational amplifier block-diagram representation.

operational amplifier; a positive voltage at e_{in_1} causes e_{out} to go negative, and a positive input at e_{in_2} causes e_{out} to go positive. Therefore the output can be represented as

$$e_{out} = -A(e_{in_1} - e_{in_2})$$

Typically, operational amplifiers have values of A of 10,000 or more; as a result, a difference voltage between e_{in_2} and e_{in_1} of 1 mV or less will provide a 10-V output. Many modern operational amplifiers have gains of 50,000 or more, meaning that a 5-V output requires only a 100-μV input difference voltage. As a consequence of this high gain and low input error, *it is reasonable for practically all operational amplifier circuit applications to assume that there is zero input error between e_{in_1} and e_{in_2}.*

Consider the circuit of Fig. A-2, which provides a voltage gain of $-K$ from e_{in} to e_{out}. The fact that the voltage gain is $-K$ can be determined in the following manner: since the input voltage $(e_{in_2} - e_{in_1})$ approaches zero and e_{in_2} is at ground potential, the voltage e_{in} must appear across the resistor R; thus a current e_{in}/R flows through the resistor R and, since the amplifier input impedance is very high, essentially all this current must flow through the feedback resistor KR. Because the input signal initially, momentarily causes e_{in_1} to rise, the output e_{out} swings negative until it is at just the right voltage to pull the current e_{in}/R through it; the output resistance KR times the current e_{in}/R gives the output voltage of $-Ke_{in}$. This output voltage has a minus sign because of the direction of current flow, and because e_{in_1} is effectively at ground potential.

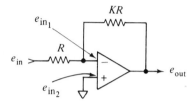

Figure A-2. Voltage amplifier with a gain of minus K.

An easier way to visualize the preceding is to picture the overall gain as $-R_{\text{feedback}}/R_{\text{input}}$; in more general terms this is $-Z_{\text{feedback}}/Z_{\text{input}}$. This last expression is very valuable and is normally used to determine the transfer functions of all operational amplifier circuits of the general form of Fig. A-2. Using this general expression, the gains of the circuits of Figs. A-4 and A-5 are developed. Figures A-4 and A-5 show an integral network and an integrator, respectively. Figure A-3 is the circuit of a subtractor with gain K; the solution of this circuit is given below the figure.

Two important imperfections of operational amplifiers are that they actually do have finite input impedances and they do require small dc input currents. The circuit of Fig. A-6 is a convenient model for visualizing operational amplifier operation, although naturally it is a great simplification. At balance, the input currents are each $i_1/2\beta$; for $i_1 = 10$ μA and $\beta = 100$, the input currents are each 50 nA. This value of current is at the high end of modern operational amplifier capabilities; using field-effect transistors in the input circuit, this current can be 50 pA or less. To show the effect of these currents, consider Fig. A-5; if e_{in} is open circuited to cause C to store its voltage, 50 nA would cause a 0.1-μF storage capacitor to charge at 0.5 V/s; 50-pA input current would cause an output voltage rate of only 0.5 mV/s.

Another effect of input current is to cause an appreciable output voltage offset for large resistors connected to the operational amplifier inputs. Consider Figure A-7: if the input current into the e_{in_2} input is 100 nanoamperes, e_{in_2} will be at -0.25 volt and therefore the voltage at e_{in_1} will have to be at -0.25 volt for the output of the amplifier to be at zero potential. The desired result of compensation is to have e_0 equal to zero volts for zero volts at e_{in}. For this to be true, e_{in_1} must be at -0.25 volt and for the same 100 nanoamperes bias current into the e_{in_1} input, this condition is satisfied for the circuit as shown. The reason that the circuit satisfies the conditions is that

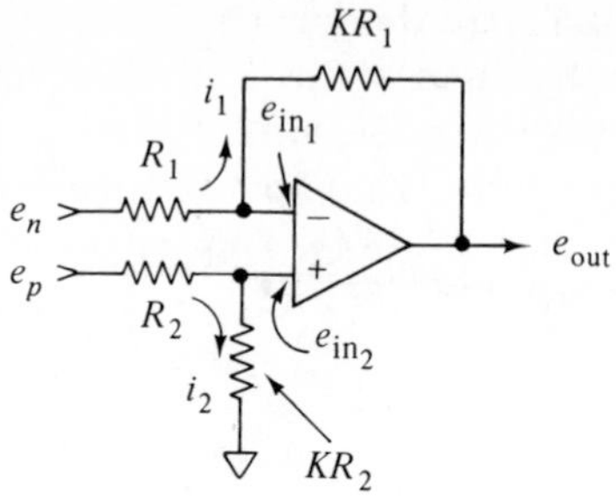

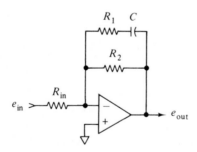

$$i_1 = \frac{e_n - e_{in_1}}{R_1} = \frac{e_{in_1} - e_o}{KR_1} \; ; i_2 = \frac{e_p - e_{in_2}}{R_2} = \frac{e_{in_2}}{KR_2} \; ;$$

$$(e_n - e_{in_2})K = e_{in_1} - e_o \; ; e_n K - e_{in_1} K = e_{in_1} - e_o \; ;$$

$$e_{in_1}(K + 1) = Ke_n + e_o \; ; e_p K - e_{in_2} K = e_{in_2} \; ;$$

$$e_{in_2}(K + 1) = Ke_p \; ; e_{in_1} = \frac{Ke_n + e_o}{K + 1} \; ;$$

$$e_{in_2} = \frac{Ke_p}{K + 1}$$

$$e_{in_2} - e_{in_1} = \frac{Ke_p}{K + 1} - \frac{(Ke_n + e_o)}{K + 1} \to 0$$

Therefore $e_o = -K(e_n - e_p)$

Figure A-3. Voltage subtractor with gain.

$$\frac{E_{out}(s)}{E_{in}(s)} = -\frac{Z_{FB}(s)}{Z_{in}(s)}$$

$$Z_{FB} = R_2 \parallel (R_1 + 1/sC) = \frac{R_2(R_1 + 1/sC)}{R_2 + R_1 + 1/sC}$$

$$= \frac{R_2(1 + R_1 sC)}{1 + (R_1 + R_2)sC}$$

$$Z_{in} = R_{in}$$

$$G(s) = \frac{E_{out}(s)}{E_{in}(s)} = \frac{1}{R_{in}} \left[\frac{-R_2(1 + R_1 sC)}{1 + (R_1 + R_2)sC} \right]$$

$$= -\frac{R_2}{R_{in}} \left[\frac{1 + R_1 sC}{1 + (R_1 + R_2) sC} \right]$$

Figure A-4. Operational amplifier implementation of integral network.

the resistance of R3 is equal to the parallel combination of R1 and R2, and the equal input bias currents cause equal voltage drops resulting in zero potential between e_{in_1} and e_{in_2}. By assuming $e_{in} = e_{out} = 0$ volts, this can be proven easily.

Most inexpensive and general-purpose operational amplifiers can be

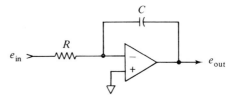

Figure A-5. Operational amplifier implementation of an inte-
grator, including solution
equation.

$$G(s) = \frac{E_{out}(s)}{E_{in}(s)} = -\frac{Z_{FB}(s)}{Z_{in}(s)} = -\frac{1/sC}{R}$$

$$= -\frac{1}{RsC} = -\frac{1/\tau}{s}$$

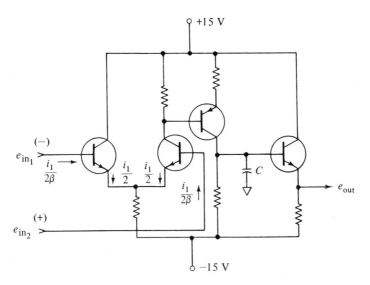

Figure A-6. Simple operational amplifier circuit.

balanced so that with e_{in_1} and e_{in_2} at the same potential at or near ground, the output can be brought to 0 V. This adjustment is to nullify the input voltage offset of the amplifier. Consider Fig. A-8: by adjusting $R_{balance}$, the effect of e_{offset} can be cancelled; this e_{offset} is a convenient representation of the various effects in the amplifier that cause the output voltage to be other than zero when both inputs are grounded.

A practical voltage offset balance circuit which can be quite useful is shown in Fig. A-9. When the switch is depressed, the amplifier has zero input

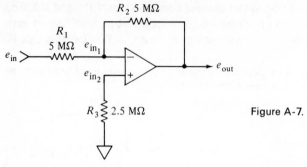

Figure A-7. Amplifier with provision for balancing voltage due to bias currents.

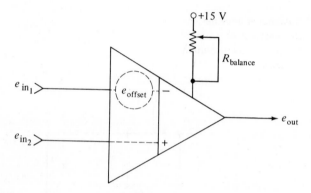

Figure A-8. Input voltage offset equivalent circuit.

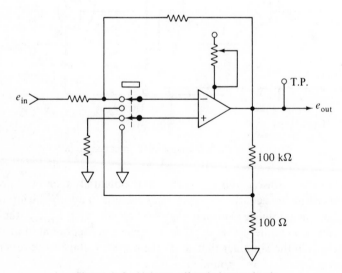

Figure A-9. Voltage offset balance circuit.

to the positive terminal, and a closed-loop gain of 1000. This provides a relatively easy adjustment to balance the voltage offset to 100 μV or less. An input offset of 100 μV in this circuit results in an amplifier output of 0.1 V.

A very useful circuit for buffering potentiometers to avoid loading errors is shown in Fig. A-10. This configuration has a gain of unity (or very close to it), and exhibits an extremely high input impedance.

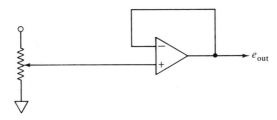

Figure A-10.   High input impedance buffer.

The preceding is intended to serve as an introduction to the use of operational amplifiers. For more theory and application information, a number of operational amplifier manufacturers publish excellent application manuals. For monolithic amplifiers, Fairchild, National Semiconductor, and other companies furnish literature on request. For discrete component amplifiers, Analog Devices and Philbrick/Nexus Research are two companies that also publish literature which may be requested.

appendix B

performance comparison curves

In this appendix, several interesting performance comparison curves are presented. These curves are derived from data given by Chestnut and Mayer.* The first of these is Fig. B-1, which gives values of M_p and of peak transient overshoot for two position loops. The general shape of the Bode plots of these position loops is shown in Fig. B-2. For both position loops $\omega_3/\omega_{cp} = 2$ and the slope from ω_3 to infinity is -2. For $\omega_2 = 0.4\omega_{cp}$, the upper pair of curves shown in Fig. B-1 result; for $\omega_2 = 0.1\omega_{cp}$, the more stable lower pair of curves in Fig. B-1 result. The abscissa of this curve is $K_v/\omega_{cp} = \alpha = \omega_2/\omega_1$, which is a useful normalized parameter for comparison purposes. It can be seen that for higher values of α, the systems generally become more unstable and values of M_p and transient overshoot approach limits. Also, the lower pair of curves "saturate" more rapidly, and indicate more stable performance.

Figure B-3 compares values of M_p for a position loop as a function of the ratio ω_{cp}/ω_3 for two values of slope from ω_3 to infinity and for three values of $\alpha = \omega_2/\omega_1 = K_v/\omega_{cp}$. The ratio ω_{cp}/ω_2 is equal to 4 for Fig. B-3. These curves demonstrate the effect on stability of variations of α, and the severe destabilizing effect of an additional pole at or near ω_3.

Figure B-4 compares values or peak transient overshoot for the same conditions as Fig. B-3.

* Harold Chestnut and Robert W. Mayer, *Servomechanisms and Regulating System Design*, Vol. 1 (New York: John Wiley and Sons, Inc., 1951), pp. 504–32.

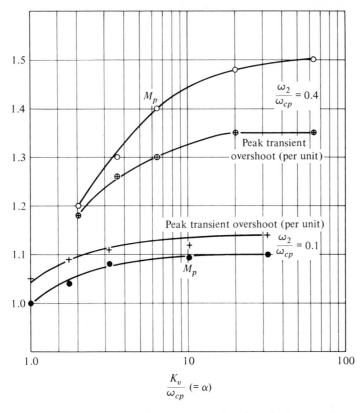

Figure B-1. Variation in peak response as a function of α for two values of ω_2/ω_{cp} ($\omega_3/\omega_{cp} = 2$, -2 slope from ω_3 to ∞).

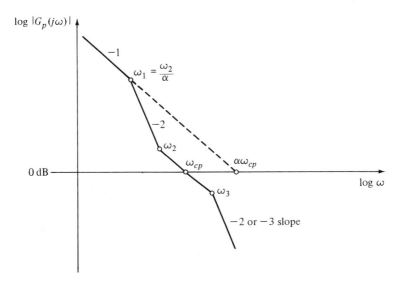

Figure B-2. Generalized open position loop gain characteristic.

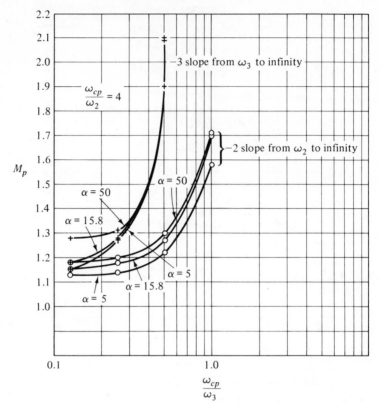

Figure B-3. Variations in M_p as a function of the ratio of ω_{cp} to ω_3 for two values of slope from ω_3 to infinity.

These curves are presented to allow the reader to assess the validity of some of the assumed relative frequency values used in this book and to make rapid determinations of the stability of various Bode plot configurations.

Consider a tachometer-stabilized servo with an integral network with $\omega_{cr} = 100$ rad/s, $\omega_{cp} = 50$ rad/s, and $K_v = 1500$ s^{-1}; find M_p and the peak transient overshoot. For this servo $\omega_3 = \omega_{cr}$, $\omega_3/\omega_{cp} = 2$, and $K_v/\omega_{cp} = \alpha = 30$. If the rate loop were closed along a -1 slope well below the next pole, then the slope from ω_{cr} to infinity could be reasonably approximated as -2. From Fig. B-1 it is then possible to predict accurately the performance of the closed position loop once a value of $\omega_i = \omega_2$ is chosen. For $\omega_2 = 0.1\omega_{cp} = 5$ rad/s, $M_p = 1.1$ and the peak transient overshoot is 14 per cent. For $\omega_2 = 0.4\omega_{cp} = 20$ rad/s, then $M_p = 1.49$ and the peak transient overshoot is 35 per cent.

For a less stable rate loop, the slope from $\omega_3 = \omega_{cr}$ to infinity would be better approximated as a -3 slope. By assuming $\omega_i = \omega_{cp}/4 = 12.5$ rad/s,

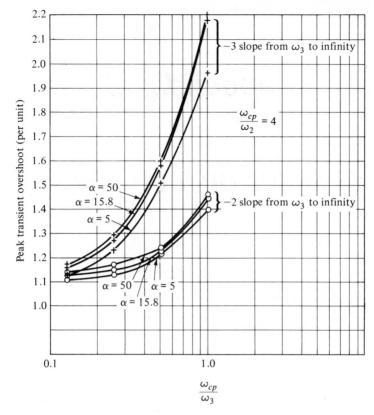

Figure B-4. Variation in peak transient response to a unit step function input as a function of ω_{cp}/ω_3 for three values of α and for two slopes from ω_3 to infinity.

Figs. B-3 and B-4 can be used. Since $\omega_{cp} = \omega_{cr}/2$, $M_p = 2.1$ and the peak transient overshoot is 60 per cent.

Although these curves are for only a limited range of parameters, they can be used to "bracket" the performance of various systems and can be useful as a guide in design.

appendix C

conversion equivalents

parameter	conversion equivalents	
length	2.54 cm	= 1 in
	30.48 cm	= 1 ft
mass	1.459×10^4 g	= 1 slug
	1 lb·s²/ft	= 1 slug
force	2.780×10^4 dynes	= 1 oz
	4.448×10^5 dynes	= 1 lb
	10^5 dynes	= 1 Newton
rotation	6.000 deg/s	= 1 rev/min (rpm)
	0.1047 rad/s	= 1 rev/min (rpm)
	1.745×10^{-2} rad/s	= 1 deg/s
	0.1667 rev/min	= 1 deg/s
	2.778×10^{-3} rev/s	= 1 deg/s
inertia	70,625 g·cm²	= 1 oz·in·s²
	1.356×10^7 g·cm²	= 1 lb·ft·s²
		= 1 slug·ft²
power	745.7 Watts	= 1 hp
	550 ft·lb/s	= 1 hp
	0.738 ft·lb/s	= 1 Watt
	10^7 ergs/s	= 1 Watt
volume	231 in³	= 1 gal
	7.481 gal	= 1 ft³
damping	$0.0497\dfrac{\text{ft}\cdot\text{lb}}{\text{rad/s}}$	$= 1\ \dfrac{\text{oz}\cdot\text{in}}{\text{rev/min}}$
torque	192 oz·in	= 1 ft·lb
	141.6 oz·in	= 1 N·m

pressure	10 dyne/cm^2	= 1 Newton/m^2
	1.453 × 10^{-4} lb/in^2	= 1 Newton/m^2
	9.716 × 10^{-6} atm	= 1 Newton/m^2
	7.501 × 10^{-3}mm(Hg)	= 1 Newton/m^2
stiffness	0.0558 oz·in/min	= 1 lb·ft/rad
	17.9 lb·ft/rad	= 1 oz·in/min
density	10^{-3} g/cm^3	= 1 kg/m^3
	0.0624 lb/ft^3	= 1 kg/m^3
	0.03613 lb/in^3	= 1 g/cm^3
flow	3.85 in^3/s	= 1 gal/min

A dependable method of converting units is to multiply the original quantity or expression by new quantities that are each identical to unity. The expressions that follow are each identical to unity:

(a) $\dfrac{1 \text{ in}}{2.54 \text{ cm}}$ (b) $\dfrac{1 \text{ gal/min}}{3.85 \text{ in}^3/\text{s}}$ (c) $\dfrac{1 \text{ min}}{60 \text{ s}}$

Consider the flow: 18.14 cm^3/min. To convert this to gallons per minute, the above three unity quantities are used as follows:

$$18.14 \frac{\text{cm}^3}{\text{min}} \times \left(\frac{1 \text{ in}}{2.54 \text{ cm}}\right)^3 \times \frac{1 \text{ min}}{60 \text{ s}} \times \frac{1 \text{ gal/min}}{3.85 \text{ in}^3/\text{s}}$$

$$= \frac{18.14 \text{ gal/min}}{(2.54)^3 \times 60 \times 3.85} = 4.78 \text{ gal/min}$$

Note that the units are cancelled algebraically to obtain the desired new expression.

appendix D

moment of inertia calculations

Hollow right circular cylinder about axis:

$$J = \tfrac{1}{8}M(D^2 + d^2)$$

where

$$M = \text{mass}$$
$$D = \text{outside diameter}$$
$$d = \text{inside diameter}$$

Solid right circular cylinder (or disk) about axis:

$$J = \tfrac{1}{2}Mr^2$$
$$= \tfrac{1}{8}MD^2$$

Homogeneous solid sphere about a diameter:

$$J = \tfrac{2}{5}Mr^2 = 0.1MD^2$$

Table of Densities

material	density, ρ	
	g/cm^3	lb/in^3
copper	8.96	0.324
steel	8.03	0.290
aluminum	2.77	0.10

Mass from density and volume:

$$M = \rho V$$

where

ρ = mass density

V = volume of object

appendix E

answers to selected problems

1-1. (a) 54.5 hp, 40,600 W
1-2.   0.0735 hp, 54.9 W
1-3. (a) 0.38 hp, 283 W
    (c) 0.57 hp, 424 W
    (e) 0.00745 hp, 5.57 W
1-4. (a) $0.99 \angle 0°$, $0.0099 \angle 0°$
    (b) $0.91 \angle 0°$, $0.091 \angle 0°$
    (c) $0.5 \angle 0°$, $0.5 \angle 0°$
    (d) $0.33 \angle 0°$, $0.67 \angle 0°$
    (e) $1 \angle -.57°$, $0.01 \angle +89.43°$
    (f) $1 \angle -5.7°$, $0.1 \angle +84.3°$
    (g) $0.707 \angle -45°$, $0.707 \angle +45°$
    (h) $0.45 \angle -63.4°$, $0.9 \angle +26.6°$
    (i) $1.3 \angle -67.5°$, $1.3 \angle +67.5°$
    (j) $11.5 \angle -87.5°$, $11.5 \angle +87.5°$
    (k) $-\infty$, $+\infty$
1-5. (a) $7 \angle +52.5°$ V
1-6. (a) 21 V·s
    (c) 16 V·s
    (e) 0.50V6 ·s
2-1. (a) $\dfrac{1}{1 + j\omega R_1 C_1}$
    (b) $\dfrac{R_2}{R_1 + R_2} \left\{ \dfrac{1}{1 + j[R_1 R_2/(R_1 + R_2)]\omega_{c_1}} \right\}$

304

2-2. (b) 1749 Hz

2-3. (a) 32.2 Hz; 183 Hz

2-8. (a) $\dfrac{s}{s + 1000}$

   (b) $\dfrac{0.1s}{s + 100}$

2-10. (b) 20

2-11. (a) 2000 Hz

2-12.   1.57

3-2. $k\left(\dfrac{1 + s\tau_1}{1 + sk\tau_1}\right)$

3-3. (c) $\dfrac{1}{1 + s/18}$

   (d) $10(1 - e^{-18t})$

3-5. $1.5(e^{-3t} - e^{-5t})$

4-1. $3°$

4-2. $0.0955°$

4-5. (a) $0.745\ \text{lb}\cdot\text{ft}\cdot\text{s}^2$

   (b) $0.083\ \text{lb}\cdot\text{ft}\cdot\text{s}^2$

4-7. (b) $80\ \text{s}^{-1}$

   (c) $\dfrac{1.25}{1 + s/80}$

   (d) $1\angle -38°$

5-1. (a) 685 rad/s

5-2. (a) $\dfrac{2.62\ \text{rad/s/V}}{1 + s/685}$

5-3. (a) $104.8(1 - e^{-685t})$ rad/s

5-6. (a) 0.0033 hp

   (b) 0.0091 hp

5-8. (a) 0.198 rad/s

6-1.   1500 rad/s

6-2.   50

6-3.   104.5 rad/s

6-4.   20.8

6-5. $2.3°$

6-6. $0.88°$

6-7.   875 rad/s

6-8. (c) 17.15 rad/s

   (d) 26.6 V/V

   (e) $35.1°$

   (f) $41.9°$

6-9. (a) $0.537°$

   (b) $0.5°$

6-11. (a) 25

      (b) 12.18 rad/s

      (c) 98.6°

      (d) 15.8°

6-14. (a) 4.22 rad/s

      (b) 0.163 s

      (c) 0.326 s

7-1.   2.5

7-3. (a) 180 rad/s

      (b) 94.2 V/V

      (f) 1.62°

      (g) 0.44°

7-5. (a) 7.65°

      (b) 0.078°

8-1. (a) -37.32 rad/s; -2.68 rad/s

      (b) -20 rad/s; -20 rad/s

      (c) $-20 \pm j24.5$ rad/s

      (f) $+0.16$ dB for Case C

8-3. (a) 20 rad/s

      (b) 0.625

      (c) 51.3°

      (d) $+0.2$ dB

8-4. (a) -0.2 dB$\angle -12°$

      (c) $+1.9$ dB$\angle -3.5°$

      (e) -2.7 dB$\angle -43°$

      (g) $+12$ dB$\angle -65°$

8-6. (b) $+2$ dB

9-2. (b) $R_1 = 5.23$ kΩ. $R_2 = 204$ kΩ. $C = 39.2$ μF

9-4. $+0.26$ dB$\angle -14°$

10-2.   113 rad/s

10-3. (a) 36.5 rad/s

10-4. (b) 701 s^{-1}

11-1. $\omega_{cp} = 11.6$ rad/s

11-2. $0.526\angle -126.9° = -5.58$ dB$\angle -126.9°$; -3.68dB$\angle -95.3°$

11-4.   33.6 kΩ

11-6.   0.05 V/s

12-2. (a) 9.67 lb·ft

      (b) 0.08°; $\epsilon_{K_v} = 0.0082°$; $\epsilon_{K_A} = 0.03°$

      (c) 53 lb·ft

12-3.   0.993°

13-2.   20.2 lb·ft

13-4.   7650 rev/min

13-5.   160 rad/s

14-1.   VCID; the simplest servo that meets the specifications

14-4.   VCID; the simplest servo that meets the specifications

appendix F

experiments

To more fully understand the material in this book, it will help greatly to perform experiments demonstrating the principles of servomechanism design. The experiments outlined below are representative of those that develop an understanding of servomechanisms.

Certain basic instruments are required to perform these experiments: a volt-ohm-milliameter, a dc cathode ray oscilloscope (CRO) and a function generator. For the servomechanisms themselves, a servo mechanical assembly and a servo electronic assembly is needed.

The *function generator* should be capable of producing sinewaves, square waves, and triangular waves in the frequency range of 0.1 hertz to 1000 hertz.

The *servo mechanical assembly* should include a dc motor, a dc tachometer, a low compliance coupling, a precision potentiometer (continuous rotation), a command potentiometer (precision not necessary), gears, hangers, a mounting plate, and miscellaneous hardware.

The *servo electronic assembly* should include at least 7 operational amplifiers, a power supply, a power amplifier to drive the motor, gain controls, and assorted resistors and capacitors.

The servo mechanical assembly and servo electronic assembly may be obtained from Humphrey Instruments Incorporated, 35 Cold Soil Road, Lawrenceville, New Jersey 08648.

The experiments described below outline the goals and general procedures involved, but do not give specific component values, gains, etc. because these vary greatly depending on the motor, tachometer, and other components used. For a particular motor and tachometer, some of the early experi-

Figure F-1   Servo mechanical assembly and power amplifier (Courtesy
of Humphrey Instruments Incorporated).

ments can be performed, and the results can be used to more completely
define later experiments.

Experiment 1   voltage amplifiers

Construct operational amplifier circuits to give closed loop gains of
1, 10, and 100. Examine their transient and frequency response characteristics
by applying sinewave and square wave signals of various frequencies.

Experiment 2   the integrator

Construct an operational amplifier integrator with a calculated gain
crossover frequency of 10 hertz. Attempt to measure its open loop gain and
phase shift at 0.1 hertz, 1 hertz, 10 hertz, 100 hertz, and 1000 hertz. Using
a second operational amplifier as a summing amplifier with a gain from either
input to the output of unity, close a loop around the integrator; measure the
combined gain and phase at the 5 frequencies mentioned above. Measure the
closed loop transient response to a 1 hertz square wave. Open the feedback
line to the summer and measure the open loop transient response.

Experiment 3   a simulated servo

An integrator in a loop acts very much like a simple servo. Using the
integrator and summing amplifier of Experiment 2, measure the closed loop
system's performance at 4 different loop gains (by varying the integrator
input resistor or summer feedback resistor). The gain crossover frequency
can be determined by measuring the closed loop frequency at which the gain
is 0.707 and the phase lag is 45°. Measure K_v for the 4 gains using a triangular
wave input.

Experiment 4   servo motor performance

Using a dc servo motor driven by a power amplifier, a tachometer coupled to the motor, the tachometer voltage as output, and the power amplifier input signal as input, measure the motor response to sinewaves of four different frequencies (the sinewave input amplitude should be as small as practical). Also measure the transient response to square wave inputs of several different frequencies (again use small input amplitudes). Vary the total inertia coupled to the motor and note the changes in response. Also add one or more resistors in series between the power amplifier and motor and note the effect (the resistors should be comparable in size to the motor armature resistance). Put a small resistor in the motor ground return, apply a small high frequency square wave to the power amplifier, prevent any motion of the motor shaft; by measuring the rise time of the voltage across the small series resistor, the electrical time constant can be measured.

Experiment 5   simple servo design

Using the results of Experiment 4, construct a servo using a feedback potentiometer, a command potentiometer, and a buffer amplifier (to prevent potentiometer loading). Adjust the position loop gain to give approximately 16% transient overshoot to a step function input (added to the command potentiometer voltage by means of another summing resistor); compare the actual gain to that based on calculation. Measure K_v using a triangular wave and K_T by applying an external torque to the motor.

Experiment 6   tachometer stabilization

Close a tachometer loop around the motor; increase the gain until there is a noticeable overshoot in the transient response (measured by applying a small square wave to the rate loop input and examining the tachometer output voltage). Decrease the gain only enough to reduce the transient overshoot to 5% or slightly less. Close a position loop around the rate loop; increase the gain to give approximately a 16% transient overshoot. Measure K_v and K_T; compare the results with those of Experiment 5. Increase the inertia by a factor of about 2 and measure K_V and K_T again.

Experiment 7   back emf stabilization

Repeat Experiment 6 using back emf stabilization. Be sure to change the back emf network when the inertia is changed.

Experiment 8   stability

Using operational amplifiers, construct an integrator in series with a simple lag and an adjustable gain. Close the loop and measure transient overshoot and M_p for Case 1, Case 2, and Case 3 gain settings.

Experiment 9   integral networks

Construct an active integral network with an ω_i of approximately one fifth of the ω_{c_p} of Experiment 6; measure its gain and phase shift in the regions of $\omega_i{}_\alpha$, ω_i, $5\omega_i$, and $10\omega_i$. Examine the transient response using square wave inputs of several frequencies.

Experiment 10   integral network compensated servo

Using the integral network of Experiment 9 in the position loop of the Experiment 6 servo, determine its destabilizing effect on the servo by measuring the frequency and transient responses. Adjust the position loop gain (and rate loop gain if necessary) to give approximately a 16% transient overshoot; measure K_V, K_T and ω_{c_p}.

Experiment 11   lead network

Construct a passive lead network; use a buffer amplifier at its output to prevent loading. Use information from Experiment 5 to select reasonable values of ω_l and γ. Examine the circuit's frequency response in the regions of $\omega_l/5$, ω_l, $\omega_l\sqrt{\gamma}$, $\gamma\omega_l$, and $5\gamma\omega_l$.

Experiment 12   lead network servo

Using the lead network of Experiment 11 in the position loop of the Experiment 5 servo, determine the stability for several values of gain in the position loop. For these gains find ω_{c_p}, K_V and K_T.

Experiment 13   scaling

Using the tachometer stabilized servo of Experiment 6, determine the maximum velocity of the servo by commanding the system with very large command potentiometer changes. Alter the values of the operational amplifier network resistors to cause the servo to have one half this maximum velocity capability while maintaining the same rate loop and position loop bandwidths.

Experiment 14   saturated instability

Using the tachometer stabilized servo of Experiment 6, increase the inertia by a factor of 4 or more and increase the rate loop gain by approximately the same amount to maintain the same rate loop stability. By applying a saturated position step input, determine if there is saturated instability; if there is not, modify the scaling to obtain a higher maximum speed. Determine how low a value of ω_{c_p} must be used to stop the saturated instability; compare this value with the calculated value determined from measured values of $\dot{\theta}_{max}$ and $\ddot{\theta}_{max}$.

index

a

Acceleration constant, 254
Acceleration damped servos, *see* Viscous coupled inertial damped servos (VCID)
Algebra, block diagram, 25-28, 129-130
Amplifier gain, calculating, 95-97
Amplifiers:
  current source, 131
  drive, 76-78
  operational, 290-295
Analysis techniques, 18-38
  block-diagram algebra, 25-28
  frequency-response, 18-21
  frequency-response solution of integrator loop, 30-32
  gain of an integrator, 28-30
  ideal motor servo, 32-35
  Laplace transforms, 23-24
  transfer functions, 24-25
  transient, 21-23
Armature inductance, 78-80
Asympotic gain crossover frequency, 90
Automatic scanning generators, 231
Automatic tracking system, 225-231
  manual position follow-up servo, 229-230
  rate memory, 230-231
  scanners, 231
  secant correction, 225-228
Azimuth error, 235

b

Back emf stabilization, 130-134
Backlash, 215-216
Bandwidths, 4-5, 282-283
  data, 216-217
  limits, 211-216
Block-diagram
  algebra, 25-28, 129-130
  alternative form, 124-126
Bode plots, 12-13
Break frequencies:
  electrical, 88
  motor, 89
Bridged-T networks, 197

c

Carrier frequency, 5
Circles, M, 153-154
Clifton Precision 13-DM dc motor, 88
Closed-loop system:
  defined, 1-2
  example, 142-145
  gain, 5-9
Coefficient, damping, 96
Component errors, 241-244
Compressibility flow, oil, 275-279
Concepts, introductory, 1-17
  basic servo defined, 1-3

Concepts (*Contd*)
Bode plots, 12-13
characteristics, 3
drive motor selection, 3-4
frequency-response approach, 9-10
frequency-response testing, 10
integration in time domain, 13-15
integrators, 11-12
servo performance, 4-5
standard diagram, 5-9
Conceptual loop, 71-72, 99
Configuration performance comparison,
288-289
Constants, 81-83
acceleration, 254
first derivative, 256
second derivative, 255
target motion error, 252-256
velocity, 53-55, 97, 193-194
Contol spool position, 267, 268
Conversion equivalents, 300-301
Current source amplifier, 131
Curves, performance comparison, 296-299

d

Damped natural frequency, 148
Dampers, viscous coupled inertial (VCID),
197-210
introduction, 197
performance, 207-209
position loop, 204-206
simple servos, 197-201
Damping coefficient, 96
Dashpot element, 57-62
dc servo motor, 68-87
armature inductance, 78-80
characteristics of, 68-73
drive amplifier, 76-78
high-value poles, effect of, 83-84
maximum power point, 84-86
servo constants, 81-83
Decaying exponentials, 41, 45
Deflection errors. 247
Design, 281-289
bandwidths, 282-283
configuration performance comparison,
288-289
drive power, 281-282
elementary, 88-110
amplifier gain, calculating, 95-97
direct design, 104-107
electric break frequency, 88
gear ratio at maximum power point, 89

Design (*Contd*)
loop, closing of, 89-95
motor break frequency, 89
torque stiffness, 97-98
velocity constant, 97
integral network servos, 180-184
lead network servo, 194-197
linearity, 104
performance calculation, 283-284
saturation, 284
system performance comparison, 284-288
torque disturbances, 98-104
Disturbance errors, 236-239
Drive amplifier, 76-78
Drive motor selection, 3-4
Drive power, 281-282
Dynamic errors, 250-265
tachometer ripple, 250
target motion, 250-260
tracking noise, 260-265

e

Electrical break frequency, 88
Electrohydraulic servos, 267-280
basic relations, 267-272
hydraulic resonance, 275-279
hydraulic servo systems, 279-280
leakage flow, 275
motor-valve analysis, 272-274
Elevation-over-azimuth systems, 225-228
Error budgets, 234-266
disturbance errors, 236-239
dynamic errors, 250-265
tachometer ripple, 250
target motion, 250-260
tracking noise, 260-265
outline, 234-235
pointing errors, 234-235
static errors, 234-250
component, 241-244
deflection, 247
gearing, 245-246
motor starting voltage, 240-241
static friction, 239-240
steady torque, 247-248
tachometer noise, 241
transducer, 244
wind gust, 248-250
tracking errors, 234-235
Error gain, 7-8
Errors, system, performance calculation,
283-284

Experiments, 307-310
Exponentials, decaying, 41, 45

f

Final value theorem, 54-55
First derivative constant, 256
First-order approximation of servo, 55-57
Follow-up servo, manual position, 229-230
Four-way spool valve, 267, 268
Frequency:
  break, 88, 89
  carrier, 5
  damped natural, 148
  domain, 39
  gain crossover, 90-95
Frequency-response, 9-10
  analysis, 18-21
  solution of integrator in loop, 30-32
  testing, 10
Friction error, static, 239-240
Friction forces, 62

g

Gain:
  amplifier, calculating, 95-97
  closed loop, 5-9
  crossover frequency, 90-95
  error, 7-8
  expressions, integral network servos,
    178-180
  integrator, 28-30
  margin, 154-155
  open-loop, 5-9
  phasor, 150-152
Gear ratio, at maximum power point, 89
Gear trains, inertia reflection through, 62-65
Gearing errors, 245-246
Generators, automatic scanning, 231

h

Hardware, specifying, 184-186
High-value poles, 83-84
Hydraulic resonance, 275-279
Hydraulic servo systems, 279-280

i

Inductance, armature, 78-80
Inertia, 61-62
  moment of, calculations, 302-303
  relected, 62-65

Inertia (*Contd*)
  See also Viscous coupled inertia damped
    servos (VCID)
Inland T-1352 torque motor, 116-117
Integral network compensation, 167-187
  design example, 180-184
  gain expressions, 178-180
  open-loop transfer function, 176-177
  performance, 172-176
  position loop, 171-172
  specifying hardware, 184-186
  torque stiffness, 177-178
Integration:
  real-time, 41-45
  in time domain, 13-15
Integrator, 11-12, 46-48
  frequency-response solution, in loop,
    30-32
  gain, 28-30
  open-loop, 29

k

Kearfott T110-36 400HZ, two-phase
    servomotor, 105

l

Laplace transforms, 39-52
  basic properties, 39-40
  integrator, 46-48
  introduction to, 23-24
  simple servomechanism, 48-50
  stability, 45-46
  transform examples, 40-41
  transform pairs table, 41-45
Lead network servos, 188-197, 210
  characteristics, 188-190
  design example, 194-197
  position loop, 191-192
  torque stiffness, 192-193
  velocity constant, 193-194
Leakage flow, in electrohydraulic
    servos, 275
Linear mechanical elements, 57-62
Linearity, 104
Load resonance, 5, 211-214
Loop:
  bandwidths, 4-5, 282-283
    data, 216-217
    limits, 211-216
  closing of, 89-95
  conceptual, 71-72, 99

Loop (*Contd*)
  frequency-response solution of integrator
    in, 30-32
  open transfer function, 176-177
  position, 121-124
    integral network servos, 171-172
    lead network servos, 191-192
    viscous coupled inertial damped
      servos, 204-206
  tachometer, 121-124
Low-pass filter, 29, 47

m

M circles, 153-154
Magnetic Technology 1937-050 torque
  motor, 77-78
Magnetic Technology 1937-063 servomotor,
  101
Mass elements, 57-62
Mechanical elements, linear, 57-62
Moment of inertia calculations, 302-303
Motor sizing, 4
Motor starting voltage error, 240-241
Motors, dc, 68-87
  armature inductance, 78-80
  characteristics of, 68-73
  drive amplifier, 76-78
  high-value poles, effect of, 83-84
  maximum power point, 84-86
  servo constants, 81-83
Motor-value analysis, electrohydraulic
  servos, 272-274

n

Network compensated servos, 167-187
  integral, 167-187
    design example, 180-184
    gain expressions, 178-180
    open-loop transfer function, 176-177
    performance, 172-176
    position loop, 171-172
    specifying hardware, 184-186
    torque stiffness, 177-178
  lead, 188-197, 210
    characteristics, 188-190
    design example, 194-197
    position loop, 191-192
    torque stiffness, 192-193
    velocity constant, 193-194
Nichols chart, 156-165
Null-seeking systems, 1

o

Oil compressability, 275-279
Open-loop:
  gain, 5-9
  integrator, 29
  system, defined, 1-2
  transfer function, 176-177
Operational amplifiers, 290-295

p

Passing track method for target motion,
  256-260
Passive integral network, 169
Performance:
  basic characteristics, 4-5
  calculation, 283-284
  comparison, system, 284-289
  comparison curves, 296-299
  first-order approximation of servo, 55-57
  integral network servos, 172-176
  linear mechanical elements, 57-62
  reflected inertia, 62-65
  velocity constant, 53-55
  viscous coupled inertial damped servos,
    207-209
Phase margin, 154-155
Phasor gain, 150-152
Pointing errors, 234-235
Poles, 136-139
  high value, 83-84
  location, transient response from, 149-150
  standard quadratic, geometric properties
    of, 147-149
Position loop, 121-124
  integral network servos, 171-172
  lead network servo, 191-192
  viscous coupled inertial damped servos,
    204-206
Positioning, manual, follow-up servo,
  229-230
Power point, maximum, dc motors, 84-86
  gear ratio at, 89
Pressure feedback, 277
Proportional-control servo, 2

q

Quadratic, standard, 96, 145-147
  poles, geometric properties of, 147-149
Quadratic response, s-plane, 139-142

r

Rate memory servo, automatic tracking systems, 230-231
Real-time integration, 41-45
Reflected inertia, 62-65
Resonance, load, 5, 211-214
Ripple error, tachometer, 250
Rotational motion, 57-62

s

Saturation, 219-225, 284
Scaling, 217-219
Scanners, 231
Secant correction, in automatic tracking systems, 225-228
Second derivative constant, 255
Sizing, motor, 4
S-plane quadratic response, 139-142
Spool value, four-way, 267, 268
Spring element, 57-62
Stability, 45-46, 111-166
  back emf, 130-134
  closed-loop system example, 142-145
  gain margin, 154-155
  geometric properties of standard quadratic poles, 147-149
  Laplace transforms and, 45-46
  M circles, 153-154
  Nichols chart, 156-165
  phase margin, 154-155
  phasor gain, 150-152
  poles, 136-139
  s-plane quadratic response, 139-142
  standard quadratic, 145-147
  tachometer, 111-130
    block diagram algebra of disturbances, 129-130
    block diagram alternatives, 124-126
    position loop around tachometer loop, 121-214
    torque stiffness, 126-129
  transient response from pole location, 149-150
  zeros, 136-139
Standard diagram, 5-9
Standard quadratic, 96, 145-147
  poles, geometric properties of, 147-149
Static errors, 234-250
  component, 241-144
  deflection, 247
  gearing, 245-246

Static errors (*Contd*)
  motor starting voltage, 240-241
  static friction, 239-240
  steady torque, 247-248
  tachometer noise, 241
  transducer, 244
  wind gusts, 248-250
Static friction error, 239-240
Steady torque errors, 247-248
Step function, 40-41
Stiffness, torque, 97-98, 126-129
  integral network servos, 177-178
  lead network servos, 192-193
System performance comparison, 284-289

t

Tachometer:
  loop, 121-124
  noise error, 241
  ripple error, 250
  stabilization, 111-130
    block diagram algebra of disturbances, 129-130
    block diagram alternatives, 124-126
    position loop around tachometer loop, 121-124
    torque stiffness, 126-129
Target motion error, 250-260
  constants, 252-256
  passing track method for analyzing, 256-260
Three-pass gear system, 63
Time-domain integration, 13-15
Tooth-to-tooth error, 245
Torque, 58-59, 61, 69-70
  disturbances, 98-104, 236-239
  errors, steady, 247-248
  stiffness, 97-98, 126-129
    integral network servos, 177-178
    lead network servos, 192-193
Total composite error (TCE), 245-246
Total indicated runout (TIR), 245-246
Tracking errors, 234-235
Tracking noise errors, 260-265
Tracking system, automatic, 225-231
  manual position follow-up servo, 229-230
  rate memory, 230-231
  scanners, 231
  secant correction, 225-228
Transducer errors, 244
Transfer functions, 24-25
  open-loop, 176-177
Transforms, Laplace, *see* Laplace transforms

Transient response:
  analysis, 21-23
  from pole location, 149-150
Translational motion, 57-62

u

Unit step function, 40

v

Valves, servo, 269-274
  four-way spool, 267, 268
Velocity constant, 53-55, 97, 193-194
  lead network servos, 193-194
Vernitron 08D4B-CCO-AI, VCID servo
  motor, 206

Viscous coupled inertial damped servos
  (VCID), 197-210
  introduction, 197
  performance, 207-209
  position loop, 204-206
  simple servos, 197-201
Viscous friction element, *see* Dashpot
  element
Voltage errors, motor starting, 240-241

w

Weight, defined, 58
Wind gust errors, 248-250

z

Zeros, 136-139